THE
INTERNATIONAL SERIES
OF
MONOGRAPHS ON PHYSICS

GENERAL EDITORS

W. MARSHALL   D. H. WILKINSON

INTERFERENCE
OF
ELECTROMAGNETIC
WAVES

BY

Ian

A. H. COOK

CLARENDON PRESS · OXFORD

1971

Oxford University Press, Ely House, London W. 1

GLASGOW NEW YORK TORONTO MELBOURNE WELLINGTON
CAPE TOWN SALISBURY IBADAN NAIROBI DAR ES SALAAM LUSAKA ADDIS ABABA
BOMBAY CALCUTTA MADRAS KARACHI LAHORE DACCA
KUALA LUMPUR SINGAPORE HONG KONG TOKYO

PRINTED IN NORTHERN IRELAND
AT THE UNIVERSITIES PRESS

PREFACE

My aim in this book has been to deal with selected topics in the interference of electromagnetic radiation in a fundamental way while yet introducing them in an elementary manner. My choice of topics has been determined both by their practical importance and by the light they shed on the basic principles of interference. Many of the more traditional interferometers and methods of treatment will therefore be found missing. On the other hand, I have tried to include most of the applications of current importance and I have also tried to show how the study of gas lasers, radio interferometers, and the idea of coherence helps to clarify a number of points often obscure to those coming first to the subject. While not providing a handbook, I have tried in a number of places to indicate important considerations in the practical handling of interferometers. The main omission among topics of importance is the subject of holography: it is already so large and growing so fast that I felt unable to do justice to it without greatly extending the book and delaying its appearance.

This book originated in a course of lectures that I gave to graduate students at the University of Colorado in 1965–6 while holding a Visiting Fellowship at the Joint Institute for Laboratory Astrophysics, Boulder, Colorado. I am most grateful to the Fellows of JILA for the opportunity to spend some months in their stimulating Institute and for the time to prepare much of the material for this book.

My approach to the subject of interference has been formed by my work at the National Physical Laboratory, with its long history of accurate measurements of wavelength and lengths, and I am especially indebted to the instruction and stimuli I have received from Dr. H. Barrell, Dr. H. A. Gebbie, and Dr. W. R. C. Rowley. I also owe much to M. Terrien, the Director of the Bureau International des Poids et Mesures, in whom I find the spirit of A. A. Michelson alive and forward-looking.

A. H. Cook

Edinburgh
March 1970

CONTENTS

NOTATION

THE following symbols are generally used throughout with the significance indicated; other symbols are used from time to time and some of those listed here are exceptionally used with a different meaning.

A	amplitude
$\mathbf{A}$	vector potential
$\left.\begin{array}{l}a\\b\end{array}\right\}$	linear dimensions
c	speed of light
$\mathbf{E}$	electric field
$\mathscr{F}$	finesse
f	fractional order of interference
$\mathbf{H}$	magnetic field
h	Planck's constant
I	intensity
$\mathbf{k}$	wave vector
k	$|\mathbf{k}| = 2\pi/\lambda$
l	length
n	wave number
R	intensity reflection coefficient
r	amplitude reflection coefficient
T	intensity transmission coefficient
t	time; amplitude transmission coefficient
V	voltage; field variable
x, y, z	distance; Cartesian coordinates
α, β	angle
Γ	coherence function
γ	mutual coherence function
δ	Dirac δ function; path difference
Δ	path difference
λ	wavelength
μ	refractive index
ν	frequency (Hz)
ρ	intensity ratio
ϱ	$4R/(1-R)^2$
τ	time
θ	angle; phase angle
Φ	phase angle
ϕ	phase angle; field variable
ψ	phase angle
ω	angular frequency (rad/s)

INTRODUCTION

THE interference of light was discovered, though not so recognized, by Newton in the form of the Fizeau fringes, or Newton's rings, formed by interference between light reflected from a mirror and from a convex lens placed on top of it. The explanation of Newton's rings in terms of interference was first given by Thomas Young (1802) and subsequently extended by him and others to many other phenomena such as the Young's double slit or the Lloyd's single mirror interferometers. An important discovery was made in 1816 by Arago and Fresnel (see Whittaker 1951 for this and other aspects of the early history of interference), who showed that beams of light polarized at right angles do not interfere; from that Young inferred that light was a transverse wave motion. As soon as sufficiently delicate apparatus could be made, interference effects could be used to measure wavelengths of light, to measure distances, and to investigate spectra. In recent years the possibility of recording photoelectrically the intensity of the light transmitted by an interferometer has made many measurements much easier and more accurate, so that the spectrometric applications of interferometry have been greatly developed, and the advent of the gas laser as a source of light is rapidly increasing the applications of interferometers in many precise measurements. At the same time interferometric methods have been applied to radio waves and many important observations in radio astronomy have been made interferometrically, while the possibilities opened up by radio and laser interferometers have directed attention anew to the fundamentals of interference phenomena so that many somewhat obscure points can now be presented in a clearer way.

The subject of this book is the co-operative effects, or correlated behaviour, of electromagnetic wave trains, as shown in interference phenomena, together with the applications of those phenomena in optical spectroscopy, metrology, and radio astronomy, among other studies.

Electromagnetic radiation is described by the electric (E) and magnetic (H) vectors, or by other field variables, such as the vector potential (A). The electric and magnetic vectors satisfy Maxwell's equations. In free space or in a medium the properties of which do not depend on the field, Maxwell's equations are linear in the components of **E** and **H**; the equations satisfied by the vector potential are similarly linear: the components of the vectors or their derivatives appear in the equations but their products do not. In such circumstances an electromagnetic wave can be expressed as the sum of components varying sinusoidally with time, that is to say, proportional to $\cos \omega t$, where $\omega/2\pi$ is the frequency of the oscillation of a component. All such components, and hence the total field itself, average out to zero over a time long compared with $1/\omega$. If two fields, each the sum of a number of components, are superposed in free space or in a medium that responds linearly as defined above, then components with the same frequency simply add together, the time average of the total field remains zero, and no new phenomenon appears. If, however, a wave train is incident on a non-linear device, the response of which is proportional to powers and products of the variables describing the incident field, then the mean value of the response may not be zero when taken over a long time, and interference phenomena, dependent on the products of the variables of the incident waves, may appear.

Consider two field variables which describe two plane wave trains. They may be, for example, the electric field vectors (which are perpendicular to the direction of propagation) or the components of the vector potential in the direction of propagation. Let the variable of one wave train vary with a speed ω_1. It may then be written as proportional to the real part of the complex exponential $e^{i\omega_1 t}$. If we write

$$\phi_1 = A_1 \exp i\{\omega_1(t-x/c)+\psi_1\}, \tag{1.1}$$

the real part of ϕ_1 will represent the field at a co-ordinate x and time t, the phase ψ_1 being included to allow for the arbitrariness of the origins of time and distance. c is the speed of light. Let the two waves travel in the same direction so that the variable of the second may be represented by the real part of

$$\phi_2 = A_2 \exp i\{\omega_2(t-x/c)+\psi_2\}.$$

The sum of the two variables is then represented by the real part of

$$\phi = \phi_1+\phi_2.$$

At low enough frequencies, devices exist that follow the variations of the field, for example, a voltage proportional to ϕ may be displayed on a cathode-ray tube, but at frequencies greater than about 10^{10} Hz the variations are too fast to follow, and signals can be derived only if a response with non-zero time average can be obtained. In particular, a detector may respond to the *intensity* of the field. The intensity is defined in Chapter 2, but roughly speaking it is proportional to the time average of the square of the modulus of a field variable, $\langle|\phi|^2\rangle$, the brackets $\langle\ \rangle$ denoting a time average.

The sum of two elementary waves is

$$\phi = \phi_1 + \phi_2 = A_1 \exp i\{\omega_1(t-x/c) + \psi_1\} +$$
$$+ A_2 \exp i\{\omega_2(t-x/c) + \psi_2\}$$
$$= \exp i\{\omega_1(t-x/c) + \psi_1\} \times$$
$$\times [A_1 + A_2 \exp i\{(\omega_2 - \omega_1)(t-x/c) + (\psi_2 - \psi_1)\}]. \quad (1.2)$$

Now the modulus of a complex exponential is 1, and therefore

$$|\phi_1 + \phi_2|^2 = |A_1 + A_2 \exp i\{(\omega_2 - \omega_1)(t-x/c) + (\psi_2 - \psi_1)\}|^2$$
$$= [A_1 + A_2 \cos\{(\omega_2 - \omega_1)(t-x/c) + (\psi_2 - \psi_1)\}]^2 +$$
$$+ [A_2 \sin\{(\omega_2 - \omega_1)(t-x/c) + (\psi_2 - \psi_1)\}]^2,$$

or

$$|\phi_1 + \phi_2|^2 = A_1^2 + A_2^2 + 2A_1 A_2 \cos\{(\omega_2 - \omega_1)(t-x/c) + (\psi_2 - \psi_1)\}. \quad (1.3)$$

Thus the intensity, proportional to $|\phi_1 + \phi_2|^2$, fluctuates at an angular frequency $(\omega_2 - \omega_1)$. Effects at this difference frequency can be observed with radio waves and with laser light, which, in certain circumstances, can be closely represented by simple wave trains. However, ordinary light from even the most monochromatic source has to be represented by wave trains with a relatively wide range of frequencies (and therefore of differences, $\omega_2 - \omega_1$) and with phases uniformly distributed from 0 to 2π. The average value of

$$\cos\{(\omega_2 - \omega_1)(t-x/c) + (\psi_2 - \psi_1)\}$$

is thus zero unless ω_2 is set equal to ω_1 and it is arranged that $(\psi_2 - \psi_1)$ is a constant independent of the separate values of ψ_2 and ψ_1. Ordinary light is the resultant of a multitude of wave trains radiated by individual atoms, each with its own frequency (within the overall spectrum) and each with its own phase. The two conditions for interference show that we can consider only interference between wave trains which initially are radiated by the same atom. Thus, the frequencies are identical and the phase difference is fixed by the difference between the separate paths that the wave trains follow between emission from the atom and recombination at the detector.

Ordinary light, from hot bodies, gas discharge lamps, and so on, is radiated by sources in which each atom behaves almost independently of the others. Interferometers for such light must therefore satisfy the condition that light from each atom must recombine independently of, but with the same phase shift as, that from every other atom. Lasers and radio transmitters are quite different sources, for in them it is arranged that the phase of radiation from many atoms or electrons is the same. The radiation from the source as a whole can be characterized by a unique phase and the phase difference between radiation from two separate devices has a definite value. Likewise, the radiation can be characterized by a single frequency (over a given time interval, definition of frequency within a given range implies definition of phase within a corresponding range), a difference of frequency is meaningful, and $\cos\{(\omega_2-\omega_1)(t-x/c)+(\psi_2-\psi)\}$ does not average out to zero, so that it is possible to see interference effects at a frequency $(\omega_2-\omega_1)$. As will be seen in more detail in the next chapter, this is not just a question of having detectors that can follow the time variation of the effects, but it involves also the relation between the amplitudes A_1 and A_2 and the phases ψ_2 and ψ_1, that is, the *coherence* of the wave trains.

In classical optical interferometry, ω_2 and ω_1 are equal, and the intensity of the light received at a detector varies as $\cos(\psi_2-\psi_1)$. The practical utility of interference phenomena depends on the variety of ways in which a phase difference $(\psi_2-\psi_1)$ can be imposed on the wave trains.

The energy radiated by a source is always spread over a range of frequencies and it is the object of spectroscopy to determine how the energy varies with frequency. Let the intensity due to a source at some place be $I(\omega)$, a function of ω, and let the corresponding amplitude be $A(\omega)$. A wave train emanating from the source can then be represented by the sum of a set of Fourier components:

$$A(t) = \sum_{\omega} A(\omega)e^{i\omega t}.$$

Since the variation of amplitude with frequency is continuous, it is more satisfactory to replace this sum by an integral, a Fourier integral:

$$A(t) = \int A(\omega)e^{i\omega t}d\omega, \tag{1.4}$$

where the range of integration covers the spectrum.

If $d\omega$ is taken to be sufficiently small, $(\omega_2-\omega_1)t/c$ is effectively zero over the time of observation and $(\psi_2-\psi_1)$ is constant for two beams from the same source of light; the interference term for the two element-ary beams reduces to $2|A|^2\cos(\psi_2-\psi_1)$ and the total effect for the source may be obtained by adding up the effects of all such beams of bandwidth $d\omega$, that is, by integrating with respect to frequency:

$$I(t) = 2\int |A(\omega)|^2 \{1+\cos(\psi_2-\psi_1)\}\,d\omega$$
$$= 2\int I(\omega)\{1+\cos(\psi_2-\psi_1)\}\,d\omega. \tag{1.5}$$

If the interferometer imposes a phase difference proportional to the frequency, so that $\psi_2-\psi_1=\omega t$, the intensity is

$$I(t) = 2\int_0^\infty I(\omega)\,d\omega + 2\int_0^\infty I(\omega)\cos\omega t\,d\omega,$$

and if the phase constant t can be varied, the detector output can be obtained as a function of t:

$$D(t) \propto 2\int_0^\infty I(\omega)\,d\omega + 2\int_0^\infty I(\omega)\cos\omega t\,d\omega. \tag{1.6}$$

The first term is just the sum of the intensities of the two wave trains, but the second is the cosine Fourier transform of $I(\omega)$ with respect to ω. Thus $I(\omega)$ can be calculated from the inverse relation

$$2I(\omega) \propto \frac{1}{\pi}\int_{-\infty}^{+\infty} \{D(t)-D(0)\}\cos\omega t\,dt,$$

(see Duffieux 1939).

The phase difference $\psi_2-\psi_1$ is proportional to a length in spectro-scopic or metrological interferometers, and t is equal to the time taken by light to traverse that distance. The more general formulation is used here to emphasize that a phase shift proportional to frequency may be produced in others ways.

Spectrometers may in general be regarded as devices that give an output that is some transform of the spectrum of the source being studied, and the Fourier transform is in fact by no means the most commonly used. An ideal prism spectrometer, for example, gives a delta-function transform:

$$D(\omega) \propto I(\omega')\delta(\omega-\omega'),$$

where $\delta(\omega-\omega')$ is zero unless $\omega=\omega'$.

The transforms for a prism, a grating, and a number of other classes of spectrometer are generated through the interference of more beams than two, and the greater the number of beams that interfere, the more closely the transform approaches the delta function. Let $A(\omega)$ be the amplitude of light incident upon a spectrometer and suppose that inside the interferometer the light is divided into a number of beams with amplitudes A_n and phases ψ_n, such that

$$A_n = F_n \cdot A(\omega)$$

and

$$\psi_n = n\psi.$$

The beams are then recombined and fall upon a detector whose output is proportional to the intensity $|\sum_n \phi_n|^2$, that is to

$$I(\omega) \, |\sum_n F_n e^{-\mathrm{i}n\psi}|^2. \tag{1.7}$$

There are two important practical cases, in the first of which the amplitude factors F_n are constant and the number of interfering beams is limited by the length of a grating or the size of the base of a prism, while in the other case the factors decrease with the number n and the number of interfering beams is in principle infinite but in effect is limited to a finite number by the decrease of amplitude. In the first case

$$I \propto \left| \sum_{n=0}^{N} e^{-\mathrm{i}n\psi} \right|^2, \tag{1.8}$$

where N, the number of interfering beams, is determined by the size of a grating; the sum must be replaced by an integration for a prism.

Now

$$\sum_{n=0}^{N} e^{-\mathrm{i}n\psi} = (1 - e^{-\mathrm{i}(N+1)\psi})/(1 - e^{-\mathrm{i}\psi}),$$

and the intensity is thus proportional to

$$\frac{|1 - e^{-\mathrm{i}(N+1)\psi}|^2}{|1 - e^{-\mathrm{i}\psi}|^2},$$

that is, to

$$\frac{1 - \cos(N+1)\psi}{1 - \cos\psi} \quad \text{or} \quad \frac{\sin^2 \tfrac{1}{2}(N+1)\psi}{\sin^2 \tfrac{1}{2}\psi}. \tag{1.9}$$

The behaviour of this function is shown in Fig. 1.1. When ψ is $2\pi p$, where p is an integer, the intensity is proportional to $(N+1)^2$ and falls to zero when $\psi = 2\pi p \pm (2\pi/N+1)$. The integrated intensity in the principal maximum is thus of order

$$\frac{1}{N} \cdot \frac{2\pi(N+1)^2}{N+1},$$

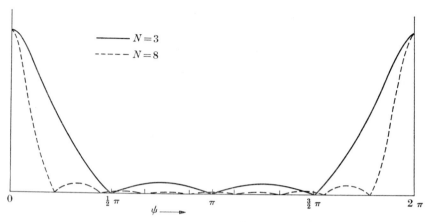

FIG. 1.1. The function $\left(\dfrac{1}{N+1}\right)^2 \dfrac{\sin^2 \frac{1}{2}(N+1)\psi}{\sin^2 \frac{1}{2}\psi}$.

since the intensity in each beam, for a given size of grating, is proportional to N^{-1}. The intensity therefore varies approximately as a delta function, the area under which is 2π, although the width is infinitesimal; the function is periodic, however, and repeats whenever $\psi = 2\pi p$. In large gratings, N is of the order of 10^5.

In the Fabry–Perot interferometer F_n is r^n, where r is less than 1. Then

$$I \propto \left| \sum_{n=0}^{N} r^n e^{-in\psi} \right|^2$$

$$= \frac{|1 - r^{N+1}\cos(N+1)\psi + ir^{N+1}\sin(N+1)\psi|^2}{|1 - r\cos\psi + ir\sin\psi|^2}, \qquad (1.10)$$

and in the limit as N approaches infinity I is proportional to

$$1/(1 + r^2 - 2r\cos\psi),$$

that is

$$\frac{1}{(1-r)^2} \cdot \frac{1}{1 + \dfrac{4r}{(1-r)^2}\sin^2 \frac{1}{2}\psi}. \qquad (1.11)$$

This again is a function that has a sharp maximum when ψ equals $2\pi p$ and so approximates to a delta function.

Applications of the two-beam Fourier transform spectrometer are simplified when the energy of the source is restricted to a narrow range of frequency. Suppose that $I(\omega)$ is appreciably different from zero only in a small range around ω_0. $I(\omega)$ may then be considered as a function

2

$I(\tilde{\omega})$ of $\tilde{\omega} = \omega - \omega_0$ and the detector output is

$$D(t) \propto 2I + 2 \int\limits_{-\omega_0}^{\infty} \tilde{I}(\tilde{\omega})\cos(\omega_0 + \tilde{\omega})t \, d\tilde{\omega}. \qquad (1.12)$$

The lower limit of integration may be replaced by ∞ since $\tilde{I}(\tilde{\omega})$ is zero when ω is much less than ω_0.

Thus
$$D(t) \propto 2I + 2(T_{\mathrm{c}} \cos \omega_0 t - T_{\mathrm{s}} \sin \omega_0 t), \qquad (1.13)$$

where
$$T_{\mathrm{c}} = \int\limits_{-\infty}^{+\infty} \tilde{I} \cos \tilde{\omega} t \, d\tilde{\omega} \quad \text{(cosine Fourier transform)}$$

and
$$T_{\mathrm{s}} = \int\limits_{-\infty}^{+\infty} \tilde{I} \sin \tilde{\omega} t \, d\tilde{\omega} \quad \text{(sine Fourier transform)}.$$

Now since $\tilde{I}$ differs from zero only in a small range of $\tilde{\omega}$, T_{c} and T_{s} are functions that vary slowly with t: if $\tilde{I}$ were a delta function, T_{c} would be 1 and T_{s} would be 0. Thus $D(t)$ is very nearly a sinusoidal function of t with slowly varying amplitude and phase.

There are three practical consequences of this result. In the first place, since the phase and amplitude of $D(t)$ vary only slowly, they need be determined at rather few values of t. Secondly, if $\tilde{I}(\tilde{\omega})$ is symmetrical, ω_0 may be uniquely defined as the centre frequency, T_{s} is zero, and the phase of $D(t)$ is constant. In such circumstances observations of the maxima and minima of $D(t)$ enable either t or ω_0 to be determined in terms of the other, for example, the interferometer may be used to find lengths in terms of wavelengths or vice versa. On the other hand, if $\tilde{I}(\tilde{\omega})$ is not a symmetrical function of $\tilde{\omega}$, the apparent value of ω_0 will change with t and a measurement of length or wavelength will have an error that depends on the total phase shift $\omega_0 t$. Thirdly, the contrast of the interference effect, (the 'visibility' of the fringes in optical terms), depends on the total phase shift, for as t increases T_{c} and T_{s} decreases. Eventually, no effect is detectable when it is small compared with the noise fluctuations of $D(t)$ and this occurs at a value of t that is greater the sharper $\tilde{I}(\tilde{\omega})$.

So far, the energy output of a source has been considered as a function of frequency, but in general it will also be a function of position over the area of the source or of the angular direction of a point in the source as viewed from an interferometer. The phase difference between the two beams of a two-beam interferometer may then be arranged to be a function of angular position as seen from the interferometer and the output of the interferometer will be a transform with respect to two variables (the two angles required to specify a direction), instead of the one variable involved in spectroscopic applications. However, in many practical cases only one of the two angles can be varied and it is necessary to consider an equivalent one-dimensional distribution of intensity, namely the distribution of intensity integrated along a strip at right angles to the plane in which the angle to the interferometer can vary. Let the angle to the interferometer be denoted by θ and suppose that the phase difference between the two interfering beams is proportional to θ: $\psi_2 - \psi_1 = \kappa\theta$. The detector output is then

$$D(\kappa) \propto 2 \int\limits_{-\pi/2}^{+\pi/2} I(\theta) \, d\theta + 2 \int\limits_{-\pi/2}^{+\pi/2} I(\theta)\cos \kappa\theta \, d\theta, \qquad (1.14)$$

by an argument which is quite analogous to that leading to eqn (1.6).

Since eqn (1.14) is formally similar to that for a two-beam spectroscopic interferometer, much of the theory of angular interferometers is similar to that for spectroscopic interferometers. In particular, the transition from two-beam to multiple-beam interferometers and the corresponding transition from Fourier transforms to delta-function transforms can be discussed in a similar way. There is not, however, great interest in a multiple-beam angular interferometer in one dimension, and in radio astronomy, in particular, the more complex case of a two-dimensional multiple-beam interferometer and the transition to a complete focusing mirror is the one of practical importance.

A distinction is usually made in elementary textbooks between interferometers employing division of amplitude and those employing division of wave front. In a general way this corresponds to the distinction made here between interferometers in which the phase shift introduced between successive beams depends on the wavelength, and those in which it depends on an angle, but no such distinctions are ever clear-cut: the output of any interferometer is a function of both the angular distribution and the spectrum of the source, and the phase shifts introduced within the interferometer are never functions of either the wavelength or a geometrical parameter alone. One of the main purposes of the detailed analysis of any interferometer is to calculate the departures from the nominal behaviour of the instrument that arise from such non-ideal interactions.

The main topic of this book is the interferometer as a device for relating some property of a source to a detector output, that is the transform property of the interferometer. In the first place it is necessary to consider in some detail the fundamental theory of the phenomenon of interference, the behaviour of detectors, the theory of coherence of electromagnetic fields and the specification and interference of polarized radiation. The detailed behaviour of various practical interferometers will then be analysed, particular attention being given to factors that are important in obtaining measurements of the very highest precision. Examples of important applications will be described. Interferometers are of course useless when the variations of the detector output that it is desired to observe are small compared with the noise fluctuations of the detector system, and the factors that determine the signal-to-noise ratio will be explained and the limitations on the performance of various interferometers that are set by noise will be analysed.

While the main emphasis of this book is on the transform properties of interferometers, the internal field of an interferometer is also important in some applications and is fundamental in the operation of a laser. An interferometer may be considered as a resonant cavity which is excited by incident waves and in which, in consequence, internal standing waves are maintained, with some energy leaking out to a detector. In the transform aspect of an interferometer, attention is concentrated on the energy leaking out, that is on the transmission properties of the system, but for lasers, it is the details of the internal field that are important.

The range of interferometric phenomena is extreme. In radio astronomy interferometers operate at frequencies as low as 30 MHz. In the infra-red, interferometers have been used from the visible to wavelengths as long as 300 μm, and applications include molecular spectroscopy, astrophysics, and lasers. The classical region is, of course, the visible and near infrared and here a great variety of systems exists with applications in high-resolution spectroscopy, in comparisons of wavelengths and measurements of length of the very greatest accuracy, in astrophysics, in optical testing and many routine mechanical gauging problems, and in lasers. The extension of interferometric methods to wavelengths below 2000 Å (200 nm)† is difficult because the absorption of optical materials increases considerably and because mechanical

† 1 nm $= 10^{-9}$ m $= 10$ Å.

adjustments at such wavelengths become very delicate, but nonetheless some successful attempts have been made to apply interferometric methods to spectroscopic problems at wavelengths as short as 140 nm. In so far as diffraction gratings may be considered as interferometric devices, interferometric methods of spectroscopy have been applied to wavelengths as short as 0·1 nm, while the study of crystal and molecular structures by X-ray diffraction really depends on the interference rather than on the diffraction of X-rays. It has even been demonstrated that two-beam interferometers can be constructed for electrons and X-rays.

Lastly, it should not be forgotten that the principles of interference apply to other fields than the electromagnetic, and that interferometers have been used in acoustics and in seismology where the linear arrays of seismometers now being employed are exact analogues of the arrays of aerials used in radio astronomy, although because of the different nature of the signals—a continuous noise signal in radio astronomy but a short burst of more or less periodic form in seismology—the methods of treating the data are somewhat different.

FUNDAMENTAL PRINCIPLES

In this chapter the behaviour of detectors, the coherence of electro-magnetic fields, and the description of a polarized field are discussed, questions that are fundamental to the behaviour of all interferometers.

The behaviour of detectors

Interference phenomena and the behaviour of detectors are divided rather clearly into two groups, a low-frequency group for frequencies low enough that the individual oscillations of a wave train can be followed and displayed, for example by an oscilloscope following the oscillations of a radio wave; and a high-frequency group for frequencies that cannot be so followed. At present, high frequencies are those above about 10 GHz, but the limit is continually being raised. At low frequencies the separate amplitudes and phases of interfering wave trains can be observed individually if the frequency is well defined and it is not really necessary to use interferometric techniques, for these direct measurements give more information than interferometric methods. However, not all signals have stable phases and amplitudes, the most important examples being the signals from astronomical sources, which, whether they have a broad spectrum or a narrow one, have a random distribution of amplitude and phase. Thus at all frequencies inter-ferometric techniques are needed and the behaviour of detectors at low as well as high frequencies requires discussion.

Another way of dividing the frequency range is according to whether or not the behaviour of a detector must be described in quantum terms, a division that is not made at the same frequency as the former. On this basis, low-frequency detectors are those that can be described entirely in terms of Maxwell's equations. Consider a detector consisting of a dipole with a thermionic diode at the centre. A complete description of the following steps can, in principle, be given by Maxwell's equations. The field induces a voltage across the two arms of the dipole, a linear process in which the voltage V is proportional to the electric component E_d parallel to the axis of the dipole. The voltage V applied to the diode then causes current to flow, the field between the electrodes and the current being calculated by means of Maxwell's equations. The actual behaviour depends on the steady voltages applied to the diode, but if the current I is space-charge limited, it is proportional to $V^{\frac{3}{2}}$, and in general it may be expressed as a series of positive powers of V:

$$I = \alpha V^2 + \beta V^4 + \dots \tag{2.1}$$

With suitable external circuits the diode can be made to follow a square law:

$$I \propto V^2 \propto E_d^2, \tag{2.1a}$$

a result that can be obtained also with semiconductor devices (the behaviour of these too can be described by Maxwell's equations).

When fields from a number of sources fall on a dipole, the total induced voltage is the sum of the voltages induced by the various fields separately. Then, if the detector follows a square-law behaviour, the detector output, proportional to V^2, is proportional to the intensity of the component of the total field parallel to the dipole.

All high-frequency detectors, in the second sense, depend on the photoelectric effect. This is obvious for any photoemissive detector, but it is true also for all solid-state detectors, for they depend on the ejection of an electron from some site in the solid. It is true also for a photographic plate and for the eye, in both of which the observable effects arise from the chemical action of electrons ejected by the photoelectric effect. Lastly, detectors depending on the thermal effect of radiation are also basically photoelectric detectors, for the absorption of radiation begins with a process such as photoionization or photodissociation.

Let $\mathbf{E}$ and $\mathbf{H}$ be field vectors satisfying Maxwell's equations and suppose that the field is that of a wave in free space. $\mathbf{E}$ and $\mathbf{H}$ are then derived from a vector potential $\mathbf{A}$:

$$\mathbf{H} = \operatorname{curl} \mathbf{A}, \qquad \mathbf{E} = -\frac{\partial \mathbf{A}}{\partial t}.$$

Now introduce a complex field vector $\mathbf{F} = \mathbf{E} + i\mathbf{H}$ and its complex conjugate $\mathbf{F}^* = \mathbf{E} - i\mathbf{H}$.

The energy density of the field is

$$\frac{1}{8\pi}(E^2 + H^2) = \frac{1}{8\pi}(\mathbf{F}^* \cdot \mathbf{F}).$$

Let the field at any frequency be written as the sum of right and left circularly polarized waves:

$$\mathbf{F} = a_\nu \mathbf{c}_\nu e^{ik_\nu x} + b_\nu \mathbf{c}_\nu^* e^{-ik_\nu x}.$$

In this expression $\mathbf{k}_\nu$ is the wave vector, a vector in the direction of propagation x, having a magnitude $2\pi/\lambda$. $\mathbf{c}_\nu$ is a complex vector:

$$\mathbf{c}_\nu = \mathbf{r}_1 + i\mathbf{r}_2.$$

$\mathbf{r_1}$, $\mathbf{r_2}$, and $\mathbf{k}_\nu$ form an orthogonal triplet, $|\mathbf{r_1}| = |\mathbf{r_2}| = (2\pi)^{\frac{1}{2}}|\mathbf{k}_\nu|$, and $\mathbf{c}_\nu\mathbf{c} = \mathbf{c}_\nu^*\mathbf{c}_\nu^* = 0$.

The energy density of the field is

$$\tfrac{1}{2}k_\nu^2(a_\nu^* \cdot a_\nu + b_\nu^* \cdot b_\nu).$$

a_ν^* and b_ν^* are respectively the complex conjugates of a_ν and b_ν.

Now suppose that

$$a_\nu = \frac{1}{2^{\frac{1}{2}}k_\nu}(p_\nu - 2\pi i\nu q_\nu), \qquad b_\nu = \frac{1}{2^{\frac{1}{2}}k_\nu}(p_\nu + 2\pi i\nu q_\nu),$$

so that the energy density may be rewritten as

$$\tfrac{1}{2}(p_\nu^2 + 4\pi^2\nu^2 q_\nu^2).$$

It will be seen that this expression is formally the same as that for the Hamiltonian of a simple harmonic oscillator if q_ν is a canonical coordinate and p_ν is the corresponding canonical momentum. Each direction of polarization corresponds to one coordinate–momentum pair for each frequency.

The a_ν, b_ν variables may be put in non-dimensional form as follows:

$$\alpha_\nu, \beta_\nu = \tau a_\nu, \tau b_\nu,$$
$$\tau = \tfrac{1}{2}(k_\nu/hc)^{\frac{1}{2}}.$$

Then, as is shown in Appendix 1, the variables, α_ν, β_ν satisfy the following relations:

$$\alpha_\nu^*\alpha_{\nu'} - \alpha_{\nu'}\alpha_\nu^* = -\delta_{\nu\nu'}$$
$$\beta_\nu^*\beta_{\nu'} - \beta_{\nu'}\beta_\nu^* = -\delta_{\nu\nu'},$$

where $\delta_{\nu\nu'}$ is the Dirac delta function, equal to 1 if $\nu = \nu'$ and otherwise zero. The same relations are satisfied by the dynamical variables used to describe an assembly of bosons, that is, a set of identical quantum particles having symmetrical wave functions and such that any number may be in a particular state. The number of bosons in a particular state is equal to

$$\alpha_\nu^*\alpha_\nu, \qquad \beta_\nu^*\beta_\nu.$$

Hence the number of bosons, or photons, with given wave vector and polarization is equal to

$$\alpha_\nu^*\alpha_\nu \quad \text{or} \quad \beta_\nu^*\beta_\nu,$$

and the total number with both polarizations is $(\alpha_\nu^*\alpha_\nu + \beta_\nu^*\beta_\nu)$ or

$$(k_\nu hc)^{-1} \times \text{energy density per unit volume}.$$

The number of photons per unit volume is in fact proportional to
V*V, where V is any of the variables **E, H, F,** or **A.**

The theory of bosons also shows that the probability of a boson being
absorbed from a particular state when an assembly of bosons interacts
with matter is proportional to the number of bosons in that state
(Dirac 1958, p. 235). But this is just the description of the photoelectric
effect, which is the interaction of light with atoms whereby light is
absorbed from the incident field. If, therefore, it is correct to identify
the behaviour of a radiation field completely with that of an assembly of
photons, the rate at which the photoelectric effect occurs is proportional
to V*V, V being, as before, any of the field variables **E, H, F, A.**

It follows from this argument that the rate of emission of electrons in
the photoelectric effect is independent of the state of polarization of the
incident field, a result that differs from that usually true for a low-
frequency detector, which, as shown above, usually has some preferred
direction. In practice, nonetheless, photo-detectors show some direc-
tional effect; the reason for the apparent discrepancy is that in the argument just given V is a field variable of the total electromagnetic field,
but the light shining on the detector may not be the only field to which
the atoms are subject, and, particularly at the surface of a metal, the
internal fields may have a preferred direction. Furthermore, the reflection coefficient of the surface may depend on the polarization of the
incident light. Thus it is found that the volume photoelectric effect is
usually independent of polarization whereas the surface effect may
frequently show some dependence on polarization.

To summarize, there are fundamental theoretical reasons for taking
the responses of detectors at both low and high frequency to be proportional to the intensity of the incident light, but there may in
practice be effects that disturb this ideal relation. The general theoretical treatment of interferometers will therefore be based on the assumption that the detector output is proportional to the field intensity,
bearing in mind that the phenomena may not be completely describable
on this basis.

The theory of the coherence of optical fields

It is sometimes possible to obtain a field that can be represented as a
simple harmonic wave train with a phase that is constant over a long
period of time or over a large area of the wave front. One may cite the
field radiated by a radio station or the beam from a laser as examples.
Such fields are described by a single Fourier component. The great

majority of fields met with in practice are far more complex, the amplitudes and phases of the Fourier components into which the field may be
analysed showing large random variations, such that the field properties are stable only in a statistical sense and over times that are long
compared with the periods of the vibrations. Such are the fields radiated by black bodies, by gas discharges, by stars, and by astronomical
radio sources.

Interference effects depend on there being some correlation between
the separate components of the total field at the detector. If there is no
such correlation, the intensity is stable in the mean. The function of the
optical components of an interferometer is to impose some correlation
upon the components by introducing a consistent phase difference
between them but this is of no effect if the incident radiation is completely free of correlation with itself. Many sources do produce fields
with some degree of autocorrelation, for example any source with a
restricted spectrum, while, in addition, correlation may be introduced
through the conditions of propagation from the source, for instance when
a large star radiating a random field appears as a point source at the
very large distance at which it is observed.

It is the purpose of the theory of coherence (Zernicke 1938) to give a
systematic and exact account of these ideas, which are fundamental
to the behaviour of interferometers.

Suppose that a beam of light is divided and that the two parts
subsequently recombine with a relative delay Δt. Let the spectrum
contain energy over a range of frequency $\Delta \nu$. At a particular frequency
ν_1, the phase of the interference fringes formed between the two parts
of the beam on recombination will be $2\pi\nu_1 \Delta t$, while at some other
frequency ν_2 it will be $2\pi\nu_2 \Delta t$. The fringes will be exactly out of phase if

$$2\pi(\nu_2 - \nu_1) \Delta t = \pi. \tag{2.2}$$

Thus we may say that $\Delta \nu$. Δt must be of order 1 or less if fringes are to
be seen.

Δt, approximately equal to $1/\Delta \nu$, is known as the *coherence time* of the
radiation, while $c \Delta t$ is known as the *coherence length*.

An idea that will recur continually is that of *quasi-monochromatic
radiation*, that is radiation such that the width of the spectrum is very
much less than the mean frequency ν_0: $\Delta\nu/\nu_0 \ll 1$.

Some typical values for $\Delta\nu/\nu_0$, the relative width of the spectrum,
are 10^{-2} to 10^{-6} for radio or television broadcasts, 10^{-6} for narrow lines
from optical spectroscopic sources, and 10^{-12} for lines from gas lasers.

TABLE 1

Properties of typical sources of radiation

	Gas discharge	Laser	Radio transmitter	Mossbauer γ^δ rays
Frequency ν_0(Hz)	6×10^{14}	5×10^{14}	10^{10}	3×10^{18}
Wavelength (nm)	500	600	3×10^7	0·1
Frequency spread $\Delta\nu$(Hz)	10^9	10^3	10^6	10^6
$\Delta\nu/\nu_0$	$1\cdot6 \times 10^{-6}$	2×10^{-12}	10^{-4}	3×10^{-13}
Coherence time (s)	10^{-9}	10^{-3}	10^{-6}	10^{-6}
Coherence length (m)	0·3	3×10^5	300	300
$h\nu_0$(J)	4×10^{-19}	$3\cdot3 \times 10^{-19}$	6×10^{-24}	2×10^{-15}
Typical power (w)	10^{-10}	10^{-3}	10^3	
Photon rate	10^6	5×10^{22}	3×10^{21}	10^3
Degeneracy	10^{-3}	10^{14}	10^{20}	10^{-20}

The photon rate is the number of photons emitted per unit area per unit frequency interval into unit solid angle in unit time.
The degeneracy is the number of photons in the coherence volume and is equal to $\frac{1}{2}(c^2/\nu_0^2) \times$ photon rate.

The properties of radiation from some representative sources over much of the accessible electromagnetic spectrum are listed in Table 1 and will be discussed further below.

Another elementary idea is that of the *area of coherence*. Consider the double pinhole interferometer shown in Fig. 2.1. A source S illuminates a screen in which there are two pinholes P_1 and P_2, and the light transmitted by the two holes forms interference fringes on the plane P. Suppose that s is a point of the source lying on the perpendicular bisector of P_1P_2; the phases of the fields at P_1 and P_2 are then the same

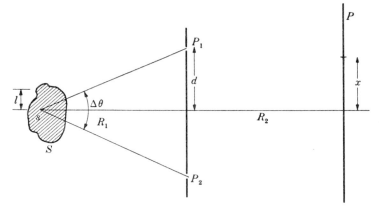

FIG. 2.1. Double pinhole interferometer.

and the maxima of the fringes formed on P occur at distances x parallel to P_1P_2 given by

$$\frac{2\pi}{\lambda}\frac{2dx}{R_2} = 2\pi n, \tag{2.3}$$

where the origin of x is taken at the point where the perpendicular bisector of P_1P_2 meets P. The distances R_2 and d are as shown in Fig. 2.1. Now consider the fringes formed by a source point displaced at distance l as shown; the positions of the maxima will satisfy

$$\frac{2\pi}{\lambda}\,2d\left[\frac{x}{R_2}+\frac{l}{R_1}\right] = 2\pi n. \tag{2.4}$$

If the fringes from the two source points are completely out of phase

$$\frac{4d}{\lambda}\frac{l}{R_1} = 1.$$

Thus if fringes are to be seen from a source of size Δl, the pinholes must subtend at the source an angle $\Delta\theta$ which satisfies the condition

$$\Delta\theta\,.\,\Delta l \leqslant \lambda, \tag{2.5}$$

and the pinholes must lie within an area ΔA equal to

$$(R_1\,\Delta\theta)^2 = R_1^2(\lambda_0/\Delta l)^2,$$

that is

$$\lambda_0^2 R_1^2/S,$$

where S is the area of the source.

ΔA is the area of coherence. The width of the spectrum of the source has been ignored and the argument applies only to the fringes close to the centre of the pattern.

It is also possible to define a *volume of coherence*, which for a nearly plane, quasi-monochromatic wave, may be written as

$$\Delta V = c\,\Delta t\,\Delta A = \frac{R^2}{S}\cdot\frac{\lambda_0}{\Delta\lambda}\cdot\lambda_0^3. \tag{2.6}$$

It is the same as the elementary cell of geometrical phase space in the quantum mechanical sense. An extension of the uncertainty principle shows that if Δp_x is the extent of one coordinate of momentum within which a particle may lie and if Δq_x is the corresponding range of the positional coordinate, then the hypervolume of the six-dimensional cell within which the momenta and coordinates are simultaneously to be found, namely

$$\Delta p_x\,\Delta p_y\,\Delta p_z\,\Delta q_x\,\Delta q_y\,\Delta q_z, \quad \text{is} \quad h^3. \tag{2.7}$$

Now the range of the longitudinal momentum of a photon, Δp_z, is $h\,\Delta\nu/c$, while the ranges of the transverse momenta, Δp_x, Δp_y, are $(h\nu_0/c)\,.\,(\Delta l/R)$, corresponding to the angle of divergence $\Delta l/R$.

It then follows that the space-like factor of phase space, ΔV, that is $h^3/[\Delta p_x \, \Delta p_y \, \Delta p_z]$, is equal to $(c\lambda_0^2 R^2)/[\Delta\nu(\Delta l)^2]$, that is $(\lambda_0^4/\Delta\lambda)(R^2/S)$, the same result as that derived on the classical picture.

The last notion that we require is that of *degeneracy*. A system is said to be degenerate in the sense of quantum mechanics if a cell of phase space is occupied by more than one photon; the degeneracies listed in Table 1 have been calculated on this basis. Fluctuation noise in a quantum mechanical system depends on the degeneracy, the greater the degeneracy, the less the noise, and in practical applications it is very much easier to work with degenerate radiation.

An outline of the theory of coherence in terms of a classical field description will now be set out. It is possible to give a description entirely in terms of quantum field theory but the results are indistinguishable from those of classical theory (Mandel and Wolf 1965, Beran and Parrent 1964).

Let $V^{(r)}(\mathbf{r}, t)$ be a real classical wave function, for example, $\mathbf{E}$ or $\mathbf{A}$; it is in general a vector ($\mathbf{r}$ is the position vector and t is the time). Let it have a Fourier representation:

$$\mathbf{V}^{(r)}(\mathbf{r}, t) = \int_{-\infty}^{+\infty} \mathbf{v}(\mathbf{r}, \nu)\exp(-2\pi i\nu t) \, d\nu. \tag{2.8}$$

Since $\mathbf{V}^{(r)}$ is real, $\mathbf{v}(\mathbf{r}, -\nu) = \mathbf{v}^*(\mathbf{r}, \nu)$ so that the negative frequency terms give no information additional to the ordinary positive frequency terms.

It is therefore possible to associate with $\mathbf{V}^{(r)}(\mathbf{r}, t)$ a complex function $\mathbf{V}(\mathbf{r}, t)$ that contains exactly the same information as does $\mathbf{V}^{(r)}(\mathbf{r}, t)$. $\mathbf{V}(\mathbf{r}, t)$ is

$$\int_0^{\infty} \mathbf{v}(\mathbf{r}, \nu)\exp(-2\pi i\nu t) \, d\nu.$$

$\mathbf{V}$ is analytic, although $\mathbf{V}^{(r)}$ need not be, and

$$\mathbf{V}(\mathbf{r}, t) = \tfrac{1}{2}[\mathbf{V}^{(r)}(\mathbf{r}, t) + i\mathbf{V}^{(i)}(\mathbf{r}, t)]. \tag{2.9}$$

$\mathbf{V}^{(r)}$, $\mathbf{V}^{(i)}$ are reciprocal Hilbert transforms:

$$\mathbf{V}^{(i)}(\mathbf{r}, t) = \frac{1}{\pi} P \int_{-\infty}^{+\infty} \frac{\mathbf{V}^{(r)}(\mathbf{r}, t') \, dt'}{t' - t},$$

$$\mathbf{V}^{(r)}(\mathbf{r}, t) = \frac{1}{\pi} P \int_{-\infty}^{+\infty} \frac{\mathbf{V}^{(i)}(\mathbf{r}, t') \, dt'}{t' - t} \tag{2.10}$$

(P denotes the Cauchy principal value of the integral at $t' = t$).

Since V contains exactly the same information as $V^{(r)}$, $V^{(i)}$ is not independent of $V.^{(r)}$

If the field is linearly polarized, V may be a scalar.

The *coherence function* $\Gamma(\mathbf{r}_1, \mathbf{r}_2, t_1, t_2)$ is defined to be

$$\langle V^*(\mathbf{r}_1, t_1) \cdot V(\mathbf{r}_2, t_2) \rangle_e$$

that is the ensemble average of the scalar products of $V(\mathbf{r}_2, t_2)$ and the complex conjugate of $V(\mathbf{r}_1, t_1)$. The ensemble average is the average taken over all values of V that satisfy the conditions of the problem.

Γ measures the correlation between the field at $(\mathbf{r}_2, t_2)$ and the complex conjugate of the field at $(\mathbf{r}_1, t_1)$. If the co-ordinates and the times are the same, Γ is the average intensity at the point:

$$\Gamma(\mathbf{r}_1, \mathbf{r}_1, t_1, t_1) = \langle V^*(\mathbf{r}_1, t_1) \cdot V(\mathbf{r}_1, t_1) \rangle_e = \langle I(\mathbf{r}_1, t_1) \rangle_e. \quad (2.11)$$

In most practical circumstances there is a great simplification, because usually the averages do not depend on the origin from which the time is reckoned; they are then said to be *stationary* and the ensemble averages are equivalent to averages with respect to time. This situation is expressed by writing $\Gamma(\mathbf{r}_1, \mathbf{r}_2, \tau)$ instead of $\Gamma(\mathbf{r}_1, \mathbf{r}_2, t_1, t_2)$, where $\tau = t_2 - t_1$, and the averages are independent of the absolute value of t_1 or t_2.

In these circumstances,

$$\Gamma(\mathbf{r}_1, \mathbf{r}_2, \tau) = \frac{1}{2T} \lim_{T \to \infty} \int_{-T}^{+T} V^*(\mathbf{r}_1, t) \cdot V(\mathbf{r}_2, t+\tau) \, dt. \quad (2.12)$$

The numerical value of $\Gamma(\mathbf{r}_1, \mathbf{r}_2, \tau)$ depends on the magnitude of the fields and it is more convenient in the applications of the theory of coherence to the study of interference phenomena to use instead the *mutual coherence function*, $\gamma(\mathbf{r}_1, \mathbf{r}_2, \tau)$, which is normalized to have a maximum value of 1:

$$\gamma(\mathbf{r}_1, \mathbf{r}_2, \tau) = \Gamma(\mathbf{r}_1, \mathbf{r}_2, \tau)/[\Gamma(\mathbf{r}_1, \mathbf{r}_2, 0) \cdot \Gamma(\mathbf{r}_2, \mathbf{r}_2, 0)]^{\frac{1}{2}}$$

$$= \Gamma(\mathbf{r}_1, \mathbf{r}_2, \tau)/\langle I(\mathbf{r}_1) \rangle^{\frac{1}{2}} \langle I(\mathbf{r}_2) \rangle^{\frac{1}{2}}. \quad (2.13)$$

The relation between coherence and interference can be understood by considering a simple example, again the two-pinhole interferometer (Fig. 2.2). Let P_1 and P_2 be the two pinholes and let P be the point at which the interference phenomena are observed. Let $\mathbf{r}_1, \mathbf{r}_2$ be the position vectors of P_1 and P_2 respectively, and $\mathbf{r}$ that of P. Let the field at P_1 be written as $V_1(\mathbf{r}_1, t_1)$ and let the field that it produces at P be $K_1 V_1(\mathbf{r}_1, t_1)$, where K_1 is a complex geometrical factor that depends on the size of

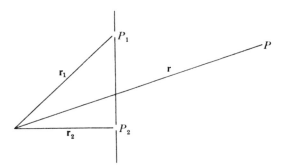

FIG. 2.2. Position vectors for pinhole interferometer.

the pinhole and the distance of P from P_1. Similarly, the field at P due to the field at P_2 is $K_2\mathbf{V}_2(\mathbf{r}_2, t_2)$. The total field at P is then

$$\mathbf{V}(\mathbf{r}, t) = K_1\mathbf{V}_1(\mathbf{r}_1, t-t_1) + K_2\mathbf{V}_2(\mathbf{r}_2, t-t_2),$$

where the time has been rewritten by putting $t_1 = |\mathbf{r}_1|/c$, $t_2 = |\mathbf{r}_2|/c$.

The average intensity of the total field at P is

$$\langle I(\mathbf{r}, t)\rangle = \langle \mathbf{V}^*(\mathbf{r}, t) . \mathbf{V}(\mathbf{r}, t)\rangle$$

$$= \langle\{K_1^*\mathbf{V}_1^*(\mathbf{r}_1, t-t_1) + K_2^*\mathbf{V}_2^*(\mathbf{r}_2, t-t_2)\} \times$$

$$\times \{K_1\mathbf{V}_1(\mathbf{r}_1, t-t_1) + K_2\mathbf{V}_2(\mathbf{r}_2, t-t_2)\}\rangle$$

$$= |K_1|^2 I_1 + |K_2|^2 I_2 + 2\operatorname{Re}\{K_1^*K_2\Gamma(\mathbf{r}_1, \mathbf{r}_2, t_2-t_1)\}, \qquad (2.14)$$

where I_1 is the intensity at P_1 at time t.

The formula may be simplified slightly by setting $I^{(1)} = |K_1|^2 I_1$, that is $I^{(1)}$ is the intensity at P due to radiation coming from the pinhole P_1. Then

$$I(\mathbf{r}, t) = I^{(1)} + I^{(2)} + 2(I^{(1)}I^{(2)})^{\frac{1}{2}} \operatorname{Re} \gamma\left(\mathbf{r}_1, \mathbf{r}_2, \frac{|\mathbf{r}_2|-|\mathbf{r}_1|}{c}\right). \qquad (2.15)$$

The first two terms are just the intensities due to the two pinholes separately and there is no interference phenomenon if the mutual coherence of the fields from the two pinholes is zero. This is a quite general result: the magnitude of the interference effect depends on the magnitude of the mutual coherence function.

Suppose that we are to consider quasi-monochromatic light with a centre frequency ν_0. Then write

$$\gamma(\mathbf{r}_1, \mathbf{r}_2, t) = |\gamma| \exp i(\alpha - 2\pi\nu_0 t), \qquad (2.16)$$

where α is equal to $\arg \gamma(\mathbf{r}_1, \mathbf{r}_2, t) + 2\pi\nu_0 t$.

α then varies slowly with time. It therefore varies slowly with the change in the relative positions of P_1 and P_2 with respect to P. (A fast change is one with a frequency ν_0, a slow one has a frequency of order $\Delta\nu$ or less.)

Thus

$$I(P) = I(\mathbf{r}, t) = I^{(1)} + I^{(2)} + 2(I^{(1)}I^{(2)})^{\frac{1}{2}} |\gamma| \cos(\alpha - \phi), \quad (2.17)$$

where

$$\phi = 2\pi\nu_0(r_2 - r_1)/c = k_0(r_2 - r_1),$$

with

$$k_0 = 2\pi/\lambda_0.$$

$I^{(1)}$, $I^{(2)}$, and α all vary slowly with changes in the positions of P_1 and P_2 and so the dominant variation of $I(P)$ is as $\cos k_0(r_2 - r_1)$.

There is a maximum intensity whenever $k_0(r_2 - r_1) = 2\pi n$ or, more strictly, when $\arg \gamma = \alpha - k_0(r_2 - r_1) = 2\pi n$.

These maxima lie on hyperboloids of revolution.

The contrast in the fringes is measured by the *visibility*, defined by A. A. Michelson as

$$\mathscr{V} = \frac{\langle I \rangle_{\max} - \langle I \rangle_{\min}}{\langle I \rangle_{\max} + \langle I \rangle_{\min}}. \quad (2.18)$$

Since

$$\langle I \rangle_{\max} = I^{(1)} + I^{(2)} + 2(I^{(1)}I^{(2)})^{\frac{1}{2}} |\gamma|$$

and

$$\langle I \rangle_{\min} = I^{(1)} + I^{(2)} - 2(I^{(1)}I^{(2)})^{\frac{1}{2}} |\gamma|,$$

it follows that

$$\mathscr{V} = 2 |\gamma|/(\rho + \rho^{-1}), \quad (2.19)$$

where

$$\rho = (I^{(1)}/I^{(2)})^{\frac{1}{2}}.$$

It is important to notice that the visibility depends on the ratio of the intensities of the two fields as well as on the mutual coherence.

It is shown in Appendix 2 that the coherence function satisfies the wave equation

$$\nabla_j^2 \Gamma = \frac{1}{c^2}\frac{\partial \Gamma}{\partial t} \quad (j = 1, 2), \quad (2.20)$$

where ∇_j^2 is the Laplace operator with respect to the coordinates of r_j, that is

$$\frac{\partial^2}{\partial x_j} + \frac{\partial^2}{\partial y_j} + \frac{\partial^2}{\partial z_j}.$$

Equation (2.20) may be used to examine the variation of the coherence of two fields from place to place in space, as will be seen later in connection with interferometers used to measure the angular sizes of stars.

The equation also shows that it is not in general possible to factorize Γ into a factor that is a function of the space coordinates only and one that is a function of the time only (when it is possible, the factors may not be independent).

The following definitions and formulae relating the coherence functions to the functions of the theory of spectra and correlation are sometimes required. $\Gamma(\mathbf{r}_1, \mathbf{r}_2, t)$ is the *cross-correlation function* of $V(\mathbf{r}_1)$ and $V(\mathbf{r}_2)$, while $\Gamma(\mathbf{r}, \mathbf{r}, t)$ is the *auto-correlation function* of $V(\mathbf{r}, t)$.

The power spectrum and $\Gamma(\mathbf{r}, \mathbf{r}, t)$ are Fourier transforms of each other:

$$\Gamma(\mathbf{r}, \mathbf{r}, t) = \int_{-\infty}^{\infty} W(\mathbf{r}, \mathbf{r}, \nu)\exp(-2\pi i\nu t)\,d\nu,$$

$$(2.21)$$

$$W(\mathbf{r}, \mathbf{r}, \nu) = \int_{-\infty}^{+\infty} \Gamma(\mathbf{r}, \mathbf{r}, t)\exp(2\pi i\nu t)\,dt,$$

while $\Gamma(\mathbf{r}_1, \mathbf{r}_2, t)$ is similarly related to the *cross-spectral density*:

$$\Gamma(\mathbf{r}_1, \mathbf{r}_2, t) = \int_{-\infty}^{\infty} W(\mathbf{r}_1, \mathbf{r}_2, \nu)\exp(-2\pi i\nu t)\,d\nu,$$

$$(2.21a)$$

$$W(\mathbf{r}_1, \mathbf{r}_2, \nu) = \int_{-\infty}^{+\infty} \Gamma(\mathbf{r}_1, \mathbf{r}_2, t)\exp(2\pi i\nu t)\,dt.$$

These relations are the basis of spectroscopic methods using Fourier transforms.

As has already been mentioned and as will be discussed in more detail later, there are simplifications in the formulae for quasi-monochromatic light, that is when W is negligible except for frequencies close to ν_0.

Polarization

Polarization is also a phenomenon that involves correlation, for in unpolarized light there is no relation between perpendicular components of the field vectors, whereas in polarized radiation they are correlated. Thus in unpolarized radiation, a resultant field vector has constant amplitude but random direction. The relation between the pependicular components of a field vector in polarized radiation can be shown by the locus of the end of the resultant vector, as indicated in Fig. 2.3. If the field is linearly polarized, the vector lies always in the same straight line

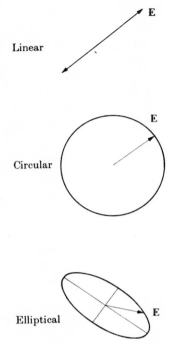

FIG. 2.3. Types of polarization.

and the ratio of the components E_x and E_y, say, is a real constant, while if the resultant vector is of constant amplitude but rotates uniformly in a plane, the field is circularly polarized. Generally, the end of the vector traces out an ellipse and the field is elliptically polarized.

Fresnel and Arago found in 1816 that two beams of light polarized at right angles do not interfere and inferred from this that light is a transverse wave motion. Let the two wave trains a and b be represented by the Cartesian components of the field vectors:

$$\mathbf{E}_a = (a_1 e^{-i\theta_1},\ a_2 e^{-i\theta_2},\ a_3 e^{-i\theta_3}),$$
$$\mathbf{E}_b = (b_1 e^{-i\phi_1},\ b_2 e^{-i\phi_2},\ b_3 e^{-i\phi_3}).$$

$$(2.22)$$

Let

$$\theta_1 - \phi_1 = \psi_1, \qquad \theta_2 - \phi_2 = \psi_2, \qquad \theta_3 - \phi_3 = \psi_3.$$

The total intensity is then

$$|E_a|^2 + |E_b|^2 + 2(a_1 b_1 \cos\psi_1 + a_2 b_2 \cos\psi_2 + a_3 b_3 \cos\psi_3). \qquad (2.23)$$

Let the direction of propagation be chosen to be the direction 3.

If the polarization of train b is rotated by 90° about direction 3 relative to the polarization of train a, the scalar product of the projections of the field vectors on to the plane normal to direction 3 is zero, that is

$$a_1 b_1 e^{i\psi_1} + a_2 b_2 e^{i\psi_2} = 0.$$

If the further experimental conditions are imposed that the light should be linearly polarized ($\theta_1 = \theta_2$, $\phi_1 = \phi_2$) and that the interferometer should shift the phase and change the amplitude of all components independently of direction of polarization, it follows that

$$\psi_1 = \psi_2 = \psi, \qquad \text{say,}$$

and since

$$a_1 b_1 e^{i\psi_1} + a_2 b_2 e^{i\psi_2} \qquad \text{is zero,}$$

so is $(a_1 b_1 + a_2 b_2)\cos\psi$.

The interference term therefore reduces to $2a_3 b_3 \cos\psi_3$ and since experiment shows it to be zero, it follows that both a_3 and b_3 are zero, that is that light has no longitudinal component (see Whittaker 1951, pp. 114, 115).

Historically this was a very important result, although nowadays it is deduced from Maxwell's equations.

Four parameters are necessary to give a complete description of polarized radiation, for example, the intensities of the polarized and unpolarized components, the ratio of the major and minor axes of the ellipse described by a field vector, and the direction of the major axis. The traditional parameters were introduced by Sir George Stokes, but others are sometimes more convenient. A complex representation is often useful but the one used here is the *coherency matrix* introduced by Born and Wolf (1959); it is defined as follows. Let the field components in two perpendicular directions be E_x and E_y. The coherency matrix **J** is then

$$\left\langle \begin{pmatrix} E_x \\ E_y \end{pmatrix} \cdot (E_x^*, E_y^*) \right\rangle = \begin{pmatrix} \langle E_x E_x^* \rangle \langle E_x E_y^* \rangle \\ \langle E_y E_x^* \rangle \langle E_y E_y^* \rangle \end{pmatrix}. \tag{2.24}$$

Now the Stokes parameters are

$$I = |E_x|^2 + |E_y|^2,$$
$$Q = |E_x|^2 - |E_y|^2,$$
$$U = |E_x|\,|E_y|\cos\delta,$$
$$V = |E_x|\,|E_y|\sin\delta,$$

where δ is the phase difference between E_x and E_y. The coherency matrix is then

$$\begin{pmatrix} I+Q & U+iV \\ U-iV & I-Q \end{pmatrix}.$$

It may also be written in terms of the Pauli spin matrices,

$$\boldsymbol{\sigma}_1 = \begin{pmatrix} 0 & 1 \\ 1 & 0 \end{pmatrix}, \qquad \boldsymbol{\sigma}_2 = \begin{pmatrix} 0 & -i \\ i & 0 \end{pmatrix}, \qquad \boldsymbol{\sigma}_3 = \begin{pmatrix} 1 & 0 \\ 0 & -1 \end{pmatrix},$$

namely

$$\mathbf{J} = I\mathbf{1} + U\boldsymbol{\sigma}_1 - V\boldsymbol{\sigma}_2 + Q\boldsymbol{\sigma}_3.$$

(**1** is the 2×2 unit matrix).

In unpolarized light there is no statistically stable relation between E_x and E_y so that the mean values of $E_x E_y^*$ and $E_y E_x^*$ are zero and, since there is no preferred direction, $\langle E_x E_x^* \rangle = \langle E_y E_y^* \rangle$. Hence

$$\mathbf{J} \propto \begin{pmatrix} 1 & 0 \\ 0 & 1 \end{pmatrix}. \tag{2.25}$$

In linear polarization, E_x/E_y is a constant, α say:

$$\mathbf{J} \propto \begin{pmatrix} 1 & \alpha \\ \alpha & \alpha^2 \end{pmatrix}. \tag{2.25a}$$

In circular polarization, $E_x = ae^{i\omega t}$, $E_y = ae^{i(\omega t+\frac{1}{2}\pi)}$, and

$$\mathbf{J} = a^2 \begin{pmatrix} 1 & -i \\ i & 1 \end{pmatrix}. \tag{2.25b}$$

Two fields are said to be *oppositely polarized* if the sum field is unpolarized. If the two fields 1 and 2 are independent, so that quantities such as $\langle E_{1x} E_{2x}^* \rangle$, $\langle E_{1x}^* E_{2y}^* \rangle$ are zero, it follows directly from the definition (2.25) that the coherency matrix of the sum field is the sum of the coherency matrices of the separate fields:

$$\mathbf{J} = \mathbf{J}_1 + \mathbf{J}_2.$$

If the sum field is unpolarized its coherency matrix is proportional to the unit matrix

$$\begin{pmatrix} 1 & 0 \\ 0 & 1 \end{pmatrix},$$

and so the coherency matrices of the separate fields must be of the form

$$\begin{pmatrix} A & B \\ B^* & C \end{pmatrix} \quad \text{and} \quad \begin{pmatrix} C & -B \\ -B^* & A \end{pmatrix}.$$

Fields with coherency matrices so related are oppositely polarized. The off-diagonal terms of the matrices then satisfy the conditions:

$$\langle E_{1x}E_{1y}^{*}\rangle = -\langle E_{2x}E_{2y}^{*}\rangle$$

and

$$\langle E_{1y}E_{1x}^{*}\rangle = -\langle E_{2y}E_{2x}^{*}\rangle. \tag{2.26}$$

Let $E_{1x} = \alpha_1 + i\beta_1$, $E_{1y} = \gamma_1 + i\delta_1$ and so on.

The conditions (2.26) than lead to the equations

$$\alpha_1\gamma_1 - \beta_1\delta_1 = -\alpha_2\gamma_2 + \beta_2\delta_2,$$

$$\beta_1\gamma_1 + \alpha_1\delta_1 = -\beta_2\gamma_2 - \alpha_2\delta_2, \tag{2.27}$$

which are satisfied by

$$\alpha_2 = -\gamma_1, \qquad \beta_2 = +\delta_1,$$

$$\alpha_1 = +\gamma_2, \qquad \beta_1 = -\delta_2. \tag{2.28}$$

With these values, the conditions on the diagonal terms of the coherency matrices, namely

$$\langle E_{1x}E_{1x}^{*}\rangle = \langle E_{2y}E_{2y}^{*}\rangle,$$

$$\langle E_{1y}E_{1y}^{*}\rangle = \langle E_{2x}E_{2x}^{*}\rangle, \tag{2.29}$$

are also satisfied.

The intensity of the sum of two oppositely polarized fields is

$$\langle (E_{1x}+E_{2x}).(E_{1x}^{*}+E_{2x}^{*})\rangle + \langle (E_{1y}+E_{2y}).(E_{1y}^{*}+E_{2y}^{*})\rangle$$

$$= I_1 + I_2 + (\langle E_{2x}E_{1x}^{*}\rangle + \langle E_{2y}E_{1y}^{*}\rangle) + (\langle E_{1x}E_{2x}^{*}\rangle + \langle E_{1y}E_{2y}^{*}\rangle). \tag{2.30}$$

The interference term is

$$2(\alpha_1\alpha_2 + \beta_1\beta_2 + \gamma_1\gamma_2 + \delta_1\delta_2),$$

which vanishes by the condition for opposite polarization (2.28). Thus, *oppositely polarized fields do not interfere.*

Consider, as an example, two beams of linearly polarized light. Let the electric vectors of the one beam be

$$E_x = a_1 e^{i\nu t}, \qquad E_y = b_1 e^{i\nu t},$$

and of the other

$$E_x = a_2 e^{i(\nu t + \phi_1)}, \qquad E_y = b_2 e^{i(\nu t + \phi_2)}.$$

The total intensity is

$$I = |a_1 + a_2 e^{i\phi_1}|^2 + |b_1 + b_2 e^{i\phi_2}|^2$$

$$= a_1^2 + a_2^2 + 2a_1a_2 \cos\phi_1 + b_1^2 + b_2^2 + 2b_1b_2 \cos\phi_2, \tag{2.31}$$

from which it appears that the two polarizations interfere independently. The conditions for opposite polarization are

$$\phi_1 = \phi_2, \qquad a_1 = b_2, \qquad a_2 = -b_1.$$

Thus the total intensity is $2(a_1^2 + b_1^2)$ and there is no interference effect.

Particular cases of interference of polarized light, both wanted and unwanted, will arise in later chapters; it can be seen quite generally from the above arguments that for optimum performance of an interferometer, any polarization introduced by the interferometer must be the same for all interfering beams and, further, that any scattered or parasitic light that may interfere with the desired beams should have no constant polarization relation to them.

MICHELSON–FIZEAU INTERFEROMETERS

I—THEORY

THE Michelson spectroscopic interferometer is one of the simplest but at the same time one of the most important of all interferometers. It is distinguished here as a spectroscopic interferometer because there is another interferometer, also due to A. A. Michelson, that is an angular interferometer used to measure the angular diameter of stars.

The parallel-plate arrangement

The principle of the spectroscopic interferometer is readily demonstrated with a laser source by means of very simple apparatus such as is shown in Fig. 3.1(a). The source S is a gas laser producing a highly collimated, highly monochromatic, coherent beam directed on to the semi-reflecting mirror M_s, which reflects a fraction of the incident light on to the fully reflecting mirror M_1, and transmits another fraction to the second fully reflecting mirror M_2. M_1 and M_2 reflect the respective partial beams back to the semi-reflecting mirror where a portion of each is transmitted or reflected to the detector D, which is supposed to be a photoelectric device. The three mirrors are adjusted so that the two beams, when they fall on the detector, are coincident and parallel. This is easy to do with a laser source because the beams are so small and so bright that there is no difficulty in seeing when they coincide on the detector.

Now suppose that the distance of M_2 from some point in the semi-reflecting surface of M_s is l greater than that of M_1 from the same point. These distances are of course well defined because when the mirrors are properly adjusted, the beams reflected from them coincide on the semi-reflecting surface. The phase of the light reflected from M_2 therefore lags behind that of the beam reflected from M_1 by $4\pi l/\lambda_0$, that is, if $t = 2l/c$, the phase lag is $\omega_0 t$. λ_0 and ω_0 are the centre values of wavelength and angular frequency for a quasi-monochromatic source and, with a gas laser, variations from them can often be neglected.

When the mirrors are correctly adjusted, light from a ray that originally passed through a particular point on the semi-reflecting surface combines with light that also originally passed through the same point, and the beams, when they fall on the detector, may be considered to be

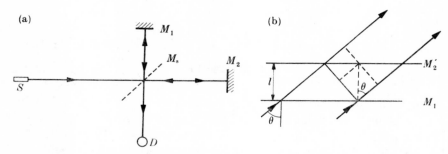

FIG. 3.1. Elementary two-beam interferometer.

spatially quite coherent. The variation of the intensity at the detector will therefore be proportional to $\cos \omega_0 t$, and if one mirror is moved parallel to itself through a distance x, while maintaining the angular adjustment of the system, the intensity will vary like $\cos 2kx$, where $k = 2\pi/\lambda_0$. The system with source, detectors, and mirrors is only practicable because a gas laser produces a highly collimated beam in a well-defined direction.

For purposes of analysis it is often possible to replace the actual system of beam divider and two mirrors by a model consisting of two parallel mirrors, namely a mirror in the position of M_1 and a second in the position of the image of M_2 formed in M_s (as seen from the detector). If the mirrors of the model are supposed to be semi-reflecting in the sense that a beam can be reflected once only by either mirror, the properties of the model are equivalent to the actual fully reflecting mirrors and semi-reflecting mirror, but it is easier to analyse the geometry of the two-mirror model.

With the equivalent pair of plates, consider a beam of light incident at an angle θ to the common normal to the plates (the plates are assumed to be parallel). Let the separation of the plates by l (Fig. 3.1(b)). Where the rays intersect a plane perpendicular to the incident beam, the path difference between the beam that passes through the plates without reflection and the one that suffers one reflection between the plates is $2l \cos \theta$. In general the direct and once-reflected beams will not coincide on a detector because the reflected one is displaced laterally from the direct one; if, however, a lens is placed after the plates, the two beams, being parallel, will come to a focus at the same point and will interfere on a detector placed there; on account of the fundamental property of a lens, the phase difference at the focus will be the same as on any plane perpendicular to the beams in front of the lens. It must be emphasized that the fundamental reason for placing a lens in front of the detector of a Michelson interferometer is to bring beams that are parallel, but have been displaced by reflection between the plates, into coincidence at the detector. The focusing process reduces the coherence of the two beams slightly because the beams are no longer parallel when they intersect at the detector and the field vectors are therefore also not parallel. The coherence is therefore reduced by the cosine of the angle between the vectors (which depends on the polarization of the light) but the effect is small and usually neglected.

Evidently all rays that lie on the cone of semi-angle θ about the normal to the plates suffer the same retardation; the corresponding locus in the focal plane of the lens is a circle with its centre at the

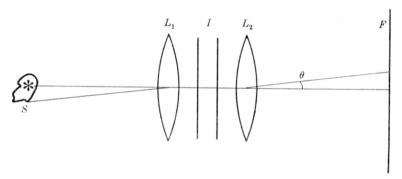

Fig. 3.2. Lens system for parallel-plate interferometer.

intersection of the normal with the focal plane. The intensity of the light will be a maximum on rings for which $2l \cos \theta = n\lambda_0$ and will be a minimum on rings for which $2l \cos \theta = \frac{1}{2}(n + 1)\lambda_0$. To see the rings in the focal plane of the lens, an extended area of the focal plane must be illuminated, that is, the interferometer must be illuminated with light over a wide range of angles. The usual arrangement is shown in Fig. 3.2 S is an extended source and L_1 is a lens with its focal plane close to the source. I is the interferometer and L_2 is a lens that focuses parallel rays on the focal plane F. If S is in the focal plane of L_1 it will be imaged on F and the brightness of the image on F will be a maximum. The clarity of the fringes is not dependent on the position of the source and it is only necessary that F should be at the focus of L_2 so that the circle of confusion on F for parallel light is least. If a photographic plate is placed at F a photograph of the rings will appear. If a diffusing screen is placed at F the rings can be seen by eye because the screen scatters light from the direct and reflected beams with the same phase shift, so that light from these two beams reaches a point on the retina in the same phase relation as it left the interferometer; interference then occurs in the retina, where the photoelectric effect takes place.

With monochromatic light the angular radii of the rings in the plane F are given by

$$2l \cos \theta = n\lambda, \qquad (3.1)$$

where n is an integer.

At the centre of the pattern, where $\cos \theta = 1$,

$$2l = (n_0 + \epsilon)\lambda. \qquad (3.1a)$$

n_0 is the integral part of the order of interference; ϵ is the fractional part at the centre.

If f is the focal length of the lens L_2, and if r is the linear radius of a bright ring,

$$\cos \theta = \frac{f}{(f^2 + r^2)^{\frac{1}{2}}} \doteqdot 1 - \tfrac{1}{2}r^2/f^2. \qquad (3.2)$$

Hence

$$1 - \tfrac{1}{2}r^2/f^2 = n\lambda/2l, \qquad (3.2a)$$

while

$$1 = (n_0 + \epsilon)\lambda/2l.$$

Now let $n_0 - n = p$, the number of the ring counting outwards from the centre of the pattern. Then

$$\frac{r^2}{f^2} = (p + \epsilon)\frac{\lambda}{l}. \qquad (3.3)$$

The linear radius of a ring is proportional to the focal length of the telescope lens L_2, proportional to the square root of the wavelength, and inversely proportional to the square root of the separation of the interferometer plates. Rings of this pattern are known as *Haidinger rings*.

The Michelson interferometer in the parallel plate arrangement is an angular filter with the transmittance in a particular direction proportional to $\cos(2\pi l \cos \theta/\lambda)$.

The essential function of the auxiliary optical system is to separate directions. If the source is a laser producing a very narrow beam, no auxiliary system is needed because the laser beam itself defines the direction, but with other sources, a particular direction is selected by the lens L_2 and a position in the focal plane F; the collimating arrangement is not critical and only affects the overall intensity of the transmitted light. It is important that fringes formed with an extended source should be viewed in the focal plane of the lens L_2, for if not, directions are not well defined by position in the plane in which the detector is placed and the fringes are not sharp.

The fringes formed in monochromatic light may be observed in three ways. Michelson himself worked visually. The distance l is fixed and the viewing plane F is located in the focal plane of an eyepiece. Fringe diameters may be measured with a micrometer eyepiece, a wire moving in the plane F being set tangentially to each fringe in succession. In photographic use, a photographic plate is placed in the plane F, and, after development, diameters of rings may be measured on the plate. Visual and photographic observations have nowadays little application with the Michelson interferometer and a discussion of details of experimental arrangements and the numerical treatment of the data will be deferred until the chapter on the Fabry–Perot interferometer, with which similar observations are still of importance. The modern use of the Michelson interferometer involves almost exclusively photoelectric observations: the light transmitted within a small solid angle around the normal to the plates is isolated by a diaphragm and is measured photoelectrically. The intensity of the transmitted light is proportional to $\cos 2\pi l/\lambda$; the length l is not kept constant but is varied over a range of one or two wavelengths so that the phase and amplitude of the sinusoidal intensity variation may be determined.

The Michelson interferometer is the most versatile of all interferometers and its applications are extensive, as will be seen in detail in Chapter 4. In spectroscopy it is used to study both quasi-monochromatic and extended spectra, for in all cases the intensity of the light transmitted normally to the plates is a function of the separation l and is the Fourier transform of the spectrum of the incident light. Michelson himself made the first observations of this sort with quasi-monochromatic light, estimating the visibility and phase of the fringes from visual observations; his choice of the red line of cadmium to provide the wavelength standard was made on the basis of detailed studies of the profiles of a number of lines carried out by these means (see also Pérard 1928, 1953; Duffieux 1939). Now that a large computer can be used to calculate the Fourier transformations, extended spectra and not just isolated line spectra can be studied with the Michelson interferometer.

It was also Michelson himself who first made metrological use of the interferometer. In the first place very accurate measurements of ratios of wavelengths can be obtained from the relative positions of the fringes formed in the different lines. Then, by relating the separation l to a mechanical standard of length, wavelengths may be determined in terms of such a standard, as Michelson did in his classical work. Nowadays wavelengths are taken as the basic standards of length and mechanical lengths are found in terms of them, most simply by counting electronically the number of fringes passing the detector as one of the plates is moved through the distance to be measured; this is quite easy to do with a laser source but other less direct means were employed before lasers became available (see Chapter 8).

The inclined-plate arrangement

If the pair of virtual semi-reflecting mirrors equivalent to the actual interferometer are at a slight angle instead of being parallel, and if the system is illuminated with light perpendicular to M_1, the path difference between light reflected from M_1 and M_2' is $2l$, but now l varies over the face of the mirror-pair, and the intensity of the transmitted light, which is proportional to $\cos(2\pi 2l/\lambda)$, varies with position over the mirrors, so that the optical system used to view the fringes formed through inclined plates must distinguish between different positions across the plates instead of different angles of transmission through them. At the same time the direction of the incident light must be limited to a narrow range.

Because the plates M_1 and M_2' are not parallel, the beams of light reflected from them are also not parallel and in general they will not recombine at a detector unless a suitable optical system is provided. The requirements of the system can be seen from the diagrams in Fig. 3.3. When light is transmitted through or reflected from the pair of plates equivalent to the interferometer, the direct and reflected beams intersect on a surface, the location of which depends on the inclinations of the plates to the incident beam. In order to see the fringes at their sharpest, the detector must be focused on the surface, real or virtual, that is the locus of the intersection of the interfering rays. The fringes formed by inclined plates are said to be *localized* because the interfering beams diverge from virtual object points in the surface. Fringes formed by parallel plates are said to be *non-localized* or *localized at infinity*. Localized fringes appear to be formed in certain positions, non-localized fringes are formed at certain angles. The inclined plate form of the interferometer is often used to study the topography of one of the plates, in which case the optical system should form an image of that plate as well as of the fringes.

Let θ be the angle between the plates, and ϕ the angle of incidence of

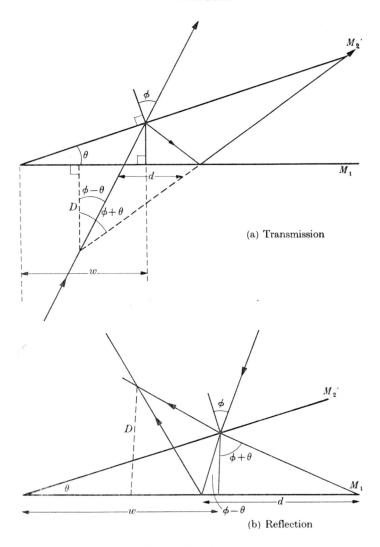

(a) Transmission

(b) Reflection

Fig. 3.3. Localization of fringes.

the light upon the second plate of a pair in transmission (Fig. 3.3(a)). Let D be the perpendicular distance of the point of intersection of the transmitted and reflected rays from the first plate and let d be the separation of the intersections of that plate with the incident and reflected rays. Let w be the distance shown in Fig. 3.3.

Then

$$D\{\tan(\phi+\theta)-\tan(\phi-\theta)\} = d$$
$$= w \tan \theta\{\tan(\phi+\theta)+\tan(\phi-\theta)\},$$

or

$$D = \tfrac{1}{2}w \sec^2\theta \sin 2\phi, \tag{3.4}$$

unless $\theta = 0$, when D is indeterminate.

The intersection of the two rays thus lies on a plane making an angle χ with the front plate, where

$$\tan \chi = \tfrac{1}{2} \sec^2\theta \sin 2\phi.$$

If θ and ϕ are small, D is very nearly $w \sin \phi$. In any case, the point of intersection of the incident and reflected rays lies in front of the first plane if ϕ is negative and behind it if ϕ is positive.

If the fringes are formed by reflection from both plates, and if ϕ is the angle of incidence of light on the front plate (Fig. 3.3(b)), it is again found that

$$D = \tfrac{1}{2}w \sec^2\theta \sin 2\phi.$$

For the incident and reflected rays to intersect, they must lie in the plane perpendicular to the line of intersection of the plates.

Fringe maxima occur whenever

$$2l \cos \phi = n\lambda; \tag{3.5}$$

usually ϕ is 0 and the separation of the maxima is given by

$$x = \lambda/2m, \tag{3.6}$$

where

x is the separation of the maxima

and

m is the gradient of the plate spacing: $(m = \delta l/x)$

The Michelson interferometer in the inclined plate arrangement has many metrological uses. It can be adapted to the measurement of gauge blocks in terms of wavelengths of light, to the study of the form of a reflecting surface, to measurements of refractive index and to testing optical instruments. Further, the theory of the Michelson interferometer in this form applies almost unchanged to interferometers (known as Fizeau interferometers) which are actually constructed of two nearly parallel plates. With suitable coatings on the plates, the optical properties of a Fizeau interferometer can be made very similar to those of the equivalent Michelson interferometer.

If the mirrors of a Michelson interferometer are equidistant from the beam divider along some line on their surfaces, that is if the virtual mirror M_2 intersects the mirror M_1, the path difference along the line of intersection is zero and the beams of light reflected from the two mirrors are in phase for all wavelengths. At this line, therefore, a fringe is seen in white light; to each side of it there is a narrow band in which the phase difference for all wavelengths of visible light is half a wavelength and which therefore appears as a dark fringe in white light, although it is slightly coloured because the minima do not coincide for all wavelengths as the central maxima do. Going further from the centre, the fringes become progressively less distinct as the maxima and minima in different colours get more and more out of step until no more fringes can be distinguished and the field appears uniformly illuminated. The number of distinct fringes depends on the spectrum of the source.

In practice, the optical arrangement has to be modified slightly for fringes to be seen in white light. In the simple system so far considered, the beam divider is a semi-reflecting metal or dielectric film supported on a plate of glass. A plate of thickness t and refractive index μ introduces an additional retardation into one arm of the interferometer but not the other, the additional phase shift being

$$2t(\mu-1)2\pi/\lambda.$$

At a single wavelength, this is compensated by an adjustment of the mechanical spacing of the mirrors and is frequently of no importance in measurements with a few discrete wavelengths, but it prevents the observation of fringes in white light because the refractive index is a function of wavelength and so the additional retardations in a continuous spectrum cannot be compensated by a single readjustment of the mirror positions. In particular, if the positions are adjusted so that the path difference is zero at some wavelength, it will not be zero at other wavelengths, and so no central bright fringe will be seen in white light. For fringes in white light to be seen, an equal thickness of glass of the same dispersion as the divider plate must be inserted in the second arm of the interferometer so that the paths through the glass in the two arms compensate.

The consequences of practical defects in the Michelson interferometer will be analysed in the following sections of this chapter and detailed accounts of the applications of the instrument will be given in Chapter 4.

Michelson's analysis of the interferometer

In the account of his work on the determination of the metre, Michelson published (in an appendix to Michelson and Benoît 1895) a detailed analysis of the behaviour of the interferometer which appears to be almost unknown nowadays, no doubt because the journal is not generally accessible. This is unfortunate, for Michelson deals with a number of problems that cause trouble in practice but that are ignored in text books. In the next few pages, therefore, Michelson's treatment is described, following his own account very closely.

Michelson imagined the actual source and collimator to be replaced by a distribution of intensity across one of the mirrors, a step that is

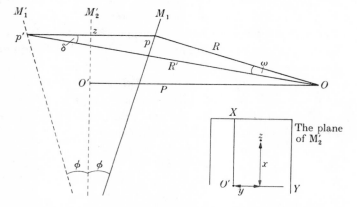

FIG. 3.4. Geometry of Michelson's analysis of his interferometer.

clearly permissible because the incident light is parallel and the distributions of the phase and intensity of the incident light across the mirror do not depend on the distance of the mirror from the collimator. Hence we may imagine an extended source, of area equal to the aperture of the collimator, to lie on the mirror M_1 (Fig. 3.4). In the figure, M_2' is, as before, the image of the actual mirror M_2 in the beam divider. M_1' is the image of M_1 in M_2'. Let p be a point in M_1 and let p' be its image point in M_1'. Denote the distance pp' by $2t$.

Consider first the resultant field at some arbitrary point O due to the source at p and its image at p'.

Let
$$Op = R, \qquad Op' = R',$$
$$R' - R = \Delta.$$
Call the angle $O\hat{p}'p$, δ and the angle $p\hat{O}p'$, ω.

By imagining a perpendicular dropped from p to Op' it can be seen that

$$\Delta = 2t \cos \delta - R(1 - \cos \omega); \tag{3.7}$$

since

$$\sin \omega = \frac{2t}{R} \sin \delta,$$

$$\Delta = 2t \cos \delta \left(1 - \frac{t}{R} \sin^2\delta\right). \tag{3.8}$$

In general t/R or $\sin \delta$, or both, are so small that Δ may be taken to be $2t \cos \delta$. This is certainly true for parallel mirrors and it is nearly true for inclined mirrors with a small path difference, but there are cases in which the assumption needs examination. The subsequent analysis depends on Δ being taken to be $2t \cos \delta$.

Now let the position of the source point be variable. Let O' be the foot of the perpendicular dropped from O on to the mirror M_1'. Let the distance OO' be P.

Let the angle between M_1 and M_1' be 2ϕ.

Take Cartesian axes $O'X$ and $O'Y$ in the plane of M_1', $O'Y$ being parallel to the intersection of the planes M_1 and M_1'. Let the line pp' intersect M_1' in z; let the coordinates of z be x and y, and let x subtend the angle i at O and y the angle θ.

Let $2t_0$ be the separation of M_1 and M_1' at O'. $2t$, the separation pp', is then given by

$$2t = 2t_0 + 2x \tan \phi, \tag{3.9}$$

that is

$$2t = 2(t_0 + P \tan i \tan \phi). \tag{3.9a}$$

Since the angle $p'\hat{O}O'$ equals δ, the angle $z\hat{O}O'$ equals $\delta + \frac{1}{2}\omega$ very nearly, that is $\delta(1 + t/R)$; in most cases, it is sufficient to take $z\hat{O}O'$ to be δ.

Now

$$\tan^2\delta = \tan^2 i + \tan^2\theta,$$

so that

$$\cos \delta = (1 + \tan^2\delta)^{-\frac{1}{2}}$$

$$= (1 + \tan^2 i + \tan^2\theta)^{-\frac{1}{2}}$$

and therefore

$$\Delta = \frac{2(t_0 + P \tan i \tan \phi)}{(1 + \tan^2 i + \tan^2 \phi)} . \tag{3.10}$$

It is evident that Δ is in general quite arbitrary, corresponding to uniform illumination of a plane containing P; we therefore ask whether in any particular conditions there is a distance P for which the variation of phase Δ is a minimum, for an interference fringe corresponds to a line along which the phase is stationary. Michelson answered this question by discussing the behaviour of the derivatives $\partial\Delta/\partial i$ and $\partial\Delta/\partial\theta$, but, if the planes are very nearly parallel so that the fringes are nearly circular, it is simpler to recast the formula in polar coordinates and to consider the radial gradient of Δ.

Put
$$r^2 = \tan^2 i + \tan^2\theta, \qquad \cos\psi = r^{-1}\tan i,$$
and
$$k = \tan\phi.$$

Then
$$\Delta = \frac{2(t_0 + Pkr\cos\psi)}{(1+r^2)^{\frac{1}{2}}} \tag{3.11}$$

and
$$\frac{\partial\Delta}{\partial r} = \frac{2(Pk\cos\psi - t_0 r)}{(1+r^2)^{\frac{1}{2}}}, \tag{3.12}$$

which vanishes if
$$P = t_0 r/k\cos\psi. \tag{3.13}$$

The focus conditions for the Michelson interferometer follow from this formula. If the plate separation is zero, $P = 0$ whatever the inclination of the plates, that is the fringes are localized on the plates, while if the plates are parallel, so that $k = 0$, P is infinite for all separations and fringes will be seen through a lens focussed for infinity.

If the plates of an interferometer are nominally parallel but are not exactly so, the fringes cannot be focused simultaneously over the whole field. Suppose that the fringes are viewed through a lens of focal length f placed at distance d from the mirror M_2'. The object at O is then at a distance $d - P$ from the lens and so the image distance v is given by
$$\frac{1}{v} = \frac{1}{f} - \frac{1}{d-P} = \frac{1}{f} - \frac{1}{d - t_0 r/k\cos\psi}. \tag{3.14}$$

Hence
$$v - f = \frac{f^2 k\cos\psi}{(d-f)k\cos\psi - t_0 r}. \tag{3.15}$$

In a typical case, d will be comparable to the focal length and, especially if t_0 is large, the denominator will be dominated by the term $t_0 r$. In that case $(v-f)$ changes sign with $\cos\psi$, in other words, on one side of the centre the fringes come to a focus in front of the focal plane for infinity, while on the other side they come to a focus behind that plane; the fringes are in focus on the focal plane for infinity when $\cos\psi = 0$, that is when $\psi = \frac{1}{2}\pi$ or $\frac{3}{2}\pi$.

This behaviour of the fringes is commonly used for checking whether the plates are parallel and provides an indication of the adjustments that should be made to bring them parallel.

Consider now the form of the fringes. Put $O'x = P\xi$, $O'y = P\eta$, so that

$$\tan i = \xi, \qquad \tan \theta = \eta.$$

The phase Δ is then constant along loci having the equations

$$(\Delta^2 - 4P^2k^2)\xi^2 + \Delta^2\eta^2 - 8t_0Pk\xi + \Delta^2 - 4t_0^2 = 0. \tag{3.16}$$

These are the equations of conic sections with axes parallel to the intersection of the plates. If the surfaces are parallel ($k = 0$)

$$\xi^2 + \eta^2 = \left(\frac{2t_0}{\Delta}\right)^2 - 1. \tag{3.17}$$

The fringes as seen in parallel light at infinity are concentric circles with the centre on the line OO', they are in fact Haidinger rings. To see this, put $\Delta = 2t_0 - (p + \epsilon)\lambda$, where p is an integer and ϵ a fraction. Then if p is much less than $2t_0/\lambda$,

$$\left(\frac{2t_0}{\Delta}\right)^2 - 1 = (p + \epsilon)\frac{\lambda}{t_0} \tag{3.18}$$

and the radii of the successive maxima are $(p\lambda/t_0)^{\frac{1}{2}}$.

If the plates are not quite parallel but k^2 is small, less than $\Delta^2/4P^2$, the loci are real ellipses and the ratio of the major and minor axes is

$$\Delta/(\Delta^2 - 4p^2k^2)^{\frac{1}{2}}. \tag{3.19}$$

It is possible to see such ellipses if t_0 is very small and the telescope is not exactly adjusted for infinity.

The centre of the ellipses is displaced by the distance

$$4t_0Pk(\Delta^2 - 4P^2k^2)^{\frac{1}{2}}$$

from the normal to the plane M'.

Finally, if t_0 and Δ are both very small but the plates are not parallel, the fringes are hyperbolae,

$$\frac{4P^2k^2}{\Delta^2}\xi^2 - \eta^2 = 1, \tag{3.20}$$

which, when η is small, are very nearly the straight lines given by

$$\xi = \pm\frac{\Delta}{2Pk}. \tag{3.20a}$$

The separation of these lines at the distance P is

$$\lambda/2t.$$

We now consider the errors in the form of the fringes formed with nominally parallel plates that are in fact slightly inclined. In the first place, the whole fringe system is slightly displaced. Let the fringes be viewed through a lens with a radius L placed at a distance D from the plane M_2' (Fig. 3.5). For a point p at a distance L from O',

$$\Delta = 2(t_0 + L\phi)\cos i. \tag{3.21}$$

If the lens is adjusted for parallel light,

$$L = D \tan i$$

and

$$\Delta = 2(t_0 \cos i + D\phi \sin i). \tag{3.22}$$

Now at the centre of the ring system $\partial\Delta/\partial i = 0$ by symmetry, and so

$$\tan i_0 = D\phi/t_0 \tag{3.23}$$

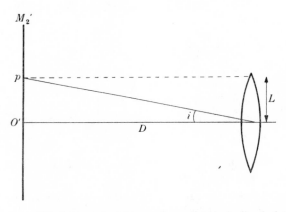

Fig. 3.5. Displacement of fringes from slightly inclined plates.

for the central ray. This formula gives the amount by which the centre of the ring system is displaced from the normal to M_2'. It is not a significant effect if the fringes are observed photographically since the direction of the normal to the plates is not recorded on the photograph, but it might matter with photoelectric recording where the aperture is fixed with respect to the normal to the plates.

There is also a phase change at the centre of the ring system. On substituting for i_0 in the expression for Δ, it will be seen that since

$$\cos i_0 = (1+\tan^2 i_0)^{-\frac{1}{2}} = (1+D^2\phi^2/t_0^2)^{-\frac{1}{2}},$$

$$\Delta = 2\left(t_0 + \frac{D^2\phi^2}{t_0}\right)^{\frac{1}{2}} \tag{3.24}$$

instead of $2t_0$ at the centre.

Hence

$$\frac{\delta\Delta}{\lambda} = \frac{D^2\phi^2}{\lambda t_0}. \tag{3.25}$$

The effect is very small. For example, let D be $0\cdot2$ m, t_0 be 10 mm, λ be 500 nm, and ϕ be 10^{-5}. Then $\delta\Delta/\lambda$ is 8×10^{-5}, which is negligible except in work of the very highest precision. (See Cook 1961 for a case in which it was allowed for in the analogous Fabry–Perot system.)

Application of the theory of coherence to the analysis of the effects of defects in a Michelson interferometer—parallel-plate interferometer

While Michelson's own analysis of the behaviour of the interferometer is of particular importance for understanding the geometry of the fringes, it is cumbersome when applied to the calculation of the effects of defects upon the visibility and phase of the fringes; the theory of coherence enables a more compact and satisfactory account of defects to be given (De 1956).

Consider an interferometer comprising two nominally parallel plates together with a lens that focuses light passing through the plates upon a small aperture behind which a detector is placed. Let V_1 be the complex field variable of light reflected from plate 1 and let V_2 be that of light from plate 2.

V_1 and V_2 are evaluated at the detector. Let V_2 differ from V_1 by a complex reflection coefficient ρ equal to $re^{i\psi}$ and by a phase shift $k\Delta$ due to the path difference Δ. Then

$$\Gamma = \langle rV_1^*V_1 \exp i(\psi-k\Delta)\rangle, \tag{3.26}$$

where Γ is evaluated at the detector. Since the intensities of the two fields at the detector are respectively $\langle|V_1|^2\rangle$ and $\langle r^2|V_1|^2\rangle$,

$$\gamma = \exp i(\psi-k\Delta). \tag{3.26a}$$

ψ is a differential phase shift on reflection at the plates and may in many cases be included as a change of the zero from which Δ is measured. It will therefore be ignored in the rest of this chapter, especially as for most Michelson interferometers it is very small, being the difference between two nearly equal phase shifts at the two mirrors.

In general, Δ, ρ, and V_1 are not constant over the plates. Γ must then be integrated over the area of the plates and the general formula for γ is

$$\langle |V_1|^2 \Big\langle \int_S re^{i\psi}e^{-ik\Delta}\,\mathrm{d}S \Big\rangle \Big/ \Big\langle \int_S |V_1|^2\,\mathrm{d}S \Big\rangle^{\frac{1}{2}} \Big\langle \int_S r^2\,|V_1|^2\,\mathrm{d}S \Big\rangle^{\frac{1}{2}}, \qquad (3.27)$$

where S denotes the area of the plates.

If r and $|V_1|$ are constant over the plates and if ψ is neglected

$$\int_S |V_1|^2\,\mathrm{d}S = S\,|V_1|^2$$

and

$$\gamma = \frac{1}{S}\int_S e^{-ik\Delta}\,\mathrm{d}S. \qquad (3.28)$$

If Δ is also constant, $\gamma = e^{-ik\Delta}$ and the visibility of the fringes is 1 when $r = 1$.

If Δ is not constant, the visibility of the fringes is reduced. Let

$$\Delta = \Delta_0 + \Delta_1,$$

where Δ_1 is a function of position over the plates. Then

$$\gamma = \frac{1}{S}\,e^{-ik\Delta_0}\int_S e^{-ik\Delta_1}\,\mathrm{d}S \qquad (3.29)$$

and $|\gamma|$ is

$$S^{-1}\left| \int_S \exp(-ik\Delta_1)\,\mathrm{d}S \right|.$$

Two cases are of particular practical importance. Suppose, first, that Δ_1 represents the random irregularities of the surface contour that are always present. Let Δ_1 have zero mean over S and a second moment equal to σ^2. Since

$$\int_S \exp(-ik\Delta_1)\,\mathrm{d}S = \int_S (1-ik\Delta_1-k^2\Delta^2+\ldots)\,\mathrm{d}S, \qquad (3.30)$$

$$|\gamma| = 1-\sigma^2k^2\ldots. \qquad (3.30a)$$

and the visibility is reduced by the factor $1-\sigma^2k^2$, which is independent of the mean phase shift Δ_0.

Suppose, in the second place, that the plates are inclined at an angle α so that $\Delta_1 = \alpha x$, x being measured at right angles to the line of intersection.

Then

$$\int_S \exp(-ik\Delta_1)\,\mathrm{d}S = \int_S \exp(-ik\alpha x)\,\mathrm{d}S. \qquad (3.31)$$

The value of the integral depends on the form of the area S. If S is a rectangle of sides $2a$ and $2b$, the former being parallel to the x axis, the integral is

$$2b \int_{-a}^{+a} \exp(-\mathrm{i}k\alpha x)\,\mathrm{d}x = \frac{4b}{k\alpha} \sin(k\alpha a) \tag{3.32}$$

and

$$|\gamma| = \frac{\sin k\alpha a}{k\alpha a}. \tag{3.32a}$$

If the plates are circles of radius a, take polar coordinates (r, θ), where θ is measured from the x-axis.

Then

$$x = r \cos \theta,$$
$$dS = r\,\mathrm{d}r\,\mathrm{d}\theta,$$

and

$$\gamma = \frac{1}{\pi a^2}\int_S \exp(-\mathrm{i}k\alpha r \cos \theta)r\,\mathrm{d}r\,\mathrm{d}\theta$$

$$= \frac{1}{\pi a^2}\int_0^a r\,\mathrm{d}r \int_0^{2\pi} \exp(-\mathrm{i}k\alpha r \cos \theta)\,\mathrm{d}\theta$$

$$= \frac{2}{a^2}\int_0^a r\,\mathrm{d}r\, J_0(k\alpha r)$$

$$= \frac{2}{k^2\alpha^2 a^2}\int^{k\alpha a} J_0(z)z\,\mathrm{d}z,$$

where $J_0(z)$ is the Bessel function of zero order (Whittaker and Watson 1940, p. 362).

Since $J_0(z)$ is approximately $1 - \frac{1}{4}z^2$ when z is much less than 1, γ is approximately

$$1 - \tfrac{1}{6}k^2\alpha^2 a^2$$

when $k^2\alpha^2 a^2 \ll 1$.

Once again, the reduction of visibility is independent of the mean phase shift between the plates.

These two cases, although important, are still idealizations, and practical situations are usually more complex. In particular, account must usually be taken of variations of intensity over the area S.

The above results have been derived for a single wavelength and they are now extended to quasi-monochromatic light. The integral for γ must be taken over the spectrum as well as over the area S.

Let the intensity in the range k to $k+\delta k$ be $I_k\,\mathrm{d}k$. The contribution to γ at one wavenumber is independent of that at another and so

$$\gamma = (IS)^{-1}\int_v \mathrm{d}k\int_S \mathrm{d}S I_k\,\exp\{-\mathrm{i}(k_0+k')(\Delta_0+\Delta_1)\}$$

$$= \mathrm{e}^{-\mathrm{i}k_0\Delta_0}\int_v \mathrm{d}k\frac{I_k}{I}\,\mathrm{e}^{-\mathrm{i}k\Delta_0}\int_S \frac{\mathrm{d}S}{S}\,\mathrm{e}^{-\mathrm{i}k\Delta_1}, \qquad (3.33)$$

which may be written as

$$\mathrm{e}^{-\mathrm{i}k_0\Delta_0}\gamma_k\gamma_S,$$

where γ_k is a factor describing the effect of the finite spectrum and γ_S is a factor describing the effect of plate irregularities.

This factorization property of γ is very important in the practical use of the Michelson interferometer. When $\Delta_0 = 0$, γ_k is 1 and the visibility is determined solely by the plate defects. γ_S can thus be found from measurements at small path differences, and visibilities at greater path differences can be corrected for the effect of plate irregularities simply by multiplication by $|\gamma_S|^{-1}$.

Stray light and unequal intensities also reduce the visibility by factors that are constant at all path differences. If the intensities of the two beams are I_1 and I_2 and if there is, in addition, stray light of intensity I_3, uncorrelated with the fields V_1 and V_2, the visibility of the fringes is

$$\frac{2(I_1I_2)^{\frac{1}{2}}\,|\gamma|}{I_1+I_2+I_3}, \qquad (3.34)$$

where $|\gamma|$ has the value obtained above. Stray light in phase with one of the fields V_1 or V_2 will of course alter γ.

Consider now the effect of a detector aperture that is not very small. If a ray of light makes an angle θ with the normal to the interferometer plates (Fig. 3.6), the path difference Δ is $2l\cos\theta$. If the angular radius

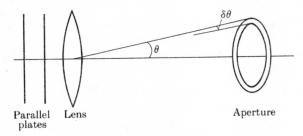

Parallel   Lens   Aperture
plates

Fig. 3.6. Interferometer with limiting aperture.

of the (circular) aperture is α, the value of γ integrated over the aperture is given by

$$\pi\alpha^2\gamma = \int_S \exp(-2ikl\cos\theta)\,\mathrm{d}S\dagger \qquad (3.35)$$

for a single wavelength, while for quasi-monochromatic light

$$\pi\alpha^2\gamma = I^{-1}\int_\nu \mathrm{d}k \int_S \mathrm{d}S I_k \exp(-2il(k_0+k')(1-\tfrac{1}{2}\theta^2)\}, \qquad (3.36)$$

where $\cos\theta$ has been replaced by $1-\tfrac{1}{2}\theta^2$. Thus

$$\pi\alpha^2\gamma = e^{-2ilk_0}\,I^{-1}\int_\nu \mathrm{d}k\,I_k e^{-2ilk'}\int_S e^{ilk_0\theta^2}\,\mathrm{d}S. \qquad (3.36a)$$

Suppose first that the centre of the aperture lies upon the normal to the interferometer plates. Then $\mathrm{d}S = \pi\,\mathrm{d}\theta^2$ and, for a single wavelength,

$$\pi\alpha^2\gamma = \pi\int_0^{\alpha^2} \exp(ilk_0\theta^2)\,\mathrm{d}\theta^2, \qquad (3.37)$$

that is

$$\gamma = (e^{ilk_0\alpha^2}-1)/ilk_0\alpha^2$$

$$= \exp(\tfrac{1}{2}ilk_0\alpha^2)\frac{\sin\tfrac{1}{2}lk_0\alpha^2.}{\tfrac{1}{2}lk_0\alpha^2} \qquad (3.38)$$

This result shows that the visibility of the fringes is reduced by the factor

$$\frac{\sin\tfrac{1}{2}k_0l\alpha^2}{\tfrac{1}{2}k_0l\alpha^2}\,;$$

in addition the phase of the fringes formed in the light integrated over the whole of the aperture is shifted with respect to the phase for a pinhole of infinitesimal size, a new feature that did not appear in the effects of plate defects. The phase shift is $\tfrac{1}{2}k_0l\alpha^2$ and since it depends on the path difference, it must be allowed for explicitly in measurements of wavelength. α can in fact be fairly large: for an example, let l be 0·1 m, let the wavelength be 500 nm so that k is $4\pi\times10^6$ m^{-1} and let α be 10^{-3}, corresponding to a pinhole of 2 mm diameter at a focal distance of 1 m; the phase shift is then 0·6π. The shift can usually be calculated with sufficient accuracy.

Now let the aperture be slightly off centre. The geometry is shown in Fig. 3.7. The centre of the pinhole lies at an angular distance β from the normal to the plates. If an element of area lies at a distance ϕ from

† S is now the area of the detector aperture, not of the interferometer plates.

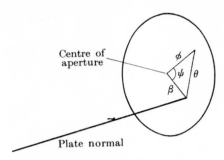

Fig. 3.7. Off-centre aperture.

the centre of the pinhole and at an azimuth ψ from the direction of the normal, the angular distance θ of the element from the normal is given by

$$\cos\theta = \cos\beta\cos\phi - \sin\beta\sin\phi\cos\psi, \tag{3.39}$$

that is

$$\cos\theta \doteqdot 1 - \tfrac{1}{2}(\beta^2 + \phi^2) - \beta\phi\cos\psi. \tag{3.40}$$

Hence

$$\int_S e^{ik_0 l\theta^2}\,\mathrm{d}S = e^{ik_0 l\beta^2}\int_0^{2\pi}\int_0^{\alpha} e^{ik_0 l(\phi^2 + 2\beta\phi\cos\psi)}\phi\,\mathrm{d}\phi\,\mathrm{d}\psi$$

$$= e^{ik_0 l\beta^2}\int_0^{\alpha}\phi\,\mathrm{d}\phi\, e^{ik_0 l\phi^2}\int_0^{2\pi}\mathrm{d}\psi\, e^{2ilk_0\beta\phi\cos\psi}. \tag{3.41}$$

Now

$$\int_0^{\pi} e^{iz\cos\theta}\,\mathrm{d}\theta = \pi J_0(z). \tag{3.42}$$

Since

$$J_0(z) = J_0(-z),$$

$$\int_0^{2\pi} e^{+iz\cos\theta}\,\mathrm{d}\theta = 2\pi J_0(z), \tag{3.43}$$

and so

$$\int_0^{2\pi} e^{+2ilk_0\beta\phi\cos\psi}\,\mathrm{d}\psi = 2\pi J_0(2lk_0\beta\phi). \tag{3.44}$$

This result is exact. To perform the further integration, the Bessel function is expanded:

$$J_0(2lk_0\beta\phi) = 1 - l^2 k_0^2\beta^2\phi^2 + \tfrac{1}{4}l^4 k_0^4\beta^4\phi^4\ldots. \tag{3.45}$$

Thus

$$\gamma = \frac{2}{\alpha^2} e^{-ilk_0\beta^2}\int_0^{\alpha^2} e^{-ilk_0\phi^2}\{1 - l^2 k_0^2\beta^2\phi^2 + \tfrac{1}{4}l^4 k_0^4\beta^4\phi^4\}\,\mathrm{d}\phi^2. \tag{3.46}$$

The first term of the series is

$$\frac{2e^{-ilk_0\beta^2}}{ilk_0\alpha^2}[e^{-ilk_0\alpha^2}-1];$$

(3.47)

the second term is

$$2lk_0\beta^2 e^{\frac{1}{2}ilk_0\alpha^2}\frac{\sin\frac{1}{2}lk_0\alpha^2.}{\frac{1}{2}lk_0\alpha^2}$$

(3.48)

Hence

$$\gamma = e^{ilk_0(\beta^2+\frac{1}{2}\alpha^2)}(i+lk_0\beta^2)\frac{\sin\frac{1}{2}lk_0\alpha^2}{\frac{1}{2}lk_0\alpha^2}.$$

(3.49)

Now $lk_0\alpha^2$ is usually made less than 1 and so $lk_0\beta^2$ may be taken to be much less than 1 since, in practice, β will not exceed about 0.1α. The factor by which the visibility is reduced can therefore be taken to be

$$\frac{\sin\frac{1}{2}lk_0\alpha^2}{\frac{1}{2}lk_0\alpha^2}$$

as before, while the phase shift with respect to an infinitesimal centred pinhole is $lk_0(\beta^2+\frac{1}{2}\alpha^2)$.

The great advantage of the Michelson interferometer used with photoelectric recording is that even if the angular diameter of the aperture is as small as 10^{-4}, in which case the phase shifts due to the finite size and incorrect centring of the aperture can certainly be ignored, the intensity of the light transmitted is still in most cases great enough to give a good signal-to-noise ratio without an unduly long integration time (see Chapter 9).

Coherence analysis of inclined-plate interferometer

The coherence of two beams reflected from non-parallel plates is reduced by four factors: the angle between the interfering beams, which gives a factor of $\cos 2\alpha$, α being the angle between the plates; the inequality of the intensities of the beams reflected from the plates; the spectrum of the light; and the range of angles at which light is incident on the plates. The first is not a serious matter, while at the spacings usually employed and with the sources now available, the effect of the spectrum can also usually be neglected. If the amplitudes are unequal, the fringe visibility is less than it would be for equal amplitudes by the factor $(\rho+\rho^{-1})^{-1}$, ρ being the ratio of the intensities. In many practical applications of the Michelson as well as of the Fizeau interferometer, it may not be possible or convenient on account of the different reflectivities of different materials, to have equal amplitudes, and the reduction in visibility, which may be quite considerable, has to be accepted.

The effect of the range of angles over which light is transmitted through the plates is of great importance in practical metrological applications, where the range is determined by the size and location of the apertures through which the plates are illuminated and viewed. Suppose that the angle of incidence is θ for a ray passing through some point of the aperture, usually that through which the fringes are viewed, which limits the cone of rays. The fields of the beams reflected from the two plates may be written as $e^{i\omega t}$ and $e^{i(\omega t \Delta + k\Delta)}$ respectively, the amplitudes of the two beams being taken to be the same. Δ is the difference of path between the two beams, and is equal to $2l \cos \theta$.

Thus for a single wavelength

$$\gamma = \frac{1}{S} \int_S e^{i 2kl \cos \theta} \, \mathrm{d}S, \tag{3.50}$$

where S is the area of the limiting aperture. Hence

$$\gamma = \frac{1}{S} e^{i2kl} \int_S e^{-ikl\theta^2} \mathrm{d}S. \tag{3.51}$$

If the limiting aperture is a circle centred on the plate normal (the plates may usually be treated as parallel for this purpose),

$$\gamma = \frac{1}{\alpha^2} e^{i2kl} \int_0^{\alpha^2} e^{-ikl\theta^2} \mathrm{d}\theta^2$$

$$= e^{2ikl} e^{-\frac{1}{2}ikl\alpha^2} \frac{\sin \frac{1}{2}kl\alpha^2}{\frac{1}{2}kl\alpha^2} \tag{3.52}$$

The visibility is thus reduced by the factor $(\sin \frac{1}{2}kl\alpha^2)/\frac{1}{2}kl\alpha^2$ and there is a phase shift equal to $-\frac{1}{2}kl\alpha^2$.

The effect of an aperture that is not centred can be calculated along the lines of the calculation for an off-centre aperture for the parallel-plate interferometer.

Rectangular apertures are commonly employed in practice. Let the lengths of the sides of the rectangle be given in non-dimensional form as $2a$ and $2b$; if the aperture is centred,

$$\gamma = \frac{1}{4ab} e^{2ikl} \int_{-a}^{+a} \int_{-b}^{+b} e^{-ikl(x^2+v^2)} \mathrm{d}x \, \mathrm{d}y, \tag{3.53}$$

where x, y are non-dimensional Cartesian coordinates in the plane of the aperture.

This integral may be expressed in terms of the Fresnel integrals

$$C(z) = \int_0^z \cos(\tfrac{1}{2}\pi t^2)\, \mathrm{d}t,$$

$$S(z) = \int_0^z \sin(\tfrac{1}{2}\pi t^2)\, \mathrm{d}t.$$

(Abramowitz and Stegun 1964, p. 300.)

Put

$$\alpha = \frac{2kl}{\pi}\, a^2, \qquad \beta = \frac{2kl}{\pi}\, b^2.$$

Then

$$\int_{-a}^{+a} e^{-iklx^2}\mathrm{d}x = 2\left(\frac{\pi}{2kl}\right)^{\frac{1}{2}}\{C(\alpha) - iS(\alpha)\} \tag{3.54}$$

and so

$$\frac{1}{4ab}\int_{-a}^{+a}\int_{-b}^{+b} e^{-ikl(x^2+y^2)}\mathrm{d}x\,\mathrm{d}y = \frac{1}{ab}\frac{\pi}{2kl}\{C(\alpha)-iS(\alpha)\}\{C(\beta)-iS(\beta)\}$$

$$= \frac{1}{ab}\frac{\pi}{2kl}\begin{bmatrix}C(\alpha)C(\beta)-S(\alpha)S(\beta)-\\-i\{C(\alpha)S(\beta)+S(\alpha)C(\beta)\}\end{bmatrix}. \tag{3.55}$$

The modulus is then

$$\frac{1}{ab}\frac{\pi}{2kl}\{C^2(\alpha)+S^2(\alpha)\}^{\frac{1}{2}}\{C^2(\beta)+S^2(\beta)\}^{\frac{1}{2}} \tag{3.56a}$$

and the phase is

$$-\arctan\frac{C(\alpha)S(\beta)+S(\alpha)C(\beta)}{C(\alpha)C(\beta)-S(\alpha)S(\beta)}. \tag{3.56b}$$

If α, β are less than about 0·5, that is, a and b are less than $\frac{1}{2}(\pi/2kl)^{\frac{1}{2}}$, a condition that is in general satisfied, then the Fresnel integrals may be approximated by

$$C(z) = z - \frac{1}{10}\left(\frac{\pi}{2}\right)^2 z^3,$$

$$S(z) = \frac{1}{3}\frac{\pi}{2} z^3.$$

Thus

$$C^2(z) + S^2(z) = z^2 - \frac{1}{5}\left(\frac{\pi}{2}\right)^2 z^4,$$

$$\frac{S(z)}{C(z)} = \frac{1}{3}\frac{\pi}{2} z^2.$$

The modulus of γ is therefore

$$\frac{1}{ab}\frac{\pi}{2kl}\,\alpha\beta\left\{1-\frac{\pi^2}{40}(\alpha^2+\beta^2)\right\}$$

$$=1-\frac{\pi kl}{20}(a^2+b^2)$$

and the phase shift is $-\frac{1}{3}kl(a^2+b^2)$.

Strictly speaking, the expressions for γ should be obtained in a calculation in which all factors are included simultaneously, but it will readily be seen that since the effects are all small, it is sufficient to calculate the influence of each separately and add them in the final stage of the calculation.

The phase shifts arising from the finite size of the aperture and from any offset of the aperture from the normal to the plates, are almost always significant in metrological applications. Consider, for example, a gauge of length 0·1 m measured in an interferometer with a rectangular aperture 1 mm × 1 mm at the focus of a lens of 0·5 m focal length.

The measured phase is

$$2kl-\tfrac{1}{3}kl(a^2+b^2),$$

that is to say, the measured length is in error by $\frac{1}{6}l(a^2+b^2)$.

With the values assumed, a and b are each 10^{-3} and the error is $3\cdot3\times10^{-7}$ or $0\cdot033\ \mu$m, an amount that is often significant.

Some very thorough discussions and detailed calculations have been given for the aperture errors in wedge-type interferometers (Ignatowsky 1935; Hopkins 1957; Bruce 1955a,b 1957; Landwehr 1959a,b).

Wide-field interferometers

An important advantage of the parallel-plate form of the Michelson interferometer, shared with the Fabry–Perot interferometer (Chapter 6) is that the angular aperture for a given range of phase shift is very much greater than for a grating spectrometer and other instruments relying on a narrow slit to isolate a line (see Chapter 10). The reason for this is that the parallel-plate interferometers are rotationally symmetrical about the normal to the plates. Consider light passing through the plates at an angle θ to the normal. The range of path difference for angles from 0 to θ is

$$2l(1-\cos\theta),$$

or $l\theta^2$ if θ^4 can be neglected. Let this range be denoted by δ.

The solid angle Ω included by directions from 0 to θ is $\pi\theta^2$, so that Ω/δ is π/l. With slit-instruments the solid angle is of order ws, where w is the angular width of the slit and s the angular length. s is commonly an order of magnitude greater than θ whereas w is three or four orders less. The light transmitted for a given range of path difference is thus two or three orders of magnitude less for the slit instrument.

The performance of the simple parallel-plate instrument is not, however, the best possible. Consider the performance of such an instrument with a medium having a refractive index μ between the plates. If light is incident on the plates at an angle θ_i to the normal, then it traverses the space between the plates at an angle θ to the normal given by

$$\frac{\sin \theta_i}{\sin \theta} = \mu.$$

The solid angle within which light is received by the detector is determined by the angle θ_i, whereas the spread of path difference is determined by the angle θ. Thus for cones with semi-angle θ_i and θ respectively,

$$\Omega = \pi\theta_i^2$$

and

$$\delta = 2\mu l(1 - \cos \theta)$$

and for angles such that θ^4 is negligible

$$\frac{\Omega}{\delta} = \frac{\pi\mu}{l}. \tag{3.57}$$

Detailed analysis (Hilliard and Shepherd 1966) shows that the advantage can be very much greater if the two arms of a Michelson interferometer are treated differently. Consider a mirror faced with a slab of refractive index μ (Fig. 3.8). Let the path of a ray through this slab be as shown by the full lines and let the position of the image of the mirror of the other arm of the interferometer, as imaged in the beam divider, be shown by the broken line; broken lines also show the path of a ray reflected from this second mirror as projected on to the space of the first mirror. With the symbols shown in Fig. 3.8, the path difference Δ between rays in the two arms of the interferometer is

$$\Delta = 2\mu a - b - s.$$

Since

$$a = t/\cos \phi_n,$$
$$b = t'/\cos \phi,$$

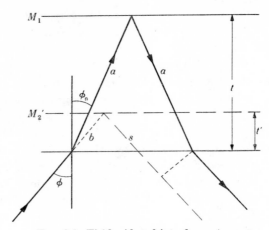

FIG. 3.8. Field-widened interferometer.

and

$$s = 2 \sin \phi(t \tan \phi_n - t' \tan \phi),$$

while

$$\sin \phi = \mu \sin \phi_n,$$

$$\Delta = \frac{2\mu t}{\cos \phi_n} - \frac{2t'}{\cos \phi} - \frac{2\mu t \sin^2\phi_n}{\cos \phi_n} + \frac{2t' \sin^2\phi}{\cos \phi}$$

$$= 2\mu t \cos \phi_n - 2t' \cos \phi. \tag{3.58}$$

At normal incidence,

$$\Delta = 2(\mu t - t').$$

Now

$$\cos \phi = 1 - \tfrac{1}{2}\phi^2 + \tfrac{1}{24}\phi^4 + \cdots$$

and

$$\cos \phi_n = \left(1 - \frac{\sin^2\phi}{\mu^2}\right)^{\frac{1}{2}}$$

$$= 1 - \frac{\phi^2}{2\mu^2} + \frac{\phi^4}{2\mu^2}\left(\frac{1}{3} - \frac{1}{4\mu^2}\right) + \cdots.$$

Hence

$$\Delta = 2\mu t - 2t' - (t/\mu - t')\phi^2 + \left\{\frac{t}{\mu}\left(\frac{1}{3} - \frac{1}{4\mu^2}\right) - \frac{t'}{12}\right\}\phi^4 + \cdots. \tag{3.59}$$

This expression contains no odd powers of ϕ and the term proportional to ϕ^2 vanishes if $t' = t/\mu$. (If t' is zero, the result given above (3.57) is obtained.)

If, then, the path difference is chosen to have the particular value $2t(\mu - 1/\mu)$, Δ is constant up to terms of order ϕ^4 or less.

Let $\Delta_0 = 2t(\mu - 1/\mu)$ and let t' depart from the value t/μ by a small amount e.

Then

$$\Delta - \Delta_0 = -2e + e\phi^2 + \left(\frac{\Delta_0}{8\mu^2} - \frac{e}{12}\right)\phi^4 + \ldots \qquad (3.60)$$

For a special value of path difference, therefore, $\Delta - \Delta_0$ is very small for a wide range of ϕ. The comparative values are: Grating spectrometer:

$$\Delta - \Delta_0 = 2t \sin \phi \rightleftharpoons 2t\phi;$$

Michelson and Fabry–Perot interferometers:

$$\Delta - \Delta_0 = -2t(1 - \cos \theta) \rightleftharpoons t\phi^2;$$

Field-widened Michelson, $\Delta_0 = 2t(\mu - 1/\mu)$:

$$\Delta - \Delta_0 = \frac{\Delta_0}{8\mu^2}\phi^4.$$

The special field-widened system is thus valuable for special studies of weak extended sources for which a very large aperture is an advantage, but it is evidently inflexible and of no general use.

The field-widened interferometer with a medium of high refractive index is difficult to make with a variable path difference and it is evident that this particular way of improving the ratio Ω/δ is not very useful. The principle can be applied in other ways, however. The essential point is to set up a relation between the angles θ_i and θ so as to increase the solid angle subtended by the detector over that within which light travels between the interferometer plates. System of lenses and of prisms have been used (Mertz 1959, 1965; Bouchareine and Connes 1963; Steel 1963; Connes 1956).

4

MICHELSON–FIZEAU INTERFEROMETERS
II—APPLICATIONS

THE optical system of a practical Michelson interferometer used in the parallel-plate mode is shown in Fig. 4.1. An extended source is placed at the focus of a collimating lens and the beam divider is illuminated by the collimated light. The conventional arrangement is for the beam divider to be at 45° to the incident light and accordingly for the two mirrors to be at right angles. It is also usual for the beam divider to be a plate of glass with a semi-reflecting coating on one face and for the compensating plate to be a separate parallel plate. These conventional arrangements are not necessarily the best or simplest. It is convenient to combine the beam divider and compensator by putting them in optical contact on the face that carries the semi-reflecting coating. Reflections from the supposedly non-reflecting surface of the beam divider or compensating plate bear a constant phase relationship to the principal beam and cause a small displacement of the fringes, as well as a change of visibility that cannot be eliminated by observations at zero path difference, as can the effects of incoherent stray light. Such reflections can be reduced to a considerable extent by coating the surfaces with dielectric non-reflecting films, but Terrien, in his adaptation of Michelson's original interferometer at the International Bureau of Weights and Measures (Michelson and Benoît 1895, Terrien 1958), has arranged that the light shall be incident on the beam divider and compensating plates at the Brewster angle for the glass of the plates, so ensuring that plane polarized light is transmitted through the interferometer without reflection at the inclined surfaces of the plates.

The semi-reflecting coatings are often aluminium or silver films for an interferometer working in the visible, but semi-reflecting dielectric coatings are as effective and must be used in the far infra-red (Chamberlain, Chantry, Findlay, Gebbie, Gibbs, Stone, and Wright 1966). If the reflectance of the beam divider is R, the transmittance T, and the absorptance A, and if all other losses in the interferometer are neglected, the overall transmittance of the interferometer is RT. The maximum occurs, of course, when R equals T and both are 50 per cent, but provided the absorptance is kept low, the overall transmittance varies

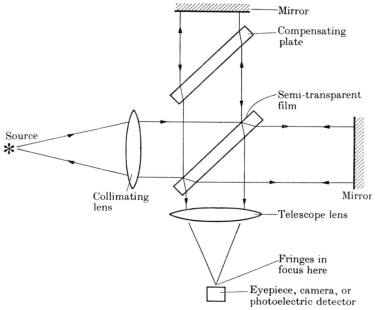

Fɪɢ. 4.1. Optical System of Michelson interferometer in parallel-plate mode.

rather slowly with the reflectance and indeed the reflectance can be as low as 15 per cent before the overall transmittance falls to half the maximum value.

The mirrors of a Michelson interferometer are usually aluminized glass plates worked optically flat to $0\cdot1\lambda$ or better according to the application. Great care must be given to the mechanical design of the supports of the mirrors to ensure that they do not distort the mirrors and that it is possible to make the very delicate adjustments needed to align the mirrors in a quite positive manner and to ensure that the mirrors will remain in alignment during the use of the interferometer. As will be seen below, systems that are to a large extent self-aligning are available but they have some disadvantages. The problem of maintaining the alignment of the mirrors is more acute in interferometers with continuous scanning and photoelectric recording. In the earlier applications, the mirrors were set to some path difference, were aligned, and a measurement of the visibility was made visually or photographically, using a field that contained a number of fringes, so that it was not necessary to move the mirrors in order to observe the variation of intensity on passing through a fringe. With photoelectric recording of the intensity at the centre of the ring pattern, it is necessary to change the path difference. To move the mirrors themselves mechanically places very severe demands on the fabrication of the ways on which the mirrors move and can be avoided by restricting the scan at any nominal path difference to a very few wavelengths, for example by tilting the compensating plate or by some other angular movement such as was introduced by M. and Mme. Connes. It is also possible to vary the pressure of air in part of one of the optical paths, but, in contrast to practice with the Fabry–Perot interferometer, air pressure scanning is not the most convenient method for the Michelson interferometer. In the ultra-violet and the infra-red, the number of transmissions through optical components must be kept to a minimum to reduce absorption, and the compensating plate, which is not essential for observations with a restricted number of wavelengths at a time, may be omitted. In these circumstances, and working also in vacuum, one of the mirrors must be moved to scan the fringes. Recent developments make this an entirely practical matter; an example will be given later.

Prior to the introduction of lasers it was difficult to count fringes when one of the mirrors was moved because the visibility of the fringes changed greatly over useful ranges of path difference even when the sharpest lines from the available thermal sources were used. While fringe-counting interferometers had been constructed, they had not been widely employed but with the introduction of gas lasers as inter-ferometric sources the scope of such interferometers in practical applications was greatly extended, and optical systems were developed which enabled a mirror to be moved over a metre or more while the alignment was maintained. The simplest (Peck 1948, 1957) uses cube-corner reflectors, which have the property that light incident on such a reflector is reflected parallel to itself (Fig. 4.2(a)). The scheme has the disadvantages that the wave front is inverted on reflection so that irreg-ularities in the optical components have exaggerated effects, and that tilts of the reflectors cause lateral displacements of the wave fronts that change the phase and visibility of the fringes. The scheme indicated in Fig. 4.2(b) (Terrien 1959, Murty 1960) is free of these disadvantages and lends itself well to the construction of a very rigid system with the plane mirror and beam divider, on which the optical alignment depends, strongly connected. Another fact that has to be borne in mind in con-sidering cube-corner systems is that they polarize initially unpolarized light and it is desirable to have similar systems in both arms of the interferometer even though only one of the mirrors may be moved.

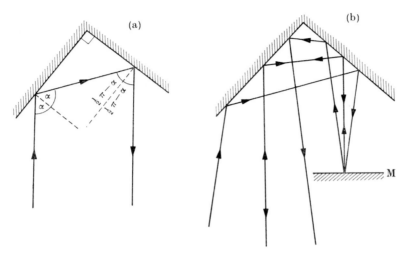

FIG. 4.2. Cube-corner reflectors for a Michelson interferometer.
(a) simple cube-corner;
(b) cube-corner with auxiliary mirror, M.

The 'Möbius strip' interferometer is another system insensitive to tilt of the mirrors (Pritchard, Sakai, Steel, and Vanasse 1967).

The adjustment of a Michelson interferometer is quite straightforward, indeed with a laser source very simple; if a gas laser with a very narrow beam is used it is easy to see by eye when the two interfering beams coincide on a surface in the position of the detector, and with a beam a fraction of a millimetre in diameter, a visual judgement of coincidence is adequate. More generally, a Michelson interferometer is adjusted by autocollimation. The telescope through which the fringes are to be viewed is provided with an autocollimating eyepiece (Fig. 4.3), one mirror is covered with a screen and the other is adjusted (or the telescope may be adjusted) until the graticule in the eyepiece is imaged back upon itself; the screen is then placed over the other mirror, which, with the telescope left untouched, is adjusted until the graticule and its image in this mirror also coincide. With a suitably fine graticule, fringes should then be seen and can, if need be, be improved by small adjustments to the mirrors until the focus of the fringes is uniform over the field (see Chapter 3). If the path difference is not too great nor the diameter of the fringes too small, it may be possible to see them visually without the telescope, accommodating the eye for infinity, and then as the eye is moved about to observe fringes formed in different regions of the plates, the fringes will be seen to open out or to contract,

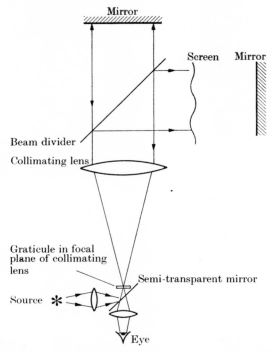

FIG. 4.3. Adjustment of Michelson interferometer by autocollimation.

corresponding to the varying separation of the plates and providing another criterion for the final adjustment. When a Michelson interferometer is used photoelectrically, the centre of the fringe pattern being observed through a small pinhole, the best way of checking the adjustment is to observe the same pinhole in autocollimation (Fig. 4.3). If the mirrors are aligned so that the pinhole is autocollimated in each to within about one-twentieth of its diameter, an adjustment that is readily made, conditions will be satisfactory (see Chapter 3).

Measurements of length and wavelength

Measurements of length and wavelength imply the use of quasi-monochromatic light. The output of the interferogram is then of the form

$$I(\Delta) = I_0 + T_c \cos k_0\Delta + T_s \sin k_0\Delta, \tag{4.1}$$

where $k = 2\pi/\lambda$, Δ is the path difference,

$$T_c = \int \tilde{I}(\tilde{k})\cos \tilde{k}\Delta \, \mathrm{d}\tilde{k},$$

$$T_s = \int \tilde{I}(\tilde{k})\sin \tilde{k} \, \Delta \, \mathrm{d}\tilde{k}, \tag{4.2}$$

and

$$k = k - k_0.$$

Unless the sine transform T_s is zero, the effective wavelength depends on the path difference; the effective wavelength, λ_{eff}, is the path difference divided by the number of equivalent zeros (those following either a maximum or a minimum) of the interferogram in that path difference. Zeros occur when

$$T_c \cos k_0 \Delta + T_s \sin k_0 \Delta = 0; \qquad (4.3)$$

for zeros following a maximum

$$k_0 \Delta = 2N\pi + \tfrac{1}{2}\pi + \arcsin\left(\frac{T_s}{T_c}\right) \qquad (4.4)$$

If T_s is zero,

$$k_0 \Delta = 2N\pi + \tfrac{1}{2}\pi \qquad (4.5)$$

and

$$\lambda_{\text{eff}} = \lambda_0. \qquad (4.5a)$$

If T_s is not zero,

$$\frac{\lambda_{\text{eff}} - \lambda_0}{\lambda_0} = \frac{1}{2N\pi} \arcsin\left(\frac{T_s(\Delta)}{T_c(\Delta)}\right). \qquad (4.6)$$

Careful studies (Rowley and Hamon 1963) have shown that even the narrowest of lines emitted by gas discharge sources, including the krypton-86 standard orange line at 605·8 nm, show some asymmetry, and that the effective wavelengths become imperfectly defined after a path difference of 1m. Only with light emitted by a gas laser operating in a single mode, the spectrum of which has a width of perhaps only 10^{-6} of that of the best gas discharge source, is the wavelength defined unambiguously out to many hundreds of metres.

The bulk of wavelength measurements are really measurements of the ratios of wavelengths, λ_1/λ_2. The only fundamental wavelength measurements are those in which the metre was compared with a wavelength of light as described in Chapter 8. In such measurements it is necessary to be able to define a path difference accurately in relation to a mechanical length defining the metre, whereas in wavelength measurements it is only necessary that the path difference should be the same when the interferometer is illuminated with light of different wavelengths. From the relative phases of the interferograms formed in the different wavelengths it is then possible to calculate the ratios. Wavelength measurements in this sense are thus somewhat simpler than measurements of length. Now that the unit of length is a wavelength, all measurements of wavelength are in fact measurements of ratios of wavelength to the krypton-86 standard (605·8 nm).

Suppose that the intensities in the interferograms formed in different radiations are

$$I_1(\Delta) = I_1(0) + T_{1c} \cos k_1\Delta,$$
$$I_2(\Delta) = I_2(0) + T_{2c} \cos k_2\Delta. \tag{4.7}$$

Observations then give values of Δ for which $\cos k\Delta$ equals 1 for a number of values of Δ and for the different wavelengths. It will be supposed that the ratios of the wavelengths are known well enough for the integral part of the order of interference to be calculated in each wavelength; then, if at some path difference Δ, $\cos k\Delta$ is 1 while the fractional part of the order of interference in another radiation is f,

$$k_1\Delta = 2\pi N,$$
$$k_2\Delta = 2\pi(N_2 + f), \tag{4.8}$$

and so

$$\frac{\lambda_2}{\lambda_1} = \frac{k_1}{k_2} = \frac{N_1}{N_2 + f}. \tag{4.9}$$

The practical problems in carrying out such a programme are the determination of a starting value of the ratio λ_2/λ_1, the measurement of the phases of the interferograms, the maintenance of a constant value of Δ, and the determination of Δ (or the integral orders).

Primitive measurements of wavelengths and wavelength ratios depend on direct counting of interference fringes over a small enough path difference to permit reliable counts; earlier determinations made before electronic counters were available are described in Chapter 8. Given approximate values of wavelength derived from such counts, orders of interference can be calculated for short path differences, improved ratios can be found from the fractional orders at those differences and so orders can be calculated for greater differences and the process can then be repeated. Thus step by step, using successively greater path differences, which at each stage are short enough to avoid ambiguity in the calculation of the integral parts of the order of interference, greater and greater precision in the determination of the ratios can be achieved.

Many methods are available for the determination of the phase of the interferogram. Attention continues to be restricted for the present to the Michelson interferometer in the parallel-plate mode, the inclined-plate mode being considered later. If observations are made visually or photographically using a field that embraces a number of Haidinger rings, then the order of interference at the centre of the ring pattern may be found by measuring the diameters of the rings and fitting them by least squares to the formula given in Chapter 3. This is not a very accurate procedure with sinusoidal fringes (it is much better adapted to the multiple-beam Fabry–Perot interferometer, Chapter 6) and is superseded by photoelectric methods. The most straightforward scheme is to measure the intensity at the centre of the fringe pattern as the path difference is varied continuously, the intensity being recorded automatically at equal intervals of path difference. A sine curve is then fitted to the observed intensities and from that the phase at some specified path difference may be calculated. The calculations are normally performed in a digital computer. Terrien (1958) has shown that very high accuracy can be obtained with a somewhat simpler method. He varies the path difference by tilting the compensating plate in his instrument and observes the intensity at the centre of the fringe pattern at three or four path differences. Let the interferogram be

$$A + B \cos(\theta + \phi), \tag{4.10}$$

where ϕ is the phase shift introduced by tilting the compensator plate. ϕ is taken to be zero at some reference position and the intensity is measured at positions for which it takes the values 0, ϕ_1, and ϕ_2. It is required to find θ. Let the photometer readings in the three positions be r_0, r_1, and r_2:

$$r_0 = A + B \cos \theta,$$
$$r_1 = A + B \cos(\theta + \phi_1), \tag{4.11}$$
$$r_2 = A + B \cos(\theta + \phi_2).$$

Then

$$B \cos \theta = \frac{r_0 \sin(\phi_2 - \phi_1) - r_1 \sin \phi_2 + r_2 \sin \phi_1}{\sin \phi_2 - \sin \phi_1 - \sin(\phi_2 - \phi_1)}. \tag{4.12}$$

It is convenient to take $\phi_1 = 120°$, $\phi_2 = 240°$, in which case

$$B \cos \theta = \tfrac{1}{3}(r_0 - r_1 + r_2).$$

Also $$B \sin \theta = 3^{\frac{1}{2}}(r_1 - r_2)/2. \tag{4.13}$$

Thus both B and θ may be found. Lastly

$$A = r_0 + \tfrac{1}{3}(r_0 - r_1 + r_2), \tag{4.14}$$

so that the visibility of the fringes can be determined.

Phases of an interferogram can be determined to about $2\pi/10^4$ using photoelectric methods.

It is evident that wavelength ratios will be in error if the path difference is not the same when observations are made in the different wavelengths. Two factors in particular can be troublesome. Temperature changes cause changes in the path difference because of mechanical changes in the structure of the interferometer and, unless observations in the different wavelengths are made simultaneously, errors can arise. (Changes in refractive index are ignored since all accurate measurements are made *in vacuo*.) The greater the desired accuracy the longer the time of observation needed to increase the signal-to-noise ratio and therefore the greater the chance of systematic errors from temperature changes. Photographic observations readily permit simultaneous observations if the interferometer is followed by a spectrograph in which the fringes in the various wavelengths may be photographed all at the same time. More elaborate methods of switching beams of light of different wavelengths are needed in photoelectric recording; one arrangement is described in Chapter 6. The second source of error is the illumination of the interferometer plates. If more than one lamp is used, as in a switching system for simultaneous photoelectric observations, the distribution of the illumination over the plates may not be the same for the different sources and then, if the plates are not perfectly flat and parallel, the effective path differences for the two lamps will not be the same.

The determination of the actual value of the path difference depends on matching the fractional values of the orders of interference in a number of wavelengths of which the ratios are already known (Perot and Fabry 1899). Suppose that wavelengths $\lambda_2, \ldots \lambda_y$ are known as multiples of λ_1. Suppose that the path difference Δ is an unknown integral order in λ_1:

$$\frac{\Delta}{\lambda_1} = N_1. \tag{4.15}$$

In some other wavelength let the measured fractional order be f_i and the unknown integral part be N_i:

$$\frac{\Delta}{\lambda_i} = (N_i + f_i). \tag{4.15a}$$

Now suppose that N_1 is increased by unity; Δ/λ_i will increase by

$$\frac{\lambda_1}{\lambda_i} = 1 + \frac{\lambda_1 - \lambda_i}{\lambda_i}, \tag{4.16}$$

and so f_i will increase by $(\lambda_1 - \lambda_i)/\lambda_i$.

The observed value of f_i will therefore recur whenever N_1 increases by $\lambda_i/(\lambda_1-\lambda_i)$. If a third wavelength λ_j is included, the measured fractions f_i and f_j will recur together when N increases by

$$\frac{\lambda_i}{\lambda_1-\lambda_i} \cdot \frac{\lambda_j}{\lambda_1-\lambda_j}.$$

With perhaps six well-distributed wavelengths, the recurrence interval can be made very large, and with a good mechanical determination of N_1 it does not take long to identify the integral order of interference.

Workers at the International Bureau of Weights and Measures have made wavelength measurements that agree to 1 in 10^9 with measurements made with a Fabry–Perot interferometer at the National Physical Laboratory (Cook 1962). This may well be near the limit of accuracy with thermal gas-discharge sources. The determination of line profiles, intimately connected with wavelength measurements, is discussed in Chapter 5.

The Michelson interferometer in the parallel-plate mode can be used for the measurement of fixed path differences by the method just described for the determination of a path difference from observations in a number of known wavelengths but the Fabry–Perot interferometer or the inclined-plate mode of the Michelson interferometer are better adapted for such measurements.

The Michelson interferometer is well adapted for the measurements of displacements by counting fringes. The introduction of lasers made fringe counting over large distances a practical possibility because it overcame the difficulty that with thermal sources the fringe visibility decreased relatively rapidly with path difference, making the design of the electronic counting circuits difficult. A diagram of a fringe-counting interferometer constructed at the National Physical Laboratory (Rowley and Stanley 1965) for the measurement of linear scales, is shown in Fig. 4.4. The scale to be measured is mounted on a carriage by which it is moved steadily beneath a detector (photoelectric microscope) that gives a signal every time a line on the scale passes beneath it. One path of the Michelson interferometer is by way of mirrors mounted on the carriage. The beam divider provides two optical signals with a phase difference of $\frac{1}{2}\pi$; the outputs from photomultipliers on which these signals fall go to a counter which, because the signals differ in phase by $\frac{1}{2}\pi$, can determine whether the count is increasing or decreasing. It is essential to be able to count in both directions since small

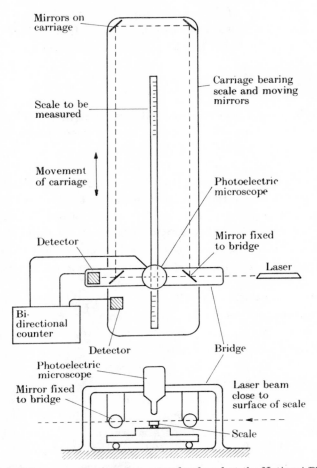

FIG. 4.4. Fringe-counting interferometer developed at the National Physical
Laboratory for the measurement of linear scales.

mechanical vibrations are sufficient to reverse the direction of movement momentarily. Two counters are provided that are started and
stopped alternately by the signals from the head detecting the transit
of a line; while one counter counts the number of fringes between successive lines, the count of the other, corresponding to the interval
between the preceding pair of lines, is recorded on punched paper tape.
An automatic record of the number of fringes between successive lines is
thus obtained. The counter gives the integral part of the order of interference and an interpolation system enables the fractional part to be
found. It is possible to determine the position of every line on a metre

bar divided into millimetres with an accuracy of about 0·01 μm in a total observation time of 15 min. The observations are made in air and all the corrections for the temperature of the scale and the refractive index of the air are applied in a computer which calculates the scale intervals from the fringe counts.

Bi-directional fringe-counting interferometers can also be used to record the changes in length of a nominally fixed distance. By setting up an interferometer with a path difference of about 100 m, it is easily possible to record continuously the variations of the path to better than 1 in 10^9 (Bostrom and Vali 1968, King, Bilham, Gerard, Davies, and Sydenham 1969). Such a system has great possibilities for geophysical observations of the state of strain at the surface of the Earth, both for components with relatively short periods, say up to one day, for which it is not necessary to be much concerned about the stability of the wavelength emitted by the laser, and for changes over much longer times for which the problem of stabilizing the laser wavelength becomes the dominant one.

When interferometers are to be used with a laser source, it is important to be sure that light from the interferometer is not reflected back into the laser; the phase of any such reflection will be related to that of the incident light in a way that depends on the path difference in the interferometer; as the latter is changed, the intensity of the light emitted by the laser will vary and it is possible to suppress the emission entirely. Interferometers using cube corners or analogous systems with mirrors do not return a beam directly into the laser, and should therefore be used with laser sources. (See, for lasers generally, Herriott 1967.)

The Fizeau interferometer and the Michelson interferometer in the inclined-plate mode

The essential components of an interferometer of this type are shown in Fig. 4.5; it is drawn for a transmission wedge but differs only in minor ways from the systems suitable for a wedge in reflection or for a Michelson interferometer. P_1 is a pinhole, which, together with the collimating lens C at the focus of which it is placed, defines the range of directions of light incident on the wedge W. T is the telescope lens, at the focus of which is a pinhole P_2 through which the fringes are viewed. L is a lens that focuses the fringes and the wedge on the focal plane F. L and F may form a photographic camera, or they may be the lens and retina of the eye. P_1 and P_2 are not both essential since one of them alone would define the direction of the light transmitted through the

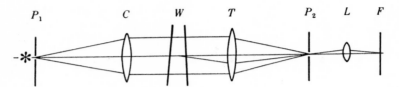

FIG. 4.5. Elements of a wedge-plate interferometer.

wedge, but it is helpful to have both to cut down stray and scattered light. They must of course be carefully imaged one upon the other.

To adjust such an interferometer, the eye is placed behind P_2 and focused on the pinhole P_1, using an eyepiece if necessary to obtain good definition. In general a number of images of P_1 will then be seen, arising not only from reflections at the inner faces of the wedge as well as the direct transmitted image, but also from reflections from the outer faces of the wedge plates, lens surfaces, and so on. The plates are adjusted to bring the direct image into coincidence with the image formed by reflection within the plates. (In the Michelson interferometer and the wedge viewed in reflection, the images reflected from the two mirrors are brought into coincidence.) Details of the adjustment and in particular of the identification of the correct images depend on the details of the instrument. When the images coincide, the plates will be sufficiently parallel to enable fringes to be seen, though usually the fringes will be very closely spaced. The final step in the adjustment is therefore to change the angle of the wedge very slightly until fringes are seen at a convenient spacing.

The Fizeau interferometer (Fizeau 1862) is the simplest of two-beam interferometers (Fig. 4.6). M_1 and M_2 are the two reflecting surfaces, of which M_1 is a fully reflecting surface and M_2 is semi-transparent. Division and recombination of the light take place at the semi-transparent surface. The same pinhole is used for illuminating and observing the fringes and the one lens L acts as both collimator and telescope. A semi-reflecting plate between the source S and the pinhole enables the fringes to be illuminated and observed through the pinhole. The fringes may be observed by eye or they may be photographed. The system provides a convenient means of examining the flatness of glass or metal plates or the shape of lens or mirror surfaces, and as such is widely used in optical and metal workshops in which surfaces are to be worked to high accuracy. If the lens L is designed carefully, fields of up to 25 cm diameter may be attained. Two types of lens aberration are

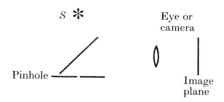

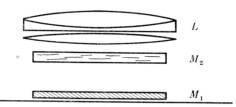

FIG. 4.6. Optical system of a Fizeau interferometer.

important. If the field is not flat, that is if all parts of the mirrors are not in focus for a given position of the pinhole, it will not be possible to use the whole field; if for a given position of the pinhole, rays through the centre of the mirrors are not parallel to those through the edges, the apparent separation of the plates at the edges will be in error on account of the obliquity of the light (Chapter 3).

In the usual procedure, the semi-reflecting mirror M_2 is the reference surface of known form, and the surface to be examined is placed beneath it. Fringes of quite sufficient intensity can be obtained from an uncoated glass surface. If the lower mirror is a metal surface of fairly high reflectivity it is well to increase the reflectivity of the upper mirror to match it, for then more than two beams can interfere and somewhat sharper fringes are obtained than with a strictly two-beam system (compare Chapter 6).

The form of the fringes is shown in Fig. 4.7; the fringes are contours that map out the separation of the two surfaces. Were the surfaces both flat, the separation would be a linear function of position and the fringes would be straight lines. If one surface departs from a plane, the fringes are curved, and the amount by which they depart from straight lines corresponds to the amount by which the surface departs from a

(a) Fringe pattern

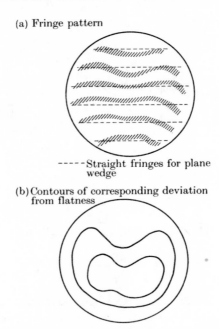

- - - - - Straight fringes for plane
                wedge

(b) Contours of corresponding deviation
       from flatness

FIG. 4.7. Fringes formed between two surfaces in a Fizeau interferometer.

plane: at the point where the fractional order of interference is not zero, as it would be if the fringes were straight, but is f, say, the surface lies either above or below a plane by the amount $f\lambda/2$. Whether the surface is concave or convex with respect to the reference surface can be determined by tilting one of the mirrors slightly in a known direction and observing the direction in which the fringes move.

The form of a surface can be determined to between 0·1 and 0·05 of a fringe, say 0·01 μm when the green line of mercury is used, by simple visual observation; methods which give much higher accuracy from the measurement of photographs have been described (Gates 1955).

When the surfaces can be brought close together, it is not necessary to use a source giving a very narrow spectrum line, and a convenient one is a high-pressure mercury lamp, the intense green line being isolated by a filter.

The Fizeau interferometer is also convenient for the measurement of engineer's block gauges (slip gauges), which are blocks of hardened steel having two optically polished flat parallel faces, the separation of which defines the gauge length. To measure such gauges in a Fizeau interferometer, the lower mirror is made the optically flat and polished surface of a metal base plate to which the blocks are wrung in molecular contact. Fringes are seen to cross the surface of the base plate and the upper surface of the gauge, and the difference of the order of interference between the two sets of fringes is equal to

$$2t/\lambda,$$

where t is the thickness of the gauge. The fractional part f of the difference of order is estimated by eye from the relative positions of the fringes on the gauge and base plate, and from observations in a number of wavelengths combined with a mechanical measurement of the gauge, the integral part of the order of interference can be determined as explained earlier.

The simple Fizeau interferometer is convenient for the rapid measurement of short gauges, on which accuracies of better than 0·01 μm can be obtained by visual observations. Gas discharge sources with cadmium or mercury-198 are used. Corrections for the refractive index of the air, calculated from the observed temperature, pressure, and humidity, amount to about 2·7 μm on a gauge 1 cm long.

A form of the Michelson interferometer convenient for the measurement of gauges up to 50 cm long is the Kösters interferometer (Fig. 4.8) (Kösters 1921, 1926). It is a Michelson interferometer of conventional form except for the disposition of one of the mirrors. As with the Fizeau interferometer, B is a base plate to which the gauge G is wrung. Fringes are formed between the reference mirror R and, on the one hand, the surface of the base plate, and on the other, the upper surface of the gauge. The characteristic feature of the Kösters interferometer is that the path difference between R and B is made to be about the same as that between R and the upper face of the gauge, though of opposite sign: in these circumstances, the image R' of the reference mirror R falls about half way along the gauge. As a result, the visibility of the fringes is the same on the gauge surface as on the base plate and because it is easier to estimate the relative positions of the fringes when they are of equal rather than of unequal contrast, the accuracy of measurements is higher than with the Fizeau interferometer, in which the fringes are necessarily of unequal visibility. Further, the maximum length of gauge for which fringes of a given visibility are obtained with a particular source is just twice that for the Fizeau interferometer. The Kösters interferometer is therefore especially useful for gauges between 0·1 and 0·5 m long.

The Kösters interferometer is similar to the interferometer introduced

6

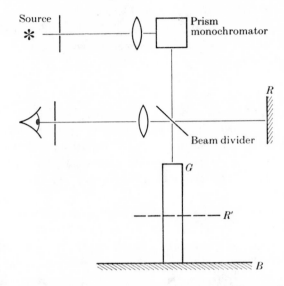

FIG. 4.8. Kösters interferometer for measurement of long end gauges.

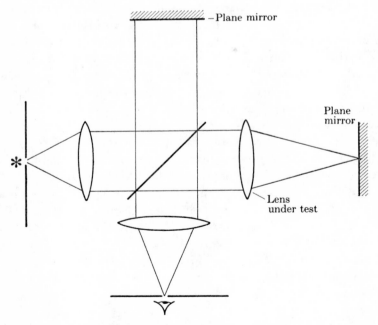

FIG. 4.9. Twyman–Green interferometer.

by Twyman and Green (1916, Hilger and Twyman 1918) for the testing of mirrors, lenses, and other optical components. A mirror that is supposed to be flat can be tested by using it as one of the two mirrors of the interferometer, a reference mirror of known form being used as the other. For more general components, auxilliary optical systems must be arranged so that the wavefronts reflected from each arm of the interferometer are plane when they meet the beam divider. Thus, a lens to be tested may be combined with a plane mirror placed at its focus so that a plane wave incident on the combination is reflected as a plane wave (Fig. 4.9); the reflected wave may then be compared with one reflected from a plane reference mirror in the other arm of the interferometer. The flatness of the mirror at the focus of the lens under test is not critical. In all cases, the imperfections of the optical components under test give rise to distortion of the nominally plane wave reflected to the beam divider and these distortions in turn are displayed as departures of the interference fringes from parallel straight lines.

The Twyman–Green interferometer can conveniently be used for the measurement of refractive index by the comparison of the refractive indices of a solid and liquid that are nearly the same. If a parallel-sided slab of the solid is immersed in the liquid contained in a tank having sides that are optically flat and parallel, and if the whole arrangement is placed in one arm of the interferometer, the field of view will be crossed by parallel fringes that show a change of order at the boundary of the solid (Fig. 4.10). With proper choice of the thickness t of the solid to avoid ambiguity of the change of the order of interference, the difference of refractive index between the liquid and the solid may be calculated from the formula

$$\delta\mu = f\lambda/t,$$

where f is the relative displacement of the fringes, λ is the wavelength and $\delta\mu$ the difference of refractive index. Although it is simplest if the solid has plane sides, it is not essential, and, in particular, the refractive indices of simple lenses and even spheres may be found in this way.

The interferometer systems so far described have relatively large fields of view and essentially give no magnification of the surface being observed. If microscope objectives are placed in the arms of the interferometer (Linnik 1933) a surface may be observed under a high magnification and fine details of the topography delineated. A diagram of the system is shown in Fig. 4.11. O_1, O_2 are well-corrected microscope

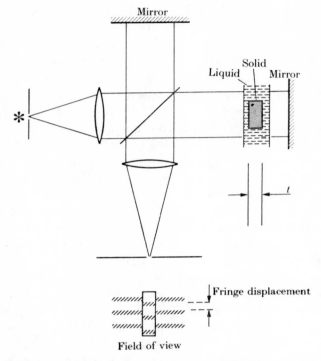

Fig. 4.10. Measurement of refractive index with Michelson interferometer.

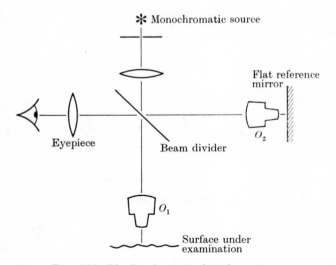

Fig. 4.11. Linnik microscope interferometer.

objectives that should be closely matched. The light falling on the surface to be examined is strongly convergent and the visibility of the fringes is therefore negligible unless the path difference between the test and reference surfaces is almost zero (see Chapter 3). It is possible to make interference microscopes of the Fizeau type (Fig. 4.12); since the path difference can never be reduced exactly to zero, the magnification is necessarily less than that possible with the Linnik type, where the path difference can be made almost exactly zero. The

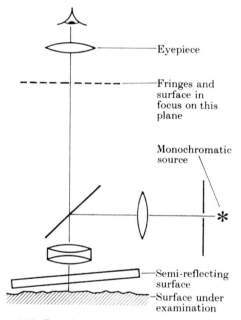

FIG. 4.12. Interference microscope of Fizeau type.

interpretation of the results obtained with any interference microscope must always be considered very carefully if the topographic slopes of the surface being examined are appreciable, as for example in studying grooves ruled on metal with a diamond. The combination of a wide angle of illumination of the surface combined with the steep angles of the surface itself can give rise to misleading fringe patterns (Ingelstamm 1960).

A very compact interferometer of the Kösters type can be made using a beam divider devised by Kösters and known as the Kösters prism (Fig. 4.13) (Kösters 1938). It consists of a prism divided into two as shown, with a semi-reflecting coating on the median plane. The

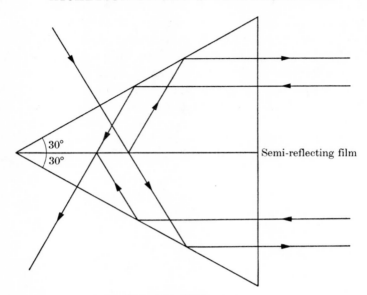

FIG. 4.13. Kösters prism.

semi-vertical angle is 30°; light incident normally on one of the inclined faces undergoes total internal reflection at one or other of the inclined faces, depending on whether it is transmitted or reflected at the median plane, and is then transmitted normally through the base of the prism. Light returned from the mirrors placed in the emergent beams is like-wise transmitted back through the prism to emerge normally from one or other of the inclined faces. The system is evidently compensated for white light fringes and, although the prism is difficult to make, the fact that it gives two parallel beams is of great advantage in laying out an interferometer. In the particular example of a gauge interferometer the gauge and the reference mirror can be placed side by side in the one temperature-controlled enclosure (Fig. 4.14).

Taking μ to be the refractive index of air, the refractivity $(\mu-1)$ is proportional to the density of the air and is 270×10^{-6} for air of normal density. The rates of change of refractivity are thus $0\cdot27 \times 10^{-6}$ per mbar† and 1×10^{-6} per °C. (The refractivity also depends slightly on the humidity of the atmosphere and on the wavelength of the light.) Suppose that a gauge $0\cdot01$ m long is to be measured to $0\cdot01$ μm, that is to 1 part in 10^6; it is sufficient to measure the pressure of the air to about 1 mbar and the temperature to about $0\cdot2$°C, measurements that

† 1 mbar = 100 N/m²; atmospheric pressure is about 1000 mbar.

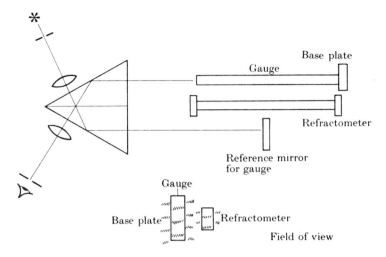

FIG. 4.14. Interferometer using Kösters prism.

are easy to make. To measure a gauge 1 m long to 0·1 μm requires measurements of pressure and temperature that are one hundred times more accurate, presenting very considerable difficulty. One solution is to make all measurements in a vacuum, but there are two disadvantages in so doing: the temperature of the gauge itself takes longer to come into equilibrium with its surroundings when in vacuum, and because the gauge is compressible, the length is slightly increased, by about 1 part in 10⁶. Provided the refractivity can be measured sufficiently accurately, there is some advantage, as well as some convenience, in working in air at normal pressure. The Kösters–Zeiss interferometer (see Hunziger 1955) incorporates a refractometer in the form of an evacuated tube placed close to the gauge to be measured, and closed by optically flat plates that extend over the sides of the tube. The refractivity of the air is found from the difference between the orders of interference inside and outside the evacuated tube. It may, if need be, be found by direct counting, since the difference is about 1000 fringes. The interferometer is in an air-tight enclosure and a convenient and accurate method of observation is to vary the air pressure until the fringes on the base plate coincide with those on the front face of the gauge—this can be done to about one-hundredth of a fringe, a precision that enables the Kösters–Zeiss interferometer to be used for wavelength comparisons of the highest accuracy (for examples, see Engelhardt 1960).

The Mach–Zehnder interferometer

The Mach–Zehnder interferometer (Fig. 4.15) is a form of Michelson interferometer suitable for the measurement of differences of refractive index in a fluid, and is used extensively to study the flow of gases in wind tunnels and shock tubes, the density being derived from the observed changes in refractive index. S_1 and S_2 are semi-transparent mirrors, while M_1 and M_2 are fully reflecting mirrors. The fringes correspond, of course, to the total difference between the two paths round

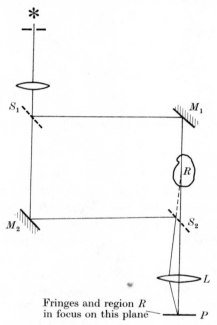

FIG. 4.15. Mach–Zehnder interferometer.

the quadrilateral, but in the great majority of applications the refactivity is constant except in a fairly restricted region R. It is then possible to adjust the mirrors so that the emergent beams diverge from that region, and then if the region is imaged by the lens L on to the plane P the fringes will also be seen in focus on the same plane (for a further discussion of localization of fringes see Born and Wolf 1959). Thus, if it is desired to examine the flow around some object in a wind tunnel, it will be arranged that the object is imaged on P and the fringes are adjusted until they also are seen in focus on P. A thorough discussion of the Mach–Zehnder interferometer has been given by Bennett and Kahl (1953).

The wedge and parallel-plate modes
of two-beam interferometers

In general, as may be appreciated from the foregoing examples, the wedge mode of the Michelson interferometer is more versatile and has more varied applications than the parallel-plate mode, but the latter is capable of higher precision. There are three main reasons why the wedge mode affords lower precision. In the first place, it is not well adapted to photoelectric work because the extended field prevents the most accurate photometric methods being applied. The bulk of the observations made with wedge-mode interferometers are made by eye. Secondly, a number of rather incidental factors reduce the visibility of the fringes in the wedge mode. It is usually difficult to ensure that the intensities of the two interfering beams are equal, although in interferometers of the Kösters type it is possible to make a reference mirror of the same reflectivity as the gauge and base plate. The optical system also usually admits more scattered light.

The most important consideration, however, is that the signal-to-noise ratio of the wedge interferometer is very poor compared with that of the parallel-plate interferometer.

Suppose that the total flux of light through the object pinhole into the solid angle subtended at the pinhole by the interferometer plates is F. This flux all passes through the exit pinhole in the ideal parallel-plate interferometer, while in the optimum practical instrument with ideal beam divider and mirrors the mean emergent flux is $\frac{1}{4}F$. The total noise will be the sum of photon noise, $\frac{1}{2}F^{\frac{1}{2}}$, and detector noise, D say, and so the signal-to-noise ratio will be

$$\frac{\frac{1}{2}FV}{\frac{1}{2}F^{\frac{1}{2}}+D},$$

where V is the visibility of the fringes.

In the wedge mode, the area of the interferometer plates is divided up into elementary areas and the flux of light through each is measured separately, whether by eye, photographically, or by some photoelectric imaging device.

If the field is observed by eye or is photographed, the number of elementary areas is set by the resolution of the eye or the photographic system. Suppose there are N elementary areas. The flux through each is then at most F/N, and may be less if successive apertures in the optical train are not properly matched. The signal-to-noise ratio for the observations of each elementary area will then be

$$\frac{\frac{1}{2}FV/N}{\frac{1}{2}(F/N)^{\frac{1}{2}}+D},$$

a quantity which lies between $1/N$ and $1/N^{\frac{1}{2}}$ of that for the parallel-plate mode. N is usually very large, possibly as great as 10^6.

Visual or photographic observations take little longer than observations on the parallel-plate interferometer since all elementary areas are observed simultaneously, but sequential photoelectric observations would have in principle to take at least N times as long.

Evidently the pinhole should be made as large as possible in the wedge mode, but a limit is placed by the range of angles of incidence, which, if large, reduces the visibility of the fringes and, in the measurement of lengths, introduces a net phase shift or obliquity error (Chapter 3). The wedge mode interferometer is therefore unavoidably a low intensity system. A corollary of this argument is that if the relative aperture of the optical system is increased, as for example in a Fizeau interferometer intended for the examination of large optical components, the area of the pinhole will be increased to maintain the intensity of illumination, and to keep the obliquity effects small the path difference in the wedge must also be kept small (see Chapter 3).

Three-beam interference

By a suitable combination of beam dividers, it is possible for beams from more than two paths to interfere. A simple system for three beams is shown in Fig. 4.16. The surfaces 1 and 3 are semi-reflecting and are placed in one arm of a Michelson interferometer while the surface 2, placed in the other arm, is imaged at 2′. The phases of the light reflected from the three surfaces are respectively

$$kl_1, \; kl_2, \; kl_3 \; = \; \theta_1, \; \theta_2, \; \theta_3.$$

If the amplitudes are $a_1,\; \alpha_2,\; \alpha_3$, the total amplitude of the combined beam is

$$a_1 \mathrm{e}^{-\mathrm{i}\theta_1} + a_2 \mathrm{e}^{-\mathrm{i}\theta_2} + a_3 \mathrm{e}^{-\mathrm{i}\theta_3}. \tag{4.17}$$

To simplify the discussion, let $a_1 = a_3$, and write $a_2/a_1 = a$. Then the intensity is proportional to

$$|\mathrm{e}^{-\mathrm{i}(\theta_1-\theta_2)} + a + \mathrm{e}^{-\mathrm{i}(\theta_3-\theta_2)}|^2. \tag{4.18}$$

Now let $\qquad \phi = \frac{1}{2}(\theta_1-\theta_3), \qquad \psi = \frac{1}{2}(\theta_1+\theta_3)-\theta_2,$

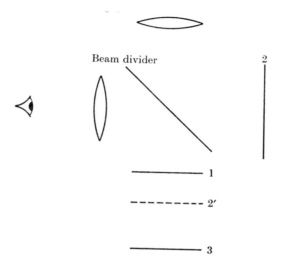

Beam divider

2

1

2'

3

FIG. 4.16. Interference of three beams.

so that the intensity may be written as

$$|e^{-1(\psi-\phi)}+a+e^{1(\psi+\phi)}|^2$$
$$= (a+2\cos\phi)^2\cos^2\tfrac{1}{2}\psi+(a-2\cos\phi)^2\sin^2\tfrac{1}{2}\psi$$
$$= a^2+4\cos^2\phi+4a\cos\phi\cos\psi. \qquad (4.19)$$

An example of the application of the interference of three beams is the measurement of the separation of the surfaces 1 and 3, when the reflectivities of these surfaces are low so that it is difficult to see directly Fizeau fringes formed between them (Cook 1957, 1961). For this purpose, it is arranged that the lines of constant ϕ are at right angles to those of constant ψ and that the spacing of the fringes corresponding to constant ψ is much less than that of the fringes corresponding to constant ϕ. Let $\cos\phi$ be greater than 0. Then the intensity I_+ is

$$a^2+4\cos^2\phi+4a\cos\psi\cos\phi, \qquad (4.20)$$

while if $\cos\phi$ is less than 0, the intensity I_- is

$$a^2+4\cos^2\phi'+4a\cos\psi\cos\phi', \qquad (4.21)$$

where

$$\phi' = \phi+\pi. \qquad (4.22)$$

Thus, the fringe pattern for $\cos\phi < 0$ is the same as for $\cos\phi > 0$ but is shifted by half the fringe spacing (Fig. 4.17). When $\phi = 0$, the intensity does not vary with ψ. It is found in practice that it is much

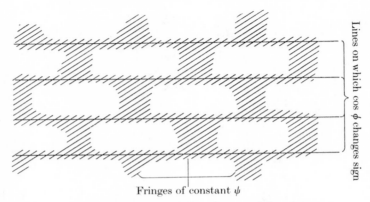

FIG. 4.17. Fringe pattern with interference of three beams.

easier to measure accurately the lines on which the phase of the ψ fringes changes than it is to measure directly the positions of the two-beam ϕ fringes of low visibility.

Three-beam systems can be used in other ways to determine phases in two-beam interference.

Polarization interferometers, X-ray and electron interferometers

A semi-reflecting surface is not the only device by which a beam of light may be divided. In particular, polarizing systems and gratings have been used.

In a polarization interferometer (Françon 1966) a birefringent component introduces a phase shift, possibly accompanied by a shear, between the ordinary and extraordinary wave fronts generated by the birefringent component. Some optical systems are indicated in Fig. 4.18.

The system shown in Fig. 4.18(a) (Françon 1951) uses two birefringent plates placed between a polarizer and an analyser. Polarized light is split into ordinary and extraordinary rays in the first birefringent plate and in the second plate they are made parallel. The system therefore introduces a lateral displacement between the two emergent beams, which then interfere. The position of the polarizing system is not critical and in particular it may be placed immediately behind a microscope objective. The interferometer is thus well adapted for the examination of small transparent objects, especially biological material. The system may also be used to examine a reflecting surface, as indicated in Fig. 4.18(b).

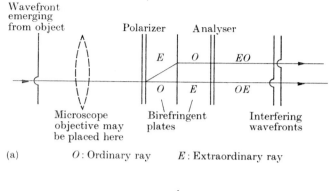

Wavefront
emerging
from object   Polarizer   Analyser

Microscope   Birefringent   Interfering
objective may   plates   wavefronts
be placed here

(a) O : Ordinary ray E : Extraordinary ray

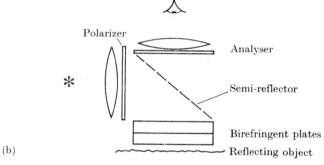

Polarizer
                                        Analyser

                                        Semi-reflector

                                        Birefringent plates
(b)   Reflecting object

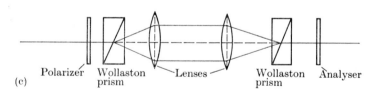

Polarizer   Wollaston   Lenses   Wollaston   Analyser
(c)   prism   prism

FIG. 4.18. Interferometers with polarizing beam dividers.

Another system is that shown in Fig. 4.18(c). It incorporates two
Wollaston prisms, and again introduces a lateral shift between the
two beams that are to interfere.

Transparent objects to be examined may be introduced between the
two beams, and the system has been used for the study of flowing gases.
The disadvantage of the system is that the angular spread of the beams
passing through the system is very limited. Nomarski (1955) has modified the Wollaston prisms so that the interferometer may be incorporated in a microscope.

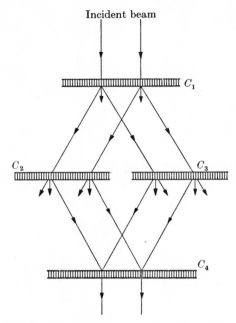

Fig. 4.19. Crystal grating X-ray interferometer (M. Hart).

Polarization interferometers have the advantage that they introduce a small (and fixed) phase difference between the two interfering beams, and may accordingly be used with white light, which, among other advantages, enables the illumination to be much more intense than it can be in monochromatic light.

François (1966) has shown that the mutual coherence function of the two beams passing through a polarization interferometer is the same as that of the two beams passing through a Michelson interferometer.

The outline of a grating system is shown in Fig. 4.19. Interferometers of this type have been set up both for X-rays and electrons, using a crystal as a diffraction grating to divide an incident beam. C_1 is a slice of a single crystal from which two first-order diffracted beams emerge symmetrically on either side of the direction of the incident radiation and, in turn, fall upon two crystals C_2 and C_3; the second-order diffracted beams from these crystals intersect at the surface of the crystal C_4 and interference occurs in the first-order diffracted beam. Such a system could of course be set up with light and transmission gratings but would not have much use. An electron interferometer has been demonstrated (Marton, Simpson, and Saddeth 1954, Simpson 1954), but the adjustment was very difficult. The X-ray system may be applied to measure the lattice spacing in the crystals in terms of visible wavelengths (Hart 1968): if crystal C_4 is moved sideways relative to the others, the intensity of the transmitted X-ray beam will pass through a maximum every time that C_4 moves by one lattice spacing. If the total movement can be made large enough (say 0·1 mm) to be measured accurately with a high resolution interferometer using a laser source, then the lattice spacing may be found in terms of the laser wavelength. The arrangement has also been applied to the study of defects in crystals using X-rays: if the crystal C_4 is replaced by two crystals one in front of the other, the interference patterns from the two crystals combine in a Moiré pattern (Hart and Bonse 1968).

Microwave interferometers

It is a relatively simple matter to construct a two-beam interferometer from waveguide components. One, devised by Froome (1954, 1958 see also Froome and Essen 1969) for the measurement of the velocity of light, is shown in Fig. 4.20. The path difference between the two sides of the interferometer can be changed by moving the detector assembly relative to the transmitter assembly and the number of wavelengths in a measured displacement can be counted. The wavelength of the radiation is then known and, from the known frequency, the velocity of the microwave radiation in air is calculated. The number of wavelengths between the receiving and transmitting horns was never very large and the diffraction pattern of the horns in the near-field region had to be discussed in great detail. The Mach–Zehnder interferometer is the closest optical analogue of this microwave interferometer.

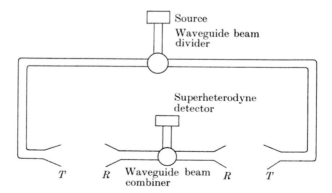

T, T, fixed transmitting horns
R, R, receiving horns on movable carriage

FIG. 4.20. Microwave Michelson interferometer (K. D. Froome).

The birefringent filter

The birefringent filter, invented independently by Lyot (1933) and Öhman (1938), is essentially a number of two-beam interferometers placed one after the other. The path differences of successive interferometers are arranged to be in the ratio of 2:1. If the order of interference in the shortest interferometer is n_1, the transmission of that interferometer will be proportional to

$$1 + \cos 2\pi n_1,$$

that is to $\cos^2 \pi n_1$, assuming ideal visibility of unity. The transmission of an assembly of $(r-1)$ interferometers will then be

$$\cos^2 \pi n_1 . \cos^2 2\pi n_1 \ldots \cos^2 2r2\pi n_1.$$

The principal maxima of the product occur whenever n_1 is an integer, and have the value 1, whereas the intervening maxima, which occur when $2n_1$, $3n_1$, etc. are integers although n_1 is not, are very small. Thus it is possible to make a filter with a pass band given by the longest interferometer, whereas the interval between pass bands is set by the shortest.

The actual interferometers comprise blocks of birefringent crystal each with polarizers on either side. Let the crystal have indices of refraction $\alpha > \beta > \gamma$ and let light travel along the direction of the β-axis. The first polarizer is set with its direction of polarization at 45° to the α- and γ-axes; incident light is thus split into two equal components that travel through the crystal with speeds c/α and c/γ. On emerging from the crystal, the light passes through a second polarizer with the direction of polarization parallel to that of the first; two parallel polarized beams of equal intensity thus emerge from the polarizer and, since they are coherent and of equal intensity, they interfere to give fringes with a visibility of 1. The phase difference is

$$\frac{d}{\lambda_\gamma} - \frac{d}{\lambda_\alpha} = \frac{d}{\lambda_{\text{vac}}} (\gamma - \alpha),$$

where d is the thickness of the crystal and λ_{vac} is the vacuum wavelength.

Birefringent filters have been made in a number of different configurations (for example, the polarizers may be sheet polarizers or Nicol prisms) and have been applied to many problems. Pass bands can be made as small as 0·01 nm. The wavelength of the pass bands can be varied over about 1 nm by altering the temperature and hence the refractive indices of the birefringent material, while a greater variation may be obtained if wedge-plate phase shifters are introduced. These, and many other developments, are discussed by Evans (1949).

Birefringent filters were developed for solar spectroscopy and they have continued to be so used; other uses in the laboratory have also been found: for example, to isolate lines in the spectrum of krypton-86.

Unlike multiple-beam interference filters (Chapter 6), birefringent filters have no reflecting elements and so the peak transmission can be very close to 100 per cent, while extremely narrow pass bands can be achieved.

5

FOURIER TRANSFORM SPECTROSCOPY

Quasi-monochromatic spectra

It has already been seen that the formulae of Fourier transform spectroscopy are especially simple when light is quasi-monochromatic, for then the interferogram is very nearly a cosinusoidal function of path difference with the amplitude and phase varying slowly with path difference. A few observations are then usually sufficient to determine the parameters of the spectrum.

Consider a Gaussian spectrum as a simple example. Let the centre of the spectrum be at a wave number k_0 and let the intensity be given by

$$I(k) = \frac{1}{(2\pi)^{\frac{1}{2}}\sigma} e^{-(k-k_0)^2/2\sigma^2},$$

or

$$I(k') = \frac{1}{(2\pi)^{\frac{1}{2}}\sigma} e^{-k'^2/2\sigma^2},$$

(5.1)

where $k' = k - k_0$.

Since $I(k')$ is an even function of k', the sine transform is zero. $\mathscr{I}(l)$, the cosine transform with respect to path difference l, is

$$\mathscr{I}(l) = \frac{1}{(2\pi)^{\frac{1}{2}}\sigma} \int_{-\infty}^{+\infty} e^{-k'^2/2\sigma^2} \cos k'l \, dk',$$

(5.2)

that is

$$\frac{1}{(2\pi)^{\frac{1}{2}}\sigma} \operatorname{Re} \int_{-\infty}^{+\infty} e^{-k'^2/2\sigma^2} e^{-ik'l} \, dk',$$

(5.2a)

or

$$\frac{1}{(2\pi)^{\frac{1}{2}}\sigma} \operatorname{Re} \int_{-\infty}^{+\infty} e^{-\frac{1}{2}l^2\sigma^2} \exp\left\{-\left(\frac{k'}{2^{\frac{1}{2}}\sigma} + \frac{il\sigma}{2^{\frac{1}{2}}}\right)^2\right\} dk'.$$

(5.2b)

Now put $z = k' + il\sigma^2$ so that

$$\mathscr{I}(l) = e^{-\frac{1}{2}l^2\sigma^2} \frac{1}{(2\pi)^{\frac{1}{2}}\sigma} \operatorname{Re} \int_{-\infty}^{+\infty} e^{-z^2/2\sigma^2} \, dz.$$

(5.3)

Thus

$$\mathscr{I}(l) = e^{-\frac{1}{2}l^2\sigma^2}.$$

(5.3a)

Hence, by equations (2.19) and (2.20), the interferogram is proportional to

$$1+\frac{2}{\rho+\rho^{-1}}\mathrm{e}^{-\frac{1}{2}l^2\sigma^2}\cos k_0 l, \qquad \left(\rho = \left(\frac{I^{(1)}}{I^{(2)}}\right)^{\frac{1}{2}}\right), \tag{5.4}$$

the visibility of the fringes is

$$\mathscr{V} = 2\mathrm{e}^{-\frac{1}{2}l^2\sigma^2}/(\rho+\rho^{-1}), \tag{5.5}$$

and

$$\ln \mathscr{V} = -\tfrac{1}{2}l^2\sigma^2-\ln(\rho+\rho^{-1})+\ln 2. \tag{5.5a}$$

The correction factor $\frac{1}{2}(\rho+\rho^{-1})$ can readily be determined and it will be convenient in the remainder of this chapter to understand by $\mathscr{V}$ the visibility multiplied by $\frac{1}{2}(\rho+\rho^{-1})$.

If the spectrum is purely Gaussian, measurements of the visibility at a few well-spaced path differences determine σ, the only parameter of the spectrum apart from k_0. Evidently these same observations will show whether the spectrum is adequately described by a Gaussian function.

An important feature of Fourier transform spectroscopy of quasi-monochromatic light is that it is often easy to separate different components of the spectrum. Suppose that the spectrum is the convolute of two elementary functions $I_1(k)$ and $I_2(k)$, a common case when a line is broadened by two mechanisms, one of which would on its own give a Lorentz profile for example, while the other by itself might give a Gaussian profile. Then

$$I(k) = \int_{-\infty}^{+\infty} I_1(k-\kappa)I_2(\kappa)\,\mathrm{d}\kappa. \tag{5.6}$$

Let $\mathscr{I}(l)$ be the Fourier transform of $I(k)$:

$$\mathscr{I}(l) = \int_{-\infty}^{+\infty} I(k)\mathrm{e}^{-\mathrm{i}kl}\,\mathrm{d}k;$$

$$I(k) = \int_{-\infty}^{+\infty} \mathscr{I}(l)\mathrm{e}^{\mathrm{i}kl}\,\mathrm{d}l. \tag{5.7}$$

Thus

$$\mathscr{I}(l) = \int_{-\infty}^{+\infty} \mathrm{d}k \int_{-\infty}^{+\infty} \mathrm{d}\kappa I_1(k-\kappa)I_2(\kappa)\mathrm{e}^{-\mathrm{i}kl}$$

$$= \int_{-\infty}^{+\infty} \mathrm{d}k \int_{-\infty}^{+\infty} \mathrm{d}\kappa I_1(k-\kappa)I_2(\kappa)\mathrm{e}^{-\mathrm{i}(k-\kappa)l}\mathrm{e}^{-\mathrm{i}\kappa l}. \tag{5.8}$$

Put $k-\kappa = \xi$; then

$$\mathscr{I}(l) = \int_{-\infty}^{+\infty} I_1(\xi)\mathrm{e}^{-\mathrm{i}\xi l}\mathrm{d}\xi \int_{-\infty}^{+\infty} I_2(\kappa)\mathrm{e}^{-\mathrm{i}\kappa l}\mathrm{d}\kappa, \tag{5.9}$$

or
$$\mathscr{I}(l) = \mathscr{I}_1(l) \cdot \mathscr{I}_2(l). \tag{5.9a}$$

This is a standard result: the Fourier transform of the convolute of two functions is the product of the Fourier transforms of those functions. Since

$$\mathscr{V}(l) = |\mathscr{I}(l)|, \tag{5.10}$$

the visibility is equal to
$$|\mathscr{I}_1(l)| \cdot |\mathscr{I}_2(l)|$$

and
$$\ln \mathscr{V} = \ln |\mathscr{I}_1| + \ln |\mathscr{I}_2| = \ln \mathscr{V}_1 + \ln \mathscr{V}_2. \tag{5.11}$$

The problem of the analysis of a spectrum that is the convolute of a Gaussian and a Lorentzian profile has been extensively studied by Terrien (1960) in the course of his examination of the wavelengths of standard lines in the spectra of krypton and mercury. In this case,

$$I_1(k) = \frac{1}{(2\pi)^{\frac{1}{2}}\sigma} e^{-\frac{1}{2}k^2/\sigma^2};$$

$$I_2(k) = \frac{1}{\pi} (1+k^2/a^2)^{-1}. \tag{5.12}$$

It has already been seen that

$$\mathscr{I}_1(l) = e^{-\frac{1}{2}l^2\sigma^2}.$$

For the Lorentz profile,

$$\mathscr{I}_2(l) = \frac{1}{\pi} \int_{-\infty}^{+\infty} \frac{e^{+ikl}}{1+k^2/a^2} \, \mathrm{d}k. \tag{5.13}$$

To evaluate the integral, replace it by the equivalent contour integral around the infinite semi-circle in the upper half plane. There is one pole, at $k = ia$, in the upper half plane, and therefore

$$\mathscr{I}_2(l) = e^{-al}. \tag{5.14}$$

If, then, the spectrum is the convolute of a Gaussian and a Lorentz function, the visibility is given by

$$\ln \mathscr{V} = -\tfrac{1}{2}l^2\sigma^2 - al. \tag{5.15}$$

Terrien has measured the visibility at a number of path differences and has plotted $l^{-1} \ln \mathscr{V}$ against l, as shown in Fig. 5.1. He found that some six points were sufficient to show that the visibility did indeed behave according to eqn. (5.15). The intercept at $l = 0$ gives the Lorentz parameter a, while the slope of the line gives the Gaussian

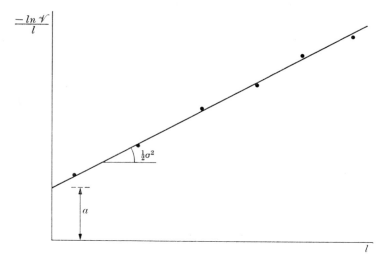

FIG. 5.1. Variation of $\mathscr{V}$ with path difference l for convolution of Gaussian and Lorentz profile.

parameter σ. The method is very sensitive: Terrien was able to determine a Lorentz parameter equal to $0\cdot2$ m^{-1} when the Gaussian parameter was 2 m^{-1}. Terrien has also investigated self-reversed lines. If the unreversed profile is Gaussian, the visibility of fringes formed in the reversed line will fall to zero at some path difference, but it will not fall to zero if the unreversed profile is Lorentzian (Cook 1968). It is almost always found that self-reversal is not symmetrical.

Multiple components can also be detected by visibility measurements. Suppose that a spectrum consists of two components with similar profiles, the amplitude of one being α times that of the other. If the two components are centred on k_1 and k_2, the intensity of the two together is

$$I = [\delta(k-k_1)+\alpha\delta(k-k_2)]*I_0(k), \tag{5.16}$$

where $I_0(k)$ is the profile of either component separately and $\delta(k-k_1)$ equals zero unless $k = k_1$, when it is unity. ($*$ denotes convolution.) The Fourier transform of $\delta(k-k_1)$ is $e^{ik_1 l}$; the Fourier transform of

$$\delta(k-k_1)+\alpha\delta(k-k_2)$$

is therefore

$$e^{ik_1 l}(1+\alpha e^{i\kappa l}), \qquad (\kappa = k_2-k_1),$$

and that of the complete profile is

$$\mathscr{I}(l) = e^{ik_1 l}(1+\alpha e^{i\kappa l}) \cdot \mathscr{I}_0(l). \tag{5.17}$$

Thus

$$|\mathscr{I}(l)| = |1+\alpha e^{i\kappa l}| \cdot |\mathscr{I}_0(l)| \tag{5.18}$$

and since
$$|1+\alpha e^{i\kappa l}| = (1+\alpha^2+2\alpha \cos \kappa l)^{\frac{1}{2}},$$

$$\mathscr{V}(l) = |\mathscr{I}(l)| = (1+\alpha^2+2\alpha \cos \kappa l)^{\frac{1}{2}} \cdot \mathscr{V}_0(l). \qquad (5.19)$$

The visibility of the fringes formed from the two components is therefore that of either component separately ($\mathscr{V}_0(l)$) on which is imposed a modulation with an amplitude of α and a period of $2\pi/\kappa$.

It will be possible to detect two components if the separation is such that there are at least two periods of the modulation over the path difference in which the fringes can be seen above noise. Suppose, for example, that with a Gaussian profile fringes can no longer be seen if $\frac{1}{2}l^2\sigma^2 > 4$. Then κ should exceed $2^{\frac{1}{2}}\pi\sigma$.

If the separation of the components is smaller, the overall spectrum should be regarded as that of an unsymmetrical line, for which the visibility does not contain all the possible information about the spectrum. If the spectrum is symmetrical, the interferogram is given by

$$\mathscr{I}(l) = T_c \cos k_0 l, \qquad (5.20)$$

while if the spectrum is unsymmetrical,

$$\mathscr{I}(l) = T_c \cos k_0 l - T_s \sin k_0 l, \qquad (5.20a)$$

where T_c and T_s are the cosine and sine transforms of $I(k')$.

Thus
$$\mathscr{I}(l) = A \cos(k_0 l - \phi), \qquad (5.21)$$
where
$$A^2 = T_c^2 + T_s^2$$
and
$$\tan \phi = -T_s/T_c.$$

To study an asymmetrical spectrum, or to demonstrate that a spectrum is or is not asymmetrical, the phase ϕ must be measured; if that cannot be done, the most that can be obtained from the observations is the form of the equivalent symmetrical spectrum, that is to say, the spectrum with a sine transform that is zero and with a cosine transform equal to
$$(T_c^2 + T_s^2)^{\frac{1}{2}}.$$

The measurement of phase requires path differences that are known to a small fraction of a wavelength, unlike the measurement of visibility, for which it suffices to know the path difference only approximately, since visibility changes slowly with path difference; the measurement of phase, on the other hand, depends on the comparison of the positions of the maxima or minima of the fringes of the interferogram. If ϕ varies rapidly with path difference, that is if the asymmetry is considerable, it is sufficient to measure the path difference interferometrically using fringes formed in a much narrrower line, but obviously the narrowest lines cannot be examined in that way and in particular, the orange line in the spectrum of krypton-86 that is now taken to be the standard line cannot be so examined for, by hypothesis, the fringes formed in it are the standard against which all others are to be compared. However,

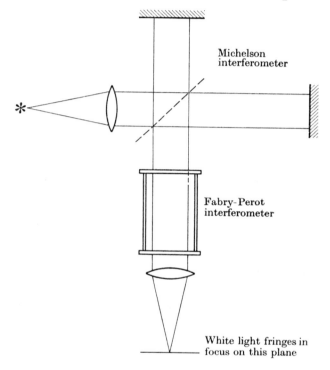

Michelson interferometer

Fabry-Perot interferometer

White light fringes in focus on this plane

FIG. 5.2. Apparatus of Rowley and Hamon for making the path difference in a Michelson interferometer equal to a multiple of that in a Fabry–Perot interferometer.

Rowley and Hamon (1963) were able to study the standard line itself by using the fringes formed in white light when the path difference in a Michelson is an integral multiple of that in a Fabry–Perot interferometer placed in series with it, to set up a number of path differences that bore simple integral relations to each other.

A diagram of Rowley and Hamon's apparatus is shown in Fig. 5.2. The path difference in the Michelson is adjusted to be n times that in the Fabry–Perot interferometer so that fringes may be formed in white light, as discussed in Chapter 6. With the Michelson so adjusted, the visibility and phase of the fringes formed in the orange line were found; the intensity of the light transmitted by the interferometer was measured photoelectrically at four path differences (preferably covering a range of about one wavelength) set up by small rotations of the compensating plate of the interferometer. If the four path differences so established are $\phi-3\alpha$, $\phi-\alpha$, $\phi+\alpha$, $\phi+3\alpha$, where ϕ is the phase for a reference position of the plate, and if the corresponding intensities are a, b, c, and d, the visibility and phase of the nearly cosinusoidal interferogram are given by

$$\tan \phi = \{(3u-v)(u+v)\}^{\frac{1}{2}}/(t-w),$$

$$\mathscr{V} = \pm \frac{2}{tn-um}\left\{\frac{u^3(m^2+np)}{p}\right\}^{\frac{1}{2}},$$

where

$$v = a-d, \qquad u = b-c, \qquad w = a+d, \qquad t = b+c,$$

and

$$m = t-w, \qquad n = 3u-v, \quad \text{and} \quad p = u+v.$$

(See also eqns (4.11)–(4.14).)

By such studies Rowley and Hamon were able to show that the standard line is slightly asymmetrical, being equivalent to a principal component with a secondary component about 1/16 the intensity of the principal component at about 0·70 m^{-1} on the blue side of the principal component.

Hamon (see Terrien 1967) has since extended these results but, instead of the rather unwieldy though absolute scheme with fringes in white light, has reverted to a comparison with a narrower line, making use of the fact that the spectrum from a stabilized gas laser is very much narrower than that from any source in spontaneous emission. He has been able to show that the visibility in a number of the narrowest lines in the spectrum of krypton falls to zero and subsequently becomes appreciable again but with a phase change of π, behaviour that is characteristic of lines that are self-reversed.

The theory of the Fourier transform study of quasi-monochromatic light was in large part given by Michelson (1891, 1892, Michelson and Benoît 1895, also Rayleigh 1889) and was applied by him to a number of spectrum lines, as a result of which he selected the cadmium red line (643·8 nm) as having the narrowest profile and one indistinguishable from Gaussian form. He found that H_α (656·2 nm) has two Gaussian components each of half-width 0·0049 nm, with intensities in the ratio

7:10 and separated by 0·014 nm; that an orange line of oxygen had three components, that each of the two lines of the yellow radiation of sodium (568·7 and 588·9 nm) had a close companion and that the half-width of the cadmium red line was 6·5 × 10⁻⁴ nm. He also studied lines of mercury, zinc, and thallium and separated Doppler and pressure broadening, and it seems that he observed self-reversal in the green line of mercury.

Extended spectra

If an extended spectrum is to be studied, no simplification of the Fourier transform relations is possible as for a narrow line. The intensity of the interferogram must be measured at a large number of path differences and the spectrum must be derived by numerical integration from the relation

$$I(k) = \frac{1}{\pi} \int_{-\infty}^{+\infty} \tfrac{1}{2}\{D(l) - D(0)\}\cos kl \; dl. \tag{5.22}$$

The necessary calculations are very heavy and it is only the advent of automatic computing machines combined with a fast method of organizing the calculations (Forman 1967) that has made Fourier transform spectroscopy practical for extended spectra. It is also necessary in practice to make the observations automatically, for very many are needed for adequate range and resolution. The greatest wave number that can be detected in the spectrum is equal to $1/\xi$, where ξ is the interval of path difference between successive measurements of the interferogram (Blackman and Tukey 1959). The resolution is similarly determined by the maximum path difference. The detector output is

$$D(l) = \int_{0}^{\infty} I(k)\cos kl \; dl, \tag{5.23}$$

assuming that absorption and scattering in the interferometer do not in effect limit the range of integration with respect to frequency over the part of the spectrum being studied. On inverting the Fourier transform, the calculated spectrum will be

$$I(k') = \frac{1}{2X} \int_{-X}^{+X} \tfrac{1}{2}\{D(l) - D(0)\}\cos k'l \; dl, \tag{5.24}$$

where X is the maximum path difference of the interferometer. (It should be noted that since the spectrum is not necessarily symmetrical about any frequency, the interferogram must be scanned symmetrically about zero path difference). Hence

$$
I(k') = \frac{1}{2X} \int\limits_{-X}^{+X} \int\limits_{0}^{\infty} \{I(k)\cos kl - \tfrac{1}{2}I(k)\} \, \cos k'l \, dk \, dl
$$

$$
= \frac{1}{2X} \int\limits_{0}^{\infty} dk I(k) \int\limits_{-X}^{+X} \tfrac{1}{2}[\cos(k-k')l + \cos(k+k')l - \cos k'l] \, dl
$$

$$
= \frac{1}{2} \int\limits_{0}^{\infty} dk I(k) \frac{\sin (k-k')X}{(k-k')X} + \frac{1}{2} \int\limits_{\infty}^{0} dk I(k) \frac{\sin(-k+k')X}{(-k+k')X} -
$$

$$
- \frac{1}{2} \int\limits_{0}^{\infty} I(k) \, dk \, \frac{\sin k'X}{k'X} \,. \tag{5.25}
$$

The integrands of the first two terms are identical; hence

$$
I(k') = I(k) * \frac{\sin k'X}{k'X} - \frac{1}{2} \frac{\sin k'X}{k'X} \int\limits_{0}^{\infty} I(k) \, dk. \tag{5.26a}
$$

The first term is the convolution of the spectrum $I(k)$ with the function $(\sin k'X/k'X)$ and tends to $I(k)$ as X becomes large, while the second term approaches zero as X becomes large. The spectrum obtained from Fourier transform procedures is similar to that derived from observations with a dispersive instrument having a slit of width X^{-1} wave numbers and the least significant interval between points on the calculated spectrum is X^{-1} (see J. Connes 1958).

The actual interferogram will be distorted by the effects of surface irregularities of the mirrors and beam divider, by the two beams being not exactly parallel, and by stray light; the overall effect of these defects may be determined, as was shown in Chapter 3, by observations of the visibility with white light at zero path difference. The effect of the finite size of the viewing aperture used with photoelectric observation varies with path difference and must be determined numerically. The treatment of the effect of the size of the aperture given in Chapter 3 was restricted to the case of quasi-monochromatic light and a less restricted analysis is needed for an extended spectrum. The detector output at a path difference Δ is

$$D(\Delta) = 2 \int_0^\infty I(k)\,dk + 2 \int_0^\infty I(k)\cos k\Delta \,dk$$

$$= 2 \int_0^\infty I(k)\,dk + 2\,\mathrm{Re} \int_0^\infty I(k)e^{ik\Delta}\,dk. \qquad (5.27)$$

Since $\Delta = l(1 - \tfrac{1}{2}\theta^2)$, where θ is the angle that a ray makes with the direction through the centre of the aperture,

$$D(l) = 2 \int_A dA \int_0^\infty I(k)\,dk + 2\,\mathrm{Re} \int_A dA \int_0^\infty I(k)e^{ikl(1-\frac{1}{2}\theta^2)}\,dk, \qquad (5.28)$$

A being the area of the aperture, of angular radius α. Thus

$$D(l) = 2\pi\alpha^2 \int_0^\infty I(k)\,dk + 2\pi\,\mathrm{Re} \int_0^\infty \int_0^{\alpha^2} dk I(k)e^{+ikl}e^{-ikl\theta^2/2}\,d\theta^2$$

$$= D(0) + 2\pi\alpha^2\,\mathrm{Re} \int_0^\infty dk I(k)e^{+ikl}e^{-ikl\alpha^2/4} \times$$

$$\times \frac{\sin\frac{1}{2}kl\alpha^2}{\frac{1}{2}kl\alpha^2}, \qquad (5.29)$$

where

$$D(0) = 2\pi\alpha^2 \int_0^\infty I(k)\,dk.$$

Hence

$$D(l) = D(0) + 2\pi\alpha^2 \int_0^\infty dk I(k) \frac{\sin\frac{1}{2}kl\alpha^2}{\frac{1}{2}kl\alpha^2} \cos kl(1-\tfrac{1}{4}\alpha^2). \qquad (5.30)$$

Since the terms giving the effect of the finite size of the aperture are functions of k and of l, the corrections to be applied to the observed interferogram vary with path difference and must be found by numerical inversion of the integrals. It would of course be preferable to keep the aperture small enough for the effects to be negligible but in the circumstances in which a wide spectrum is studied by Fourier transform methods, the signal-to-noise ratio is usually poor and it is desirable to keep the aperture as large as possible.

Fourier transform methods have been used a great deal in recent years to study extended spectra in the far infra-red in the laboratory and in the nearer infra-red with astronomical sources. Fellgett (1958) made some early observations on the infrared spectra of stars but the first extensive work was that of Mme. J. Connes and H. Gush (1959) who made a detailed study of the spectrum of the night sky. The infra-red spectra of planets have also been studied in this way, the most extensive work again being that of J. and P. Connes (Connes and Connes 1966; Connes, Connes, and Maillard 1967) who have used the 20 m telescope at Haute-Provence (see also Hunter 1968). H. A. Gebbie has developed interferometers especially suitable for use in the laboratory at very long wavelengths and has studied the pure rotational spectra of molecules such as HCl, H_2O, and HCN out to 300 m or so (Gebbie and Twiss 1966). Astronomical observations in the far infra-red are be-devilled by absorption by water vapour in the atmosphere, even when the telescope is at a great height, and in the laboratory the apparatus must be in a good vacuum.

The applications of Fourier transform spectroscopy have increased greatly in recent years (see Fellgett 1967, P. Connes 1971) mainly be-cause of astronomical uses and of uses in the infra-red. There are two main reasons for this. As will be shown in Chapter 10, Fourier transform spectroscopy gives a better signal-to-noise ratio in most circumstances than does any other spectroscopic procedure. The other reason is the essential simplicity of the technique, most evident in studies of emission spectra (see Cook 1968), where the parameters of the Fourier transform may be more directly related to the physics of a source than are those of a spectrum. But even with broad complex absorption spectra, it is arguable that the equipment and procedures of Fourier transform spectroscopy, with their high degree of freedom from systematic error, are simpler than those of other spectroscopic techniques. The main practical difficulties are now largely overcome. Various workers (Mertz 1967b; Connes, Connes, and Maillard 1967; Buijs and Gush 1967; Cusenier and Pinard 1967) have developed methods for scanning automatically, often under interferometric control, and for scanning rapidly in conditions where source fluctuations cause significant errors. Automatic digital recording is routine. The difficulty of handling transient sources has been solved by Michel (1967) who has built a number of interferometers of slightly different path difference in one instrument.

Fourier transform spectroscopy has also been applied to observation of the hydrogen 21-cm line in radio astronomy and although, as ex-plained in Chapter 10, there is no advantage of signal-to-noise ratio

(Blum 1960), the versatility of a spectrometer using the principle is of great value (Davies, Ponsonby, Pointer, and de Jager 1969).

Fourier transform methods are not restricted to the determination of spectra; the method devised by Cook and Richardson (1959) for estimating the frequency dependence of the phase shift on reflection at a semi-transparent surface (Chapter 6) used Fourier transforms, and Gebbie and his associates have used Fourier transform methods to derive refractive indices; a common feature of these two applications is that the interferogram is not symmetrical about zero path difference and the phase shifts of interest are obtained from the asymmetries, whereas the spectrum is obtained from the symmetrical part of the interferogram (Chamberlain, Gibbs, and Gebbie 1963; Chamberlain, Anderson, and Gebbie 1965; see also Mertz 1967a, Bell 1967).

Consider an interferometer with a path difference x in vacuum and let a slab of material of refractive index μ and thickness y be placed in one arm. The net path difference is then

$$x+y(\mu-1).$$

x is variable but y is constant.

The intensity of the interferogram, as a function of x, is

$$D(x) = 2\int_0^\infty I(k)\ \mathrm{d}k + 2\int_0^\infty I(k)\cos\{kx+ky(\mu-1)\}\ \mathrm{d}k. \qquad (5.31)$$

Hence, expanding the cosine on the right,

$$\tfrac{1}{2}\{D(x)-D(0)\} = \int_0^\infty I(k)\cos\{ky(\mu-1)\}\cos kx\ \mathrm{d}k - $$

$$- \int_0^\infty I(k)\sin\{ky(\mu-1)\}\sin kx\ \mathrm{d}k. \qquad (5.32)$$

It will be seen that in general the detector output is not symmetrical with respect to zero path difference.

Now take cosine and sine Fourier transforms:

$$I(k)\cos\{ky(\mu-1)\} = \frac{1}{\pi}\int_{-\infty}^{+\infty} \tfrac{1}{2}\{D(x)-D(0)\}\cos kx\ \mathrm{d}x = P\ \text{say};$$

$$I(k)\sin\{ky(\mu-1)\} = \frac{1}{\pi}\int_{-\infty}^{+\infty} \tfrac{1}{2}\{D(x)-D(0)\}\sin kx\ \mathrm{d}x = Q. \qquad (5.33)$$

Hence,

$$I(k) = (P^2 + Q^2)^{\frac{1}{2}}$$

and

$$\tan ky(\mu - 1) = Q/P,$$

giving rules for the calculation of the spectrum and of the refractive index.

6

THE FABRY–PEROT INTERFEROMETER

Principles

LET a beam of light, as in Fig. 6.1, be incident on a pair of parallel plates with surfaces that partly reflect and partly transmit the light. Let t be the fraction of the amplitude transmitted at either surface and let r be the fraction reflected. Let l be the separation of the plates. Light which is transmitted by the plates with no reflections between them then has an amplitude proportional to t^2. If the light undergoes one reflection between the plates, the transmitted amplitude will be proportional to r^2t^2 while the phase lag relative to the directly trans-mitted beam will be $2kl$; in general, after n reflections between the plates the relative amplitude will be $r^{2n}t^2$ and the phase lag will be $2nkl$, assuming the light is incident normally on the plates. The sum of the complex amplitudes of the beams transmitted normally to the plates is therefore

$$t^2 \sum_{n=0}^{\infty} r^{2n}\mathrm{e}^{-2\mathrm{i}nkl}, \tag{6.1}$$

and the intensity is

$$t^4 \left| \sum_{n=0}^{\infty} r^{2n}\mathrm{e}^{-2\mathrm{i}nkl} \right|^2, \tag{6.2}$$

which, as was seen in Chapter 1, is equal to

$$t^4/\{1 + r^4 - 2r^2 \cos 2kl\},$$

or

$$\frac{T^2}{1-R^2}\ \frac{1}{1 + \dfrac{4R}{(1-R)^2}\sin^2 kl}, \tag{6.2a}$$

where $T = t^2$ and $R = r^2$ are respectively the intensity transmission and reflection coefficients of the surfaces.

If there is no absorption, $T = 1 - R$, while if there is absorption, $R = 1 - T - A$. If there is absorption, the overall transmitted intensity is

$$\left\{1 - \frac{A}{1-R}\right\}^2 \cdot \left[1 + \frac{4R}{(1-R)^2}\sin^2 kl\right]^{-1}. \tag{6.3}$$

This expression has a maximum when $\sin kl = 0$. Let

$$4R/(1-R)^2 = \rho.$$

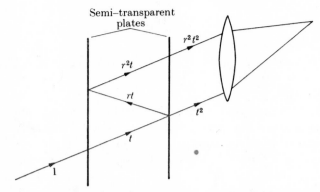

FIG. 6.1. Multiple-beam interference with parallel plates.

The transmitted intensity is then proportional to

$$1/(1+\rho \sin^2\theta), \qquad (\theta = kl),$$

the greatest value of which is 1 and the least value

$$1/(1+\rho).$$

ρ is usually large; for example, if the intensity reflection coefficient is 90 per cent, then $\rho = 360$, so that the minimum is usually quite deep.

ρ is related to the width of the intensity function at half amplitude. The mean of the greatest and least values is

$$\tfrac{1}{2}(2+\rho)/(1+\rho),$$

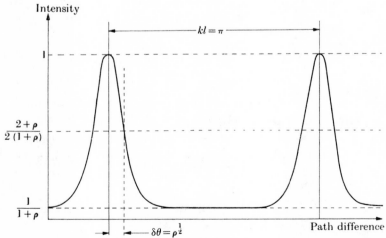

FIG. 6.2. Fringe pattern of interference of multiple beams.

and is attained when

$$\frac{1}{1+\rho \sin^2\theta} = \frac{2+\rho}{2(1+\rho)},\qquad (6.4)$$

that is

$$\sin^2\theta = (\rho+2)^{-1}$$

or

$$\sin\theta \doteqdot \pm(1-\tfrac{1}{4}\rho)\rho^{-\frac{1}{2}},\qquad (6.5)$$

$$\theta \doteqdot \pm\rho^{-\frac{1}{2}}.$$

Now the interval between successive maxima is given by $\theta = kl = \pi$, and so the relative width of the fringes at half amplitude is $1/\pi\rho^{\frac{1}{2}}$. The reciprocal relative width is called the *finesse* and will be denoted by F; $F = \pi\rho^{\frac{1}{2}}$. It is independent of the path difference (see Fig. 6.2).

The following table gives values of F for various reflectivities:

R (per cent)	90	80	70	50
ρ	360	80	31	8
minimum intensity	3×10^{-3}	$1\cdot2 \times 10^{-2}$	3×10^{-2}	$0\cdot12$
F	60	30	16	9

The first Fabry–Perot interferometer, devised by Ch. Fabry and A. Perot (1897), had plates coated chemically with films of silver, and silver, deposited by sputtering or evaporation, has been the preferred coating for many purposes since then, because it has the least absorption of any metal film over the visible spectrum. Aluminium is better for some applications because the change of phase on reflection at the plates varies little over the visible spectrum, a great convenience in measurements of wavelengths. Reflectivities of about 90 per cent can be obtained with silver and about 85 per cent with aluminium, but if multi-layer dielectric films are used, it is possible to achieve 95 per cent, with, however, the disadvantage that the reflectivity and the phase shift on reflection change rapidly with wavelength so that the optimum properties are achieved over a rather narrow band of wavelengths.

A Fabry–Perot interferometer can also be constructed for radio waves (Culshaw, Richardson, and Kerns 1960). One way of making a partially reflecting mirror is to set up a stack of dielectric quarter-wave plates, analogous to optical multilayer dielectric coatings. Very high reflectivities can be obtained; for example, with 8 sheets of perspex, a reflectivity of 0·9977 was found. Another possible mirror consists of stacks of rods set parallel to the electric field vector, and a third, a metal sheet with an array of holes; these two latter systems have reflectivities in excess of 0·999 at a wavelength of 7·3 mm. With such reflectivities, the resolution is determined almost entirely by the flatness of the mirrors.

The Fabry–Perot interferometer, like the Michelson interferometer, may be used photometrically, the optical length being changed in some way and the corresponding variation of intensity of the light transmitted through a small solid angle around the normal to the plates being recorded; or it may be used visually or photographically, the dependence of the transmitted light upon the angle of incidence being determined. If light traverses the plates at an angle θ to the common normal, the phase lag for one internal reflection is $2kl \cos \theta$ instead of

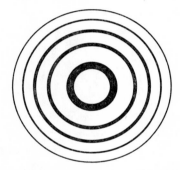

FIG. 6.3. Haidinger ring pattern, for fractional order of interference equal to 0.3.

$2kl$ for rays normal to the plates. Maxima of intensity therefore occur at the same angles as for the Michelson interferometer in its parallel-plate form and if the transmitted light is collected by a lens, a pattern of rings will be seen in the focal plane of the lens, bright rings occurring whenever

$$2kl\cos \theta = 2n\pi.$$

The rings are *Haidinger rings* (Chapter 3); an example is shown in Fig. 6.3. The fringes are very sharply defined, unlike the fringes formed by the interference of two beams in the Michelson interferometer, and it is this property that, prior to the use of photometric methods, made the Fabry–Perot interferometer so very suitable for the measurement of wavelengths.

According to the calculations above, the form of the fringes is determined by the reflectivity of the plates, but that is a simplification, and in fact they are broadened by the spread of energy in the spectrum of the incident light and by irregularities in the reflecting plates, while if the interferometer is used photometrically, the effects of the size and position of the aperture used to define the solid angle over which light is received must also be considered. In general, it is not possible to obtain explicit algebraic formulae for these effects as it is with the Michelson interferometer, for when more than two beams interfere there is no general method akin to coherence theory available for analysing the behaviour. Numerical calculations have therefore to be used at an early stage in the analysis.

Let the phase shift ϕ, equal to $2kl \cos \theta$, due to a single internal reflection, be the function of a number of variables α_i, two of which might be the coordinates of position on the interferometer plates. Suppose that the incident light is incoherent so that the intensity of light transmitted through one part of the interferometer is independent of that transmitted through any other part and that the intensity transmitted at one frequency is independent of that transmitted at any other frequency, and similarly for any other of the parameters α_i. The total intensity transmitted into a specified solid angle may therefore be calculated by integrating the contributions from elements of plate area, frequency, and so on, that is

$$I(\theta) = \int d\alpha_1 \int d\alpha_2 ... \int d\alpha_n \; \frac{1}{1 + \rho \sin^2 \phi},$$

where ϕ is a function of $\alpha_1, \alpha_2 ... \alpha_n$.

The difficulties of performing the integrations arise from the fact that the term $\rho \sin^2 \phi$ varies from zero to ρ (which is much greater than 1) over the range of integration. In the neighbourhood of the fringe maxima $\rho \sin^2 \phi$ is close to zero and it is possible to expand the integrand as a Taylor series, but that is not possible in the neighbourhood of the half-intensity points, so that elementary approximate methods are not capable of determining the width of the response curve.

Consider, for example, the effect of plate irregularities. ϕ now varies from point to point over the surface of the plates and the intensity is found by integrating over the plate area S:

$$I = \int_S \frac{dS}{1 + \rho \sin^2 \phi}. \tag{6.6}$$

This integral may be transformed to one with respect to ϕ:

$$I = \int_{\phi_1}^{\phi_2} \frac{d\phi \; \partial S / \partial \phi}{1 + \rho \sin^2 \phi} \tag{6.7}$$

where ϕ_2 and ϕ_1 are the maximum and minimum values of ϕ. $\partial S/\partial\phi$ is a distribution function that describes the relation between ϕ and area of surface.

Write

$$\partial S/\partial\phi = D(\phi'),$$

where $\phi = \phi_0+\phi'$, ϕ' being the deviation of ϕ from ϕ_0, some reference value.

Hence

$$I = \int_{\phi_1'}^{\phi_2'} \frac{D(\phi')\,\mathrm{d}\phi'}{1+\rho\,\sin^2(\phi_0+\phi')}$$

$$= \int_{\phi_1'}^{\phi_2'} \frac{D(\phi')\,\mathrm{d}\phi'}{1+\rho\,\sin^2\phi_0} +$$

$$+ \int_{\phi_1'}^{\phi_2'} \Delta_1 D(\phi')\,\phi'\,\mathrm{d}\phi' +$$

$$+ \int_{\phi_1'}^{\phi_2'} \tfrac{1}{2}\Delta_2 D(\phi')\,\phi'\,\mathrm{d}\phi' +..... \qquad (6.8)$$

The expansion is by a Taylor's series and

$$\Delta_1 = \frac{\mathrm{d}}{\mathrm{d}\phi}\left(\frac{1}{1+\rho\,\sin^2\phi}\right)\bigg|_{\phi=\phi_0},$$

$$\Delta_2 = \frac{\mathrm{d}^2}{\mathrm{d}\phi^2}\left(\frac{1}{1+\rho\,\sin^2\phi}\right)\bigg|_{\phi=\phi_0},$$

and so on.

ϕ_0 will be taken to be the mean with respect to the function D so that

$$\int D(\phi')\phi'\,\mathrm{d}\phi' \quad \text{vanishes.}$$

The second-order term is then proportional to the mean square irregularity of the plate separation.

Because the Taylor series expansion cannot be used in the neighbourhood of the half-intensity points, where $\rho\,\sin^2\phi$ is no longer small, the effects of plate irregularities and pinhole size (in the photometric use) must be determined numerically.

Chabbal (1958) has discussed this problem in a general way (see Jacquinot 1960). Consider strictly monochromatic radiation incident on a Fabry–Perot interferometer. The response of the interferometer as a function of the wave number of the incident radiation is called the *apparatus function*, $W(k)$. If the plates were perfectly flat, and the fringes were observed through an infinitesimally small pinhole, the apparatus function would just be the Airy function,

$$A(k) = \left(\frac{T}{1-R}\right)^2 (1 + \rho \sin^2 kl \cos \theta)^{-1}. \qquad (6.9)$$

When observed through a finite pinhole, the apparatus function is the convolution of the Airy function with the *diaphragm function*, $F(k)$, while if the plates are imperfect, the result must be further convolved with the *plate defect function*, $D(k)$; thus

$$W(k) = A(k) * D(k) * F(k). \qquad (6.10)$$

If the radiation has a spectrum $B(k)$, the final response of the interferometer is

$$Y(k) = W(k) * B(k). \qquad (6.11)$$

Chabbal writes the widths of the functions $W(k)$, $A(k)$, $D(k)$, and $F(k)$ as w, a, d, and f respectively, and sets w equal to the operational sum of the widths of the component functions:

$$w = a \oplus d \oplus f.$$

The width of the Airy function was found above and is equal to

$$\frac{1}{\pi \rho} \cdot \frac{1}{2l \cos \theta} \quad \text{wave numbers.}$$

$D(k)$ is the distribution function $\partial S / \partial k$, which depends on the form of the defects of the surfaces. If for example, the plates have a Gaussian distribution of errors but are on the average parallel, $D(k)$ is a Gaussian function and the half-width d is equal to $k_0 \sigma_d / 2l$, where σ_d is the standard deviation of the separation of the plates. If, as another example, the plates are spherical,

$$dS = \frac{S\, dk}{k_2 - k_1},$$

where k_2 and k_1 are the wave numbers for which the maximum intensity occurs at the centre and at the edges of the plates (Fig. 6.4), and so

$$\frac{\partial S}{\partial k} = \frac{S}{k_2 - k_1},$$

<figure>
FIG. 6.4. Distribution of area as function of wave number at maximum intensity for spherical plate.

l_2 = path difference at centre.
l_1 = path difference at edge.
Radius of ring at path difference l is $\{2R(l-l_2)\}^{\frac{1}{2}}$, where R is radius of curvature.
Area of annulus corresponding to range δl is $\delta S = 2R\,\delta l$.

Hence $\delta S = \dfrac{\delta l}{l_1-l_2} = \dfrac{\delta k}{k_2-k_1}$
</figure>

is a rectangular function that is constant for values of k between k_2 and k_1, while for values outside those limits the function is zero. Similarly, the pinhole isolates rays that are transmitted between the angles of incidence 0 and α, to which correspond the wave numbers k_1 and k_2 according to the formula

$$k = \frac{N}{2l}\left(\frac{1}{\cos\theta}\right),$$

where N is the (constant) order of interference.

The elementary annulus subtends a solid angle

$$d\Omega = 2\pi d(\cos\theta) = 2\pi\,dk/k.$$

The diaphragm function is $d\Omega/dk$, that is $2\pi/k$, again a rectangular function, zero outside the limits k_1 and k_2.

Chabbal has given curves, such as those shown in Fig. 6.5, by means of which the widths of convolutes of elementary functions may be found.

The finesse F_A, equal to the interval between fringe maxima divided by the width of the response curve, was defined above for the Airy function, and the definition can be extended to other functions. Thus if Δk is the range of wave number between successive fringe maxima, the finesse corresponding to the plate defects is

$$F_D = \frac{\Delta k}{d} = \frac{2\pi}{k_0\sigma_d},$$

while that corresponding to the aperture of the pinhole is

$$F_F = \frac{\Delta k}{f}. \qquad \text{(d and f were defined above)}.$$

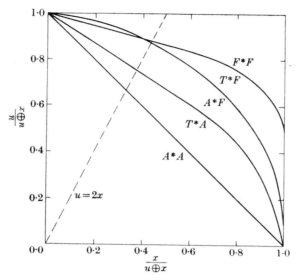

FIG. 6.5. Curves for calculating convolutions of elementary functions. U is the function A, T, or F; X is A or F. $u \oplus x$ is the width of the convolute $Z = U*X$.

An important consideration in designing a Fabry–Perot interferometer is to determine the factor that limits the overall finesse—it is usually the defects of the plates.

It is more convenient, numerically, to deal with wave numbers, equal to the number of wavelengths per metre, rather than with wave vectors; let Δn be the *free spectral range* between successive fringe maxima, that is, n_0/N. If w is expressed in wave numbers, the finesse is equal to n_0/Nw, where n_0 is the wave number of the radiation and N is the order of interference.

Thus the finesse corresponding to the defects of the plates is

$$\frac{1}{n_0 \sigma_d}.$$

Assuming that the plate defects have a Gaussian distribution, with σ_d equal to about 5 nm, or one-hundredth of the wavelength of the mercury green line, an extremely good standard of workmanship, then

$$F_D = 100$$

at a wavelength of 500 nm, but at 200 nm it is 40, while at 2000 nm it is 400. Except, possibly, in the ultra-violet, these values are less than the

finesses corresponding to reflectivities readily obtainable with multi-
layer reflecting coatings and thus it is the plate defects that in practice
limit the resolving power of a Fabry–Perot interferometer.

In order to determine the profile of a spectral line from the observed
response of a Fabry–Perot interferometer, the convolution must be
inverted, a procedure that involves a number of severe difficulties. The
apparatus function has to be determined experimentally, but, whereas
the instrumental function of a Michelson can be found from observations in white light at very small path differences and so is independent
of the spectrum of the light used in those observations, the apparatus
function of the Fabry–Perot interferometer can only be found by
observations on a line of known profile, in practice, a line with a profile
very much narrower than the one it is proposed to study. Thus prior to
the development of gas lasers with lines very much narrower than those
of spontaneous emission sources, the determination of the apparatus
function of a Fabry–Perot interferometer depended on the use of lines
with half-widths comparable with the response of a good interferometer,
and the result could be used to analyse only much wider lines with any
assurance. There is a further difficulty: the apparatus function is the
convolution of three functions that depend on wave number in different
ways, so that, unless the three functions are determined separately, it
is not possible to derive the apparatus function at one wavelength from
that at another. With the present restricted number of laser radiations, this means that the value of an apparatus function found at
say, the red line of the helium–neon laser can only be applied to the
analysis of profiles of lines with nearly the same wavelength. It is
therefore desirable to have an alternative way of expressing the response
of a Fabry–Perot interferometer that will alleviate these difficulties.

It may easily be shown that

$$\frac{1-R^2}{1-2R\cos 2kl+R^2} = 1+2\sum_{n=1}^{\infty} R^n \cos 2nkl. \qquad (6.12)$$

At a fringe maximum, $2kl = 2\pi$ and at a position intermediate
between two maxima, $2kl = 2\pi+\chi$. But $\cos(2\pi+\chi) = \cos\chi$ and thus

$$\frac{1-R^2}{1-2R\cos 2kl+R^2} = 1+2\sum_{n=1}^{\infty} R^n \cos n\chi. \qquad (6.13)$$

Eqn (6.13) is a representation of the Airy function as a Fourier
series using arguments that are multiples of the period from one

maximum to the next. Practically this is a very convenient representation to use with a scanning interferometer recording photometrically, for if the scan covers a small number of fringes it is a simple matter to express the recorder output as such a Fourier series.

Now integrate the Fourier series over the aperture of a pinhole and over the area of the irregular plates. Since

$$\cos(kl \cos \theta) = \cos k(l_0 + \delta l)(1 - \tfrac{1}{2}\theta^2), \qquad (6.14)$$

the transmitted intensity is

$$\tfrac{1}{2}S\alpha^2 + \sum_n \int dS \int_0^{\alpha^2} d\theta^2 \cos 2nk(l_0 + \delta l)(1 - \tfrac{1}{2}\theta^2), \qquad (6.15)$$

where δl is the plate irregularity and α the angular radius of the aperture.

Now

$$\cos 2k(l_0 + \delta l)(1 - \tfrac{1}{2}\theta^2) = \mathrm{Re}\ e^{2ikl_0}e^{2ik\delta l}e^{-2ikl_0\theta^2}$$
$$= \mathrm{Re}\ e^{i\chi}e^{2ik\delta l}e^{-ikl_0\theta^2}.$$

The intensity is therefore

$$\tfrac{1}{2}S\alpha^2 + \mathrm{Re} \sum_{n=1}^{\infty} R^n e^{in\chi}e^{-\frac{1}{4}inkl_0\alpha^2}\sin \tfrac{1}{4}nk_0l\alpha^2 \int e^{ink\delta l}\, dS. \qquad (6.16)$$

Thus as with the Michelson interferometer, the effects of plate defects and of the finite size of the pinhole may be separated.

The maxima of all the harmonic terms occur at the same value of χ, namely that for which

$$\chi = \tfrac{1}{4}kl_0\alpha^2.$$

The phase shift of the fringes of a Fabry–Perot interferometer due to the finite size of the pinhole is accordingly the same as that of the two-beam sinusoidal fringes.

Methods of recording and scanning

In practical use a Fabry–Perot interferometer must be associated with some filter to cut out all but the range of wavelengths within the free spectral range around the region under study. A consequence of the overlap of orders of a Fabry–Perot is that it can readily be used to study lines well separated from others but that rather elaborate means, to be described later, have to be adopted if it is to be used to study other spectra, absorption lines for example. Almost the entire discussion that follows is therefore concerned with well separated emission lines for which it is convenient to use multilayer dielectric filters adjusted to the wavelengths of the line being examined. If a number of lines is to be recorded simultaneously, the interferometer may be preceded or followed by a prism or grating monochromator. The usual arrangement is shown in Fig. 6.6. The source is placed at the focus

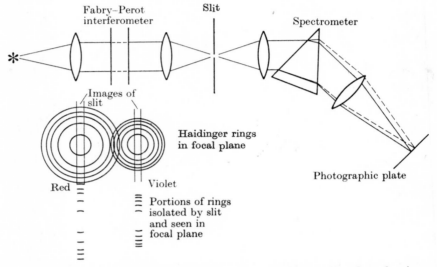

FIG. 6.6. Fabry–Perot interferometer with photographic recording through prism spectrometer.

of the collimating lens and the interferometer follows the lens. A telescope lens focuses the fringes on the slit of the spectrograph, which then images the slit and the fringes on a photographic plate or on an eyepiece. This arrangement must be adopted if fringes are to be observed visually or photographically in a number of colours simultaneously, but if just one line (or, in some cases, two) is to be observed, especially if photometric observations are to be made, it is better to place the interferometer after the filter or monochromator, for then the stray light reaching the detector is reduced. In adjusting such an optical system, the critical condition is that the fringes should be sharply focused on the photographic plate, photometric diaphragm, or eyepiece. The optical adjustment of the source is not in general critical, since it usually only affects the overall intensity of the transmitted light. To keep the solid angles of the beams of light at the various stages of the optical train as great as possible the source should be at the focus of the collimating lens, when the fringes and the source come into focus at the same place. If, however, the spectrum of the source varies over the aperture of the source, other arrangements may be adopted, either to isolate light from a particular point of the source or emitted in a particular direction, or, conversely, to average the results photometrically over the whole source.

The great majority of applications of the Fabry–Perot interferometer require the determination of the order of interference at the centre of the fringe pattern, that is the order in the direction normal to the plates, which as with the Michelson interferometer may be found by determining the fractional part of the order at the centre in a number of different wavelengths and finding the integral part from the coincidence of the values in the various wavelengths. Notwithstanding refined photometric methods of observation, there are still many applications in which visual observations can be used effectively, the fringes being observed through a telescope provided with a micrometer eyepiece so that the diameters of fringes of successive order may be measured. Visual photometric measurements are inadequate for the determination of profiles, but the eye estimates the position of the maximum intensity very effectively, and if the magnification of the optical system and the pattern of the micrometer crosswires are chosen with care, the fractional order at the centre can be determined with quite high accuracy, perhaps one-hundredth of a fringe in the best conditions. Indeed, the lower accuracy of visual observations as compared with photographic measurements is often due to the fact that visual measurements are made in circumstances when it may not be necessary or possible to ensure that the stability of the order of interference is the greatest possible.

Besides being ill-adapted for profile measurements, visual measurements cannot be applied when simultaneous observations are made in different wavelengths, as for example when it is necessary to be sure that the order of interference is the same when the fringes are recorded in the different colours. Photographic recording in the focal plane of a spectrograph is particularly suitable. When the fringes are in focus on the entrance slit of the spectrograph, the image consists of those parts of the fringe system which can be reached by light passing the slit. It is usual to arrange that the centre of the fringe system lies on the centre of the slit (Fig. 6.6). A photographic record is also valuable where the wavelength or profile may vary across a source as in some astronomical problems; in such circumstances the image of the source cannot be restricted by the slit of a spectrograph and a single wavelength must be selected by a multilayer filter. Photographic measurements of fringe diameter are capable of very high precision and particularly when differential methods for locating the maximum of the density of the image are used, accuracies approaching a few thousandths of an order of interference are possible. Prior to photoelectric recording, profiles were determined photographically, but the photographic process is not adapted to precise photometry and has been superseded in the laboratory and in many astronomical applications.

Photoelectric recording with a scanning interferometer is now the preferred method for much laboratory and astronomical work. A single wavelength must be isolated with a filter or monochromator (it is possible to observe in two wavelengths simultaneously) and the intensity at the centre of the fringe pattern is measured with a photoelectric detector placed behind a pinhole diaphragm in the focal plane of the telescope lens on the normal to the plates. The optical length of the interferometer is made to change over a few orders of interference and the intensity of the light passing the diaphragm is recorded in step with the change of the order of interference. When the method was first introduced by Jacquinot and Dufour (1948) for the study of line profiles, the pressure of air or other gas in the interferometer was varied, so changing the refractive index and thus the order of interference; the intensity was recorded on a potentiometric chart recorder. More precise methods were needed when the scanning interferometer was applied to the comparison of wavelengths, and the intensity was recorded digitally at times determined by the variation of the pressure. Pressure scanning is very suitable for interferometers with large path differences, such as are used in the laboratory with narrow lines, but becomes cumbersome for the small path differences that must be used in some astronomical applications.

We may write the refractive index as

$$(1 + \beta p),$$

where p is the pressure of the air and β is a factor that depends on the composition of the air, and is about 270×10^{-6} for a pressure of 10^5 N/m^2 (1 atm). If the separation of the interferometer plates is l, and the wavelength is λ, the order of interference is

$$2(1 + \beta p)l/\lambda.$$

The change of pressure required to give a change of order δN is thus

$$\frac{\lambda}{2\beta}\frac{\delta N}{l} \quad \text{or} \quad \frac{1}{\beta}\frac{\delta N}{N} \quad \text{very nearly.}$$

In laboratory studies of narrow lines, one may use an etalon 0.1 m long, for which the order of interference at 500 nm is $4 \cdot 10^5$; to scan over 4 orders of interference, the change of pressure must be $\frac{1}{27}$ atm or $4 \cdot 10^2$ N/m^2. In astronomical studies of much wider lines or more complex spectra, the length of the etalon may have to be kept less than 1 mm, in which case the pressure must be changed by $4 \cdot 10^5$ N/m^2 (4 atm). Changes of a fraction of an atmosphere are easily effected, but strongly built and cumbersome equipment is needed for changes of a few atmospheres (Geake, Ring, and Wolf 1959).

Mechanical methods of scanning one of the plates of an interferometer are accordingly attractive. Various flexible diaphragm supports have been devised that enable a plate to be moved over a few hundredths of a millimetre while remaining strictly parallel to itself, while piezoelectric, magnetostrictive, and electromagnetic systems, as well as purely mechanical means, have been used to move a plate.

Because the mechanical separation of the plates of a Fabry–Perot interferometer may be fixed or be variable over no more than a few micrometres, it is possible to make the interferometer very rigid. One of the most satisfactory designs was introduced by Sears and Barrell (1932). The interferometer plates are supported by a tube of invar of

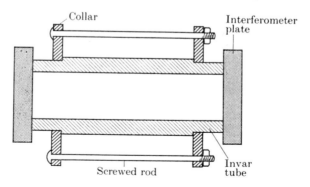

FIG. 6.7. Design of interferometer of Sears and Barrell.

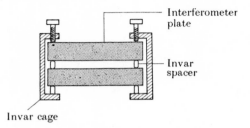

Fig. 6.8. Interferometer with small spacing.

which the ends are plated with chromium and worked to have highly polished flat surfaces so the plates may be wrung into optical contact with them. Collars are fitted near the ends of the tube (Fig. 6.7) and are pulled together with four screwed rods around the periphery of the tube, distorting the tube to bring the plates into parallelism and to make small adjustments to the separation. The design is versatile and has been used for interferometers ranging from about 0·03 to 1 m separation. The spacer is too rigid at shorter separations; a convenient arrangement is then to hold the plates in a cage and to separate them with three rods of invar or fused silica (Fig. 6.8); by altering the pressures with which the plates are clamped the rods can be more or less distorted and the parallelism thereby adjusted. If one of the plates is to be moved mechanically over a short distance, an elastic diaphragm support may be attached to the invar tube (Fig. 6.9) (cf. Chabbal and Soulet 1958). For some applications it may be necessary to vary the length of the interferometer readily over a wide range of separations while still using the same plates, and in that case it is convenient to mount the

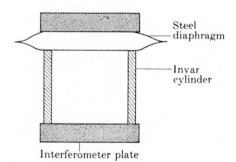

Fig. 6.9. Interferometer with support on elastic diaphragm.

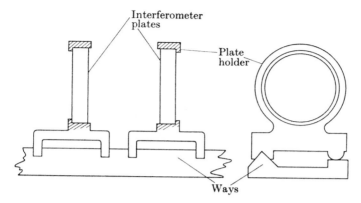

FIG. 6.10. Fabry–Perot interferometer with plates in supports sliding on ways.

plates on carriages moving on carefully worked slide ways (Fig. 6.10) (see Fabry and Perot 1901, Barrell and Teasdale–Buckell 1957).

A number of methods are available for checking when the plates of an interferometer are parallel, and the one that is adopted will depend on the separation of the plates. With small separations the ring diameters are large and the fringes formed with a mercury lamp, for example, are easily seen with the naked eye accommodated for infinity. If the eye is then moved about to observe the fringes through different regions of the plates, the ring diameters will change if the plates are not parallel and the changes of the innermost ring are readily seen; the interferometer is adjusted until no change of ring diameter can be detected. With long interferometers, multiple images of an intense pinhole source can easily be seen with the naked eye and a good criterion is to adjust the plates until all the images merge into one. It is necessary to view the fringes from a long interferometer through a telescope because the diameters are too small for the naked eye. If the plates are not parallel it will be seen that the fringes are not simultaneously in focus over the whole field of view (cf. Chapter 3) and the plates must be adjusted until the fringes are in good focus everywhere. If it is easy to remove and replace one of the two plates of an interferometer, the parallelism may be checked with an autocollimator, setting the autocollimator axis normal to one of the plates, then putting the other plate in position and adjusting it to be normal to the autocollimator axis which of course must be carefully kept fixed between the two operations. All these procedures are much easier if the source is a gas laser.

Applications of the Fabry–Perot interferometer

The prime use of the Fabry–Perot interferometer has always been for the measurement of wavelengths and of intervals between wavelengths of spectra in emission (see Fabry and Perot 1899, 1902). In such work there is no problem about the overlap of different orders of interference, for the lines that it is desired to study may be isolated by some filter or monochromator. A typical arrangement is that used for the measurement of standard wavelengths in the spectra of mercury-198 and krypton-86 (Barrell and Teasdale–Bucknell 1951) the principle of which was shown in Fig. 6.6. The interferometer is placed between the source and a spectrograph in which the fringe patterns formed in the different spectrum lines are photographed. Simultaneous photography of fringe systems in a number of wavelengths has the advantage that if there is a slow change in the optical length of the interferometer (essentially on account of temperature changes, because all the most accurate work is done with the interferometer in a vacuum enclosure) the change affects all observations similarly and there is no systematic error in the ratios of differences of wavelength derived from the observations. Nonetheless it is very important to keep the optical length as constant as possible during an exposure, which may be for some hours with weak lines, for if the length changes the fringes will be broadened. If there is a great difference in intensity between lines that are being photographed at the same time, a range of exposures must be used to get the clearest fringes on each line and then it is important to have a programme of observations that will eliminate systematic errors due to changes in optical length. The fringe diameters on the photographs are usually measured by eye on a coordinate measuring machine, although prior to photoelectric recording some studies of densitometric measurements of a photograph showed that rather higher precision could be obtained that way, but there is now no point in pursuing this method after the development of photoelectric recording, unless possibly for astronomical applications (Cook and Hitchins 1959).

Few astronomical sources have isolated emission lines but in those instances where they do, valuable studies have been made with the Fabry–Perot interferometer. Photographic recording is especially useful with large extended sources which can be imaged through the interferometer, possibly with an interference filter to isolate the appropriate part of the spectrum. Such sources include emission nebulae, H-II regions (Courtès 1958) and the solar corona (Jarrett and v. Klüber 1955). While it is easiest to use a Fabry–Perot interferometer with emission lines, ways have been devised for using it with absorption lines.

Photoelectric methods have now superseded photographic recording for the most accurate measurements of wavelength. They were introduced (Jacquinot and Dufour 1948) for profile measurements or measurements of differences of wavelength lying within one order of interference, but the double-beam system of photoelectric recording (Cook 1960) has enabled widely different wavelengths to be compared with the very highest accuracy. The main difficulty in comparing wavelengths in different orders of interference is that if pressure scanning is employed the pressures at which the fringe maxima occur in the different wavelengths must be compared with accuracies that are beyond the usual possibilities of barometric pressure measurement. If, however, the interferometer is illuminated with two wavelengths simultaneously, and the relative positions of the two sets of fringes are measured, it is not necessary to measure pressure at all, since the fringes themselves provide a scale on which the relative displacement can be measured. It is only necessary that the scale should be uniform. There are two small complications that are easily dealt with. It is easiest to record intensities at equal intervals of volume, for example at equal points on the travel of a piston moving in a cylinder, rather than at equal intervals of pressure, but the necessary numerical transformation is easy to handle in a computer programme. Secondly, if the two wavelengths are appreciably different, allowance must be made for the dispersion of the air and the absolute pressure of the air must be known, but not with the very highest accuracy. In the N.P.L. instrument (Cook 1960) the interferometer is preceded by two monochromators in front of which the two sources are placed (they may possibly be the same source from which different wavelengths are selected), and a rapidly rotating shutter obscures the two alternately. The light transmitted by the interferometer falls on a photomultiplier which is connected alternately, in synchronism with the shutter, to each of two amplifier channels. After integration, the outputs from the two channels are recorded digitally (Fig. 6.11). The shutter speed is fast compared with the integration time and the rate at which the pressure is changing, so that the two sets of fringes are recorded effectively simultaneously. With careful attention to detail, especially to ensuring that the conditions of illumination are the same for the two sources, it is possible to measure ratios of wavelengths to 1 in 10^9, whereas the accuracy attainable with photographic methods has not exceeded 1 in 10^8. A computer is used to calculate the positions of the maxima of intensity in the two sets of fringes, the scale being made uniform as indicated above, and the difference of the fractional orders

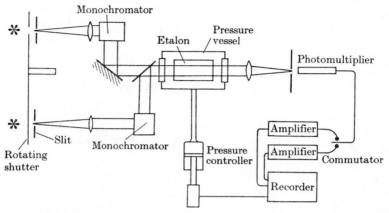

FIG. 6.11. Photoelectric recording interferometer with air pressure scanning
developed at the National Physical Laboratory.

of interference is found; thence, if the integral orders of interference
are known, the ratios of the wavelengths may be calculated.

A Fabry–Perot interferometer used as a standard of length may be
compared interferometrically with some other length that is to be
measured, or it may be incorporated itself in a system in which measurements of length are to be made (see Perot and Fabry 1899, 1901, and
Chap. 8). In these circumstances, if the integral order of interference is
known, a more precise determination of the separation of the plates is
obtained from measurements of the fractional order of interference
either photographically (see, for example, Cook 1961) or photoelectrically (Cook 1967). In such applications, careful attention must be given
to the way in which the optical length, which includes the phase shifts
on reflection at the surfaces of the plates, is related to the mechanical
length it is desired to find.

The variations of such phase shifts with wavelength affect measurements of wavelength, for they are equivalent to a change of optical
path difference with wavelength (see Fabry and Perot 1902). The
smallest change of phase shift with wavelength is found with aluminium
films, which are therefore most commonly used for determinations of
wavelengths, since in that application of the Fabry–Perot interferometer it is more important to have a small change of phase shift than to
have the very highest finesse. Silver films have somewhat lower absorption than ones of aluminium and are to be preferred in applications
where the greater change of phase shift is not a difficulty. The lowest

absorption for a given reflectivity is obtained with multi-layer dielectric films, but because the high reflectivity depends on an interference effect it is quite sensitive to the wavelength of the light, and the reflectivity and the phase shift on reflection both change rapidly with wavelength, so that these films, while valuable for studies of profiles or differences of wavelength over a restricted range of wavelength, are not suitable for comparisons of widely different wavelengths. The foregoing remarks apply to wavelengths within the visible range; outside that range, other materials may be more suitable, while in the ultra-violet, in particular, the absorption may be much greater than in the visible (see Bradley, Bates, Juulman, and Kohno 1967).

Three methods are available for the measurement of changes of phase shift. The one used in much earlier work with the Fabry–Perot interferometer (see Barrell and Teasdale–Buckell 1951) is that in which observations are made of the fringe fractions at a number of different spacings of the plates. Let the phase shift on reflection at one plate at a particular wavelength λ be ϕ, that at some standard wavelength λ_0 being taken (arbitrarily) to be zero. Let d_1 and d_2 be the spacings measured in terms of λ_0. Then the orders of interference in λ at d_1 and d_2 will be $4\pi d_1/\lambda + 2\phi$ and $4\pi d_2/\lambda + 2\phi$ respectively, and from these data ϕ may be found and the observations corrected accordingly. It is of course only possible to find the variation of ϕ with wavelength since any constant value is indistinguishable from the mechanical length as determined by matching fractional orders of interference. The main disadvantage of the method is that the final accuracy of the calculated orders of interference is determined by the measurements at the shorter path differences and the greater relative accuracy of the measurements at the longest path difference is not exploited.

Multiple-beam Fizeau fringes have been used to determine phase shifts (see Fabry and Buisson 1908, Cook and Richardson 1959). If the interferometer plates are placed very close together and with a small angle between them, very narrow fringes in monochromatic light are seen as almost parallel straight lines at a spacing of $\lambda/2\alpha$, where α is the angle between the plates (Chapter 9). Measured from the (usually inaccessible) intersection of the wedge, bright fringes are seen at distances x given by

$$\alpha x = \tfrac{1}{2}n\lambda - 2\phi.$$

If αx is small enough for the orders of interference of adjacent fringes in two colours to be the same, the calculated separation of such fringes will be

$$n \, \Delta\lambda/2\alpha,$$

while the observed separation will be $n \, \Delta\lambda/2\alpha - 2\phi/\alpha$. Careful measurements of the fringe positions on a wedge of very small angle therefore enable values of ϕ to be determined.

Phase shifts may also be found by Fourier transform methods (cf. Chapter 5). Let two Fabry–Perot interferometers be set up one after the other with the normals to the plates coincident and with the plate separations in the ratio n:1, where n is an integer (Fig. 6.12). Then, as

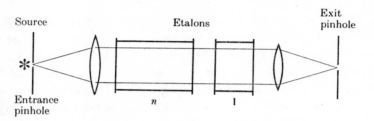

FIG. 6.12. Two Fabry–Perot interferometers in series.

will be discussed in detail below, fringes may be seen in white light, because light which has undergone one reflection in the longer interferometer has suffered a phase shift equal to light that has undergone n reflections in the shorter interferometer, a condition that is satisfied for all wavelengths. Let the light transmitted in the direction of the common normal be observed photoelectrically. It will be shown below that as the length of one of the two interferometers is varied, by air pressure scanning for example, the intensity of the transmitted light varies as

$$\int_{0}^{\infty} I(k)(1 + \cos \Phi) \, \mathrm{d}k,$$

plus a constant term from light that does not interfere. The phase Φ is equal to

$$2k(L - nl) + 2(n - 1)\phi(k),$$

where L is the length of the longer interferometer, l that of the shorter, and $\phi(k)$ is the phase shift at one surface. It is assumed for simplicity that the plates on the two interferometers have all the same properties but that condition is not necessary. The variation of the intensity of the transmitted light is therefore

$$\Delta I = \int_0^\infty \mathrm{d}k I(k)\cos\{2k(L-nl)+2(n-1)\phi\}. \tag{6.17}$$

Let $2(L-nl) = \delta$ and let δ_0 be the value of δ at which the maximum intensity occurs, that is, at the central white fringe.

Thus

$$\Delta I = \int \mathrm{d}k I(k)\cos\, k(\delta-\delta_0)\cos\{k\delta_0+2(n-1)\phi\} - $$
$$- \int \mathrm{d}k I(k)\sin\, k(\delta-\delta_0)\sin\{k\delta_0+2(n-1)\phi\}. \tag{6.18}$$

Taking Fourier transforms with respect to path difference δ' measured from δ_0 as zero, it will be seen that

$$I(k)\cos\{k\delta_0+2(n-1)\phi\} = \frac{1}{\pi}\int_{-\infty}^\infty \Delta I \cos k\delta'\, \mathrm{d}\delta'$$

$$I(k)\sin\{k\delta_0+2(n-1)\phi\} = \frac{1}{\pi}\int_{-\infty}^\infty \Delta I \sin k\delta'\, \mathrm{d}\delta'. \tag{6.19}$$

The spectrum function $I(k)$ and the phase function $k\delta_0+2(n-1)\phi$ can therefore be found from the sine and cosine Fourier transforms (see eqn (5.33)). ϕ, of course, includes a part independent of wavelength that cannot be separated from $k\delta_0$. If it is not assumed that the phase shifts are the same for the two pairs of plates, they may be determined

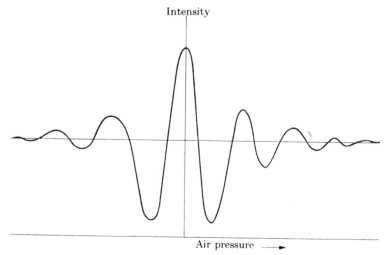

FIG. 6.13. Distribution of intensity in white light fringes.
(Cook and Richardson 1959)

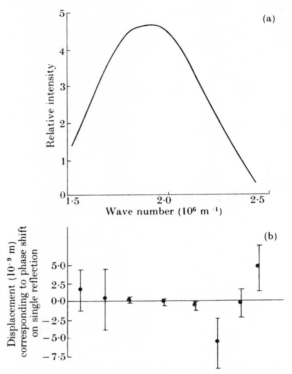

FIG. 6.14. Spectrum and phase shift derived from Fourier transform of intensity distribution in white light. (Cook and Richardson 1959.)

separately by interchanging the plates between the long and the short interferometers.

Fig. 6.13 shows an example of an interferogram obtained with a pair of etalons and the spectrum and phase shift variations derived from a number of such interferograms are shown in Fig. 6.14. The accuracy of the Fourier transform method greatly exceeds that of the phase shift variations found by measurements on multiple-beam Fizeau fringes with the same plates; the main limitation on the Fourier transform method is that the spectrum of the white light source should be sufficiently intense and, as can be seen, the uncertainties of the estimated phase shifts increase in the violet where the intensity of the spectrum is falling.

Measurements of structure and line profiles

The Fabry–Perot interferometer has frequently been used to measure the intervals between groups of close lines such as arise from hyperfine structure, Zeeman or Stark splitting, or isotope shifts. The multiple ring pattern formed with such a spectrum may be photographed, or photoelectric recording may be used with a scanning interferometer: indeed, air pressure scanning with photoelectric recording was first devised for these purposes (Jacquinot and Dufour 1948, Blaise 1958). It is one of the simplest applications of the Fabry–Perot interferometer. The fringes formed by the different lines lie within one order of interference (this is necessary to avoid overlap and confusion) and it is sufficient to know the order only approximately in order to derive the differences of wavelength from differences of the fractional order of interference. The phase shifts on reflection at the plates will be the same for all the lines. The main limitations of the Fabry–Perot interferometer are that it is less effective than the Michelson in determining the separation of close lines when the widths of the lines are comparable with the separation, and that, since the free spectral range is inversely proportional to the resolving power, it is not possible to use the highest resolving power if the overall spread of the structure is appreciable.

In recent years increasing attention has been given to the detailed study of line profiles both in astrophysics and in the laboratory. The profiles of lines that are to be used as wavelength standards must be well known, the broadening of solar or stellar lines gives information about physical conditions in the source, and line widths observed in the laboratory may be analysed in terms of pressure broadening and the lifetime of an excited state. Such studies demand a detailed knowledge of the apparatus function of the Fabry–Perot interferometer and photometry of the greatest accuracy that conditions allow; photoelectric photometry will always be used where possible but in some astronomical problems, especially with extended sources, photography may be unavoidable. The determination of the apparatus function or instrumental profile is a difficult matter with the Fabry–Perot interferometer. Since the response is the convolution of the instrumental profile with the spectrum of the light with which the interferometer is illuminated, the former can only be obtained if the latter is known. The calculations are subject to considerable uncertainty if the known profile, the apparatus function, and the profile to be studied are all of comparable width. Ideally, the apparatus function and the spectrum of the radiation with which it is determined should both be much less than that of the spectrum to be studied, for then errors in the determination of the apparatus function will not be very important in the final result, but it is difficult to achieve these conditions when the very narrowest lines are to be studied, and the standard and secondary standard lines in the spectra of krypton-86 and mercury-198 presented particular difficulties which were, however, satisfactorily overcome by W. R. C. Rowley at the National Physical Laboratory, who has used light from a gas laser to determine the apparatus function of a Fabry–Perot interferometer.† The width of a single line emitted from a gas laser is about one-millionth of the width of the apparatus function of a Fabry–Perot interferometer with plates of the highest quality, but this would be of no avail were the wavelength to vary during the observations by very much greater amounts. Such variations can indeed occur, and the oscillations of the laser must therefore be kept to a single mode and the wavelength must be stabilized, say to 1 in 10^8 or better, during the time taken by a scan through the profile. If these precautions are taken, the instrumental profile may be found with very high accuracy at the laser wavelength. However, there are at present few lasers giving suitable lines, the helium–neon laser with the red line at 632·8 nm being the most convenient, and instrumental profiles at other wavelenghts must be found by calculation from auxiliary measurements. Such calculations are most straightforwardly made by expressing the apparatus function as a Fourier series, the terms of which have periods that are multiples of that corresponding to the free spectral range.

It was shown above (eqn. 6.16) that the expression for the transmitted light is

$$\tfrac{1}{2}S\alpha^2 + \mathrm{Re} \sum_{n=1}^{\infty} R^n \mathrm{e}^{in\chi} \exp[-\tfrac{1}{4}inkl_0\alpha^2]\sin \tfrac{1}{4}nkl_0\alpha^2 \int_S \mathrm{e}^{ink\delta l}\,\mathrm{d}S.$$

The coefficient of each harmonic term is the product of three factors, namely, the reflectivity, R, an expression involving the plate irregularities, $\int_S \exp(ink\,\delta l)\,\mathrm{d}S$, and the factor depending on the pinhole size.

The product is known from the Fourier analysis with the laser at one frequency, and to estimate the product at some other frequency, the behaviour of each of the three factors with frequency must be known. The pinhole factor may be calculated, and, if the reflectivity is measured as a function of frequency, the plate irregularity term may be found from the observations at the laser frequency and may then be calculated for any other frequency. Let the apparatus function at the frequency of some line to be studied, as determined by the foregoing procedure, be written as

$$A(\nu) = \sum_r \left\{ a_p \cos \frac{p(\nu - \nu_0)}{\Delta\nu} + b_p \sin \frac{p(\nu - \nu_0)}{\Delta\nu} \right\}, \qquad (6.21)$$

† *National Physical Laboratory Report for* 1967, p. 7 (H.M.S.O., London).

where ν_0 is the centre frequency of the line being studied and $\Delta\nu$ is the free spectral range. The line profile being investigated and the response of the interferometer to that profile may similarly be written respectively as

and

$$B(\nu) = \sum_p \left\{ \alpha_p \cos \frac{p(\nu - \nu_0)}{\Delta\nu} + \beta_p \sin \frac{p(\nu - \nu_0)}{\Delta\nu} \right\} \qquad (6.21\text{a})$$

$$I(\nu) = \sum_p \left\{ C_p \cos \frac{p(\nu - \nu_0)}{\Delta\nu} + D_p \sin \frac{p(\nu - \nu_0)}{\Delta\nu} \right\} \qquad (6.21\text{b})$$

(usually b_p, β_p, and D_p will be much less than a_p, α_p, and C_p respectively). But the observed response is the convolution of the apparatus function with the line profile:

$$
\begin{aligned}
I(\nu) &= \int_{-\infty}^{+\infty} B(\nu')A(\nu' - \nu)\, d\nu' \\
&= \sum_p (\alpha_p a_p + \beta_p b_p)\cos \frac{p(\nu' - \nu_0)}{\Delta\nu} + \\
&\quad + \sum_p (\beta_p a_p - \alpha_p b_p)\sin \frac{p(\nu' - \nu_0)}{\Delta\nu}.
\end{aligned}
\qquad (6.22)
$$

Hence

$$\alpha_p = \frac{C_p a_p - D_p b_p}{a_p^2 + b_p^2},$$

$$\beta_p = \frac{C_p b_p + D_p a_p}{a_p^2 + b_p^2}.$$

$$(6.23)$$

Rowley and E. Mallia have applied this method to the study of very narrow secondary standard lines in the spectra of krypton-86 and mercury-198 and have obtained results that are essentially identical with those obtained by Fourier transform with a Michelson interferometer.[†]

Rowley has found that the accuracy of the calculations in the Fourier series method is much greater than those in which the convolution integral is inverted by iterative methods, over 50 iterations sometimes failing to give results of the same accuracy as the Fourier series.

Fabry–Perot interferometers in series

To achieve high resolution in a single Fabry–Perot interferometer, the path difference must be great and the separation between successive

† International Astronomical Union, Report of Commission 14, 1967.

orders of interference is then small. This is inconvenient if high resolution is required over a relatively large range of wavelength, especially in the study of atomic hyperfine structure, where the overall spread of the components may be many times the width of a single component. To overcome the difficulty, a second shorter interferometer is placed in series with the long one, having a length that is an integral fraction of the long one; regions of low transmittance of the short interferometer then coincide with peaks of transmittance of the longer, while by adjusting the lengths carefully, peaks of the short one may be made to coincide with every nth peak of the longer, if the ratio of the lengths is $n{:}1$. All but every nth maximum of transmittance of the longer interferometer are thus suppressed, but the resolution is the same as that of the longer etalon and so the finesse is increased n times. The disadvantage of the scheme is that the peak intensity is reduced, but the arrangement is a very powerful one for the study of hyperfine structure. With fixed path differences, as when used with photographic recording, the adjustment has to be very critical; if one or both of the interferometers can be scanned, and photoelectric recording is used, it is much easier to ensure that the peaks of the two transmittances coincide.

The most direct way of checking the coincidence of the peaks is to examine the fringes formed in white light by the two interferometers. If the path differences are in the ratio of n to 1, light that undergoes n reflections in the shorter interferometer suffers the same retardation as light that undergoes one reflection in the longer and so it is possible for interference to be observed in white light. The fringes so formed are known as *fringes of superposition* and have been used to compare one interferometer with another, so making it possible to measure a distance too long to determine by direct interferometry, by comparison with a shorter distance that could be so measured (Fabry and Perot 1897, Schuster 1924).

The transmission function of a single Fabry–Perot interferometer in an arbitrary direction is

$$T^2(1-2R\cos 2\phi+R^2)^{-1},$$

where T and R are the transmittance and reflectance of the plates and

$$\phi = kl\cos\theta.$$

The transmission function of two Fabry–Perot interferometers in series is therefore

$$T_1^2 T_2^2(1-2R_1\cos 2\phi_1+R_1^2)^{-1}(1-2R_2\cos 2\phi_2+R_2^2)^{-1}, \qquad (6.24)$$

where $\phi_2 = kl_2 \cos \theta_2$ and θ_1 and θ_2 are the angles between the common line of sight and the normals to the plates of the two interferometers.

The maximum possible transmission of the two in series is thus

$$\frac{T_1^2 T_2^2}{(1-R_1^2)(1-R_2^2)},$$

while the minimum is

$$\frac{T_1^2 T_2^2}{(1+R_1^2)(1+R_2^2)}.$$

Now

$$\frac{1-R^2}{1-2R \cos 2\phi + R^2} = 1+2[R \cos 2\phi + R^2 \cos 4\phi + ... + R^n \cos 2n\phi + ...]$$

and so the overall transmission function is

$$\frac{T_1^2 T_2}{(1-R_1^2)(1-R_2^2)} \times$$

$$\times \left[1+2 \sum_{n=1} \{R_1^n \cos 2n\phi_1 + R_2^n \cos 2n\phi_2\} + 4 \sum_{p,q \neq 0} R_1^p R_2^q \cos 2p\phi_1 \cos 2q\phi_2\right].$$

(6.25)

The last term may be written as

$$2 \sum_{p,q \neq 0} R_1^p R_2^q \{\cos(2p\phi_1 + 2q\phi_2) + \cos(2p\phi_1 - 2q\phi_2)\}. \qquad (6.26)$$

To determine the transmission of an extended spectrum, the transmission function must be integrated over the spectrum; the result will be the sum of terms such as

$$\int_{k_1}^{k_2} I(k)\cos Lk \, dk,$$

where

$$L = 2pl_1 \cos \theta_1 \pm 2ql_2 \cos \theta_2.$$

Now write $\int_{k_1}^{k_2} I(k) \, dk = I_m(k_2-k_1)$ where I_m is the mean intensity; the integral will then be approximately

$$I_m \int_{k_1}^{k_2} \cos Lk \, dk.$$

In practical cases, Lk may lie between 10^5 and 10^7 for the smaller values of p and q, so that it may be seen that all the terms of the integral will be negligible except those for which

$$2pl_1 \cos \theta_1 - 2ql_2 \cos \theta_2 \simeq 0.$$

It is only those terms in the transmission function that will vary slowly over the whole visible spectrum and so will make any significant contribution to the interference effects.

In such a term, let

$$l_2 = ml_1 + \epsilon$$

and

$$m\phi_1 - \phi_2 = (ml_1 \cos \theta_1 - l_2 \cos \theta_2 - \epsilon)k = \chi,$$

where χ is small.

The total transmitted intensity is then proportional to

$$\int I(k) \, \mathrm{d}k + 2 \sum_p R_1^{pm} R_2^p \int \mathrm{d}k I(k) \cos 2p\chi, \tag{6.27}$$

which corresponds to that of a Fabry–Perot interferometer with transmission function

$$\frac{T_1^2 T_2^2}{(1-R_1^2)(1-R_2^2)} \cdot \frac{1}{1 - 2R_1^m R_2 \cos \chi + R_1^{2m} R_2^2}. \tag{6.28}$$

It is usual for $R_1^m R_2$ to be so much less than 1 that all but the first power can be neglected, and the two interferometers in series then behave as a two-beam interferometer with a transmitted intensity proportional to

$$\int I(k) \, \mathrm{d}k + 2R_1^m R_2 \int I(k) \cos 2\chi \, \mathrm{d}k.$$

This result is the basis of the Fourier transform method for determining the phase shifts at the plates of a Fabry–Perot interferometer described above.

When used for high resolution spectroscopy (Jackson 1958), the system of two interferometers must be arranged so that the normals to the two pairs of plates are parallel while the separations must be in an exact integral ratio. To establish this condition, it is simplest to use white light fringes in just the same way as those fringes are used to compare the separations of two interferometers. The condition for obtaining the greatest maximum of the white light fringes at some point in the field of view is that

$$ml_1 \cos \theta_1 - l_2 \cos \theta_2 = 0.$$

In the spectroscopic application, the condition is achieved over as much as possible of the field of view by making θ_1 and θ_2 as nearly equal as possible, so enabling the maximum possible aperture to be used, whereas when white light is used, θ_1 and θ_2 do not in general have to be equal, the value of $(ml_1 \cos \theta_1 - l_2 \cos \theta_2)$ may vary appreciably over the field of view and fringes of different order of interference may be seen in different parts of the field; indeed, when the fringes are observed visually, it is convenient to have at least five in the field of view.

In order to vary the fringe system and to determine where exact equality of optical paths occurs, it must be possible to vary either angle or optical length to achieve the condition.†

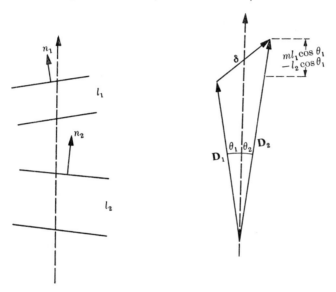

Fig. 6.15. Vector diagrams for two interferometers in series.

The relations between the retardations in the two interferometers may be conveniently represented on a vector diagram (Cabrera and Terrien 1941), as shown in Fig. 6.15. The retardation vectors, $\mathbf{D}_1$ and $\mathbf{D}_2$ are parallel to the normals n_1 and n_2 to the plates of the two interferometers and have lengths respectively ml_1 and l_2. The quantity

$$(ml_1 \cos \theta_1 - l_2 \cos \theta_2)$$

is the projection of the difference vector $\boldsymbol{\delta}$, equal to $\mathbf{D}_1 - \mathbf{D}_2$, on to the direction of a ray of light through the system. Now consider light passing through the system over a range of directions. The fringes will

† For recent spectroscopic applications of Fabry–Perot interferometers in series, see Kuhl, Steudel, and Walther (1967) and Roesler and Mack (1967).

be seen at the focus of a lens placed after the interferometers and the loci of the fringes correspond to directions of rays for which a particular condition is satisfied. In particular, the greatest maximum of the white light fringe system occurs in directions perpendicular to the difference vector δ, for then the path difference is zero for all wavelengths, while subsidiary maxima occur in directions on which the projection of δ is a small integral number of wavelengths:

$$\delta \cos \theta = p\lambda$$

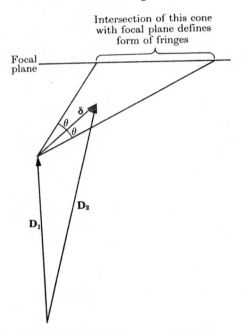

Fig. 6.16. Geometry of fringe patterns in white light.

(the greater p is, the more do the subsidiary maxima show colour since the condition is less accurately satisfied over the visible spectrum). The directions lie on a cone of semi-angle θ about the vector δ, so that the geometry of the fringes in the focal plane is determined by the angles between the vector δ and the normal to the focal plane. The fringes are of course conic sections. If the directions of D_1 and D_2 are nearly coincident, δ will be nearly parallel to D_1 and D_2 and to the normal to the focal plane, and in those circumstances the fringes will be hyperbolae and often very nearly pairs of parallel straight lines. This situation is shown in Fig. 6.16.

Three practical arrangements have been adopted for adjusting the fringes. The earliest to be used was the insertion of a wedge plate in the system (Perot and Fabry 1899, 1901, see also Chapter 8).

Sears and Barrell (1932), in their determination of the metre in terms of the wavelength of the red line of cadmium, varied the angle between the two interferometers Their arrangement is shown in Fig. 6.17. One interferometer, the one with the smaller retardation vector D_1, is aligned with the viewing telescope by autocollimation so that the vector is parallel to the optic axis of the telescope as defined by the intersection

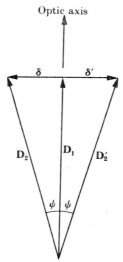

FIG. 6.17. White light system of Sears and Barrell (1932).

of cross-wires in the focal plane. The other interferometer is then tilted until the vector δ is perpendicular to the direction of the cross-wires, that is until the central white light fringe is seen to lie at the intersection of the cross-wires; the vector diagram of Fig. 6.17 corresponds to this condition. There are two such positions of the second interferometer and if the angle between the two positions is 2ψ, then the relation between the two retardations is

$$D_1 = D_2 \cos \psi.$$

If 2ψ can be measured to about 2 in 10^6, or $1''$, the ratio D_1/D_2 will be known to 5 in 10^7.

Sears and Barrell made visual observations of the position of the white light fringes, but it is evident that, if the cross-wires were to be replaced by a pinhole, the observations could be made photoelectrically. Sears and Barrell began with an interferometer 0·083 m long that they could measure directly in cadmium red light and compared it with one $\frac{1}{3}$ m long using fringes in white light; in a second stage of comparison, the second interferometer was compared with one 1 m long.

Cook and Richardson (1959) introduced the idea of altering the optical length of one of the interferometers. They used photoelectric observation and by means of autocollimation, arranged that the plates

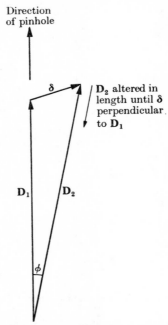

FIG. 6.18. White light system of Cook and Richardson (1959).

of one interferometer were perpendicular to the direction of a pinhole in front of a photomultiplier. The interferometers have a small angle ϕ between them, as shown in Fig. 6.18, and the length of one of the interferometers, D_2 in Fig. 6.18, is varied by altering the pressure, and therefore the refractive index, of the air in the interferometer, until the vector δ is perpendicular to the direction of the pinhole; as shown by the intensity of the light passing the pinhole reaching a maximum.

The ratio D_1/D_2 is then not exactly unity but is $(1-\cos \phi)$; however, it is easy to adjust ϕ to be so small that the ratio may be taken to be unity. The angular interval between successive fringes is $\lambda/D\phi$. In visual observation it is best not to have the fringes too widely spaced since they appear indistinct and it is difficult to make good settings on crosswires, but in photoelectric observations the spacing should be as great as possible and certainly the spacing should be four or five times the diameter of the pinhole, for otherwise the contrast of the photoelectric signal falls off seriously. It was found in practice that if the fringes were widely spaced to give good contrast in the photoelectric observations, then ϕ was small enough for D_1/D_2 to be taken equal to unity.

Cook and Richardson used their method of observation in determining the phase shifts on reflection at the interferometer plates from the Fourier transform of the white light fringes, and Cook (1967) incorporated the arrangement in the interferometric measurements of length involved in his absolute determination of the acceleration due to gravity by timing the free up and down flight of a glass ball over a measured height.

White light fringes cannot be observed if the pressures of air in the two interferometers are appreciably different, on account of the dispersion of air.

The spherical Fabry–Perot interferometer

The spherical Fabry–Perot interferometer was introduced by P. Connes (1958); a diagram of the system is given in Fig. 6.19. The particular feature of this interferometer is its very large aperture so that it may be used with very weak extended sources. Let 1 and 2 be two confocal spherical or paraboloidal mirrors; a ray entering the system through a point A on surface 1 will undergo two successive reflections from 1 and 2 in turn and will then be travelling along its original incident direction having suffered a retardation equivalent to the path length $4\mu d$, where d is the separation of the surfaces and μ is the

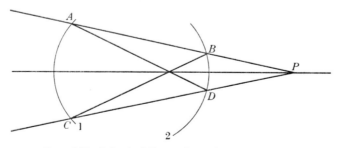

FIG. 6.19. Spherical Fabry–Perot interferometer.

refractive index of the medium between them. The result is exact for paraboloids and nearly correct for spheres; for spheres the retardation depends slightly on the angle at which the light is incident on the system. The geometry for small angles of incidence relative to the line joining the centres of curvature of the mirrors is shown in Fig. 6.19.

P is the intercept on the common axis of a ray meeting the first mirror at A at a distance h_1 from the axis. Assuming that h_1/d is very much less than 1, the ray is reflected by the second mirror at B to meet the first again at C at the same distance h_1 from the axis. PC then intersects the second mirror in D at the same distance from the axis as B, from which it will be clear that PC is the direction of the ray reflected from the point C. The symmetry of the system then shows that the ray reflected from D meets the first mirror in A and then returns to B. For rays close to the axis, the path difference for one complete circuit is $4\mu d$, but at greater distances it becomes

$$\left\{4d + \frac{1}{2d^3}\,(h_1^2 - h_2^2)^2\right\}\mu.$$

The theoretical resolving power and free spectral range are the same as for a plane Fabry–Perot interferometer of twice the separation of the spherical interferometer. The variation of phase difference between successively reflected rays over a pinhole used for photoelectric observations with either a plane or spherical interferometer must not exceed about π, which gives for the plane instrument

$$\Omega = 2\pi/\mathscr{R},$$

where Ω is the solid angle subtended by the pinhole and $\mathscr{R}$ is the resolving power. Connes has shown that, when the spherical aberration of the mirrors is taken into account, the same condition on the maximum phase difference leads to the result that the maximum value for the axial distance at which any ray enters the interferometer shall be

$$\left(\frac{32}{\mathscr{F}}\,\lambda d^3\right)^{\frac{1}{4}},$$

where $\mathscr{F}$ is the finesse of the plates.

With separations of about 0·1 m, the diameters of the plates would be about 8 mm. The product of solid angle times plate area is

$$\frac{\pi^2}{4\mathscr{F}^2}\,\lambda^2\,\mathscr{R},$$

and Connes shows that, for given finesse and resolving power, the gain of luminosity of a spherical interferometer of optimum diameter over that of a plane interferometer with plate area S is

$$\frac{\pi}{8\mathscr{F}^2} \frac{\lambda^2 \mathscr{R}^2}{S^2},$$

and that the diameter of the plates of a plane interferometer of separation d and equal luminosity is

$$1\cdot 4\, d.$$

Now the sizes of optical flats are limited by the area over which it is possible to work them flat and it appears that the spherical interferometer begins to have an advantage at separations of about 0·1 m.

The spherical Fabry–Perot interferometer can only be used with photoelectric recording and a form of scanning (in particular by air pressure variation) that does not alter the geometrical conditions.

The superiority of the spherical Fabry–Perot interferometer over the plane instrument is due to the circumstance that the maximum solid angle that can be employed is inversely proportional to the resolving power for the plane instrument whereas it is proportional to the resolving power for the spherical interferometer. On the other hand, the plate area is proportional to the solid angle instead of being independent of it as for the plane interferometer.

Despite its elegance, the applications of the spherical Fabry–Perot interferometer are restricted and it has found only specialized use (Fork, Herriot, and Kogelnik 1964). Interferometers with one plane and one spherical mirror were first employed in gas lasers and have been subsequently used in spectroscopy.

The Fabry-Perot interferometer as a filter

The Fabry–Perot interferometer is a filter that transmits light for which $kl \cos \theta = 2\pi n$. If a Fabry–Perot interferometer is placed in series with a dispersive spectrometer and illuminated with white light, bright fringes will be seen in the focal plane of the spectrometer wherever

$$kl \cos \theta = 2\pi n.$$

If coordinates x and y are taken in the focal plane of the spectrometer (Fig. 6.20) such that x is in the direction of the dispersion and y is at right angles to it, then over a small range of x and y,

$$\lambda = \lambda_0(1+\alpha x),$$

$$\cos \theta = 1 - \beta y^2 \quad (\alpha \text{ and } \beta \text{ are geometrical factors})$$

and

$$l(1 - \beta y^2) = n\lambda_0(1 + \alpha x)$$

or

$$n\lambda_0 \alpha x + l\beta y^2 = l - n\lambda_0, \tag{6.29}$$

that is to say, the bright fringes map out parabolae in the focal plane. These fringes, which are also the envelopes of the Haidinger rings

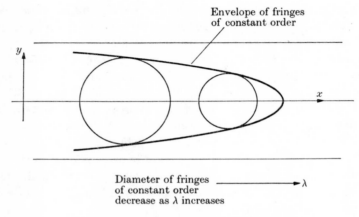

Fig. 6.20. Origin of parabolic channels.

of given order in successive colours, are known as *parabolic channels* and can be used for the study of absorption lines, since wherever an absorption line occurs, the bright parabola will be crossed by a dark line. Channelled spectra have been used in the study of solar spectra both for the measurement of wavelengths of absorption lines (Adam 1952, 1955, Adam and Nickols 1958) and for the study of profiles (Hindmarsh 1955, Treanor 1957).

If a Fabry–Perot interferometer is to be used as a filter to isolate a particular frequency, all the other frequencies that can be transmitted by the interferometer must be cut out; the only filter that is sufficiently sharply tuned to discriminate between adjacent fringes of a Fabry–Perot interferometer is another Fabry–Perot interferometer. If two interferometers have free spectral ranges r_1 and r_2, a range r_2 may be isolated by setting r_2 equal to nr_1, where n is an integer; this is the usual arrangement adopted when two interferometers are used in series for high resolution spectroscopy (Jackson 1958). There is, however, another possibility, namely to set

$$r_2 = \frac{n}{n-1} r_1,$$

when the peaks again coincide after r_2/r_1 peaks of the shorter range. There is no point in adopting this choice with plane interferometers but it is necessary to follow it with spherical Fabry–Perot interferometers since otherwise it is not possible to match the apertures (Connes 1958). Prior to the development of gas lasers, Fabry–Perot filters of very narrow pass bands were constructed to isolate a section of a natural line to provide an artificial source for interferometric measurements over very long distances. The central frequency of the pass band depends on the length of the interferometer and servo-systems have been devised to keep the plates of the interferometer parallel and to maintain the separation at some value fixed by reference to a standard length or wavelength (see Bruce 1966). The problem of finding a suitable set of path differences for a number of interferometers in series can be made much easier by isolating the desired range of frequency with coloured glass filters. The overall transmission of a set of Fabry–Perot interferometers with conventional glass plates coated with metal films would be very low while the pass band would be unnecessarily narrow if all that was required was to isolate a particular line in the spectrum by selecting a pass band of a few angstroms. Much higher transmissions at the cost of a greater pass band may be obtained by coating one transparent material with another of very different refractive index, relying on the difference of refractive indices to produce a reflectivity that will give perhaps three or four effective reflections. The fringes obtained with such a system will be somewhat sharper than sinusoidal fringes while the transmittance will be very high and the absorption low. It is now not necessary to make the path differences more than a few wavelengths and a filter may be built up of a sequence of low refractive index layers separated by layers of high refractive index, the various thicknesses being chosen to select the desired pass band. A system of such dielectric layers cannot however be regarded as a set of independent interferometers because light reflected from any interface can interfere with that reflected from any other in the stack; the design of interference filters of this type is therefore a rather complex matter best carried out on a computer (Heavens 1960).

The design and production of multilayer dielectric filters have been brought to a high degree of perfection and these filters are widely used. Typically, they have a peak transmittance of 80 per cent and a band pass of no more than about 0·1 nm.

7

THE THEORY OF MODES IN A FABRY–PEROT INTERFEROMETER

In the ordinary interferometric use of the Fabry–Perot interferometer the significant question is the dependence of the intensity of the light transmitted through the interferometer upon the angle of incidence and upon the wavelength of the light, and the distribution of the optical field between the plates is almost always ignored. When, on the other hand, a Fabry–Perot interferometer is used as the resonant system in an optical maser, the significant question is the distribution of the internal field, for the operation of a particular system depends on whether successive reflections at the interferometer plates produce such a pattern that the losses caused by reflection and diffraction at the plates are balanced by stimulated emission from the active medium.

The treatment of the modes that can be established in a Fabry–Perot interferometer differs from that of a microwave cavity because the Fabry–Perot is not completely enclosed and so the fields do not vanish upon some completely closed boundary. Boundary conditions are given upon the reflectors but nowhere else. The treatment therefore depends upon calculating the diffraction pattern of a wave reflected by one of the reflectors. The present account, following the methods introduced by Fox and Li (1961), is based on the use of scalar diffraction theory to calculate the field distribution over one of the plates given that over the other; the distributions themselves are then derived by applying the condition that they should be identical apart from a scalar factor representing the losses and a phase factor corresponding to the time of transit between the plates. The general method will be illustrated for circular confocal paraboloidal mirrors because the results can be expressed in an analytical form with fairly familiar functions; applied to other configurations the procedure may involve numerical solutions as in the original work of Fox and Li.

The diffraction is calculated by means of scalar Kirchhoff theory. Let V be a field variable expressed as the product $\psi(x, y, z)e^{i\omega t}$. Since V satisfies the wave equation, ψ satisfies

$$\nabla^2\psi + k^2\psi = 0, \quad (k = \omega/c). \tag{7.1}$$

Let S be a surface enclosing a volume T. Then according to Green's theorem,

$$\int_{T} (\psi_1 \nabla^2 \psi_2 - \psi_2 \nabla^2 \psi_1) \, d\tau = \int_{S} \left(\psi_1 \frac{\partial \psi_2}{\partial n} - \psi_2 \frac{\partial \psi_1}{\partial n} \right) dS. \qquad (7.2)$$

If ψ_1 and ψ_2 are solutions of (7.1), then

$$\psi_2 \nabla^2 \psi_1 - \psi_1 \nabla^2 \psi_2 = 0.$$

Now let ψ_1 be any solution of (7.1) and let ψ_2 be $r^{-1}e^{-ikr}$, which is also a solution of (7.1). Then

$$\int_{S} \left\{ \frac{e^{-ikr}}{r} \frac{\partial \psi}{\partial n} - \psi \frac{\partial}{\partial n} \left(\frac{e^{-ikr}}{r} \right) \right\} dS = 0. \qquad (7.3)$$

Now consider a point P inside S and draw round it a small sphere σ of which P is the centre. On σ the direction of the outward normal coincides with the radial direction and $\partial/\partial n \equiv \partial/\partial r$.

Hence on σ the surface integral is

$$4\pi\rho^2 \left[\frac{e^{-ik\rho}}{\rho} \frac{\partial \psi}{\partial r} - \psi \frac{\partial}{\partial r} \left(\frac{e^{-ikr}}{r} \right) \right]. \qquad (7.4)$$

$$(r = \rho, \quad \text{a constant, on } \sigma).$$

Now

$$\frac{\partial}{\partial r} \left(\frac{e^{-ikr}}{r} \right)_{r=\rho} = -\frac{e^{ik\rho}}{\rho^2} - \frac{ike^{-ik\rho}}{\rho},$$

and the integral over σ reduces to $4\pi\psi_P$ as ρ approaches zero.

ψ satisfies eqn (7.1) in the space between S and σ, so that the surface integrals taken over S and σ together are zero, that is to say, the integral over S is equal to minus the integral over σ, or

$$\psi_P = \frac{1}{4\pi} \int_{S} \left[\frac{e^{-ikr}}{r} \frac{\partial \psi}{\partial n} - \psi \frac{\partial}{\partial n} \frac{e^{-ikr}}{r} \right] dS.$$

On S, $\partial\psi/\partial n = \cos\theta \, \partial\psi/\partial r$ where θ is the angle between the normal and the radius vector.

Furthermore, at large distances from P, ψ behaves like e^{-ikr} and so $(\partial\psi/\partial r) \sim -ik\psi$.

Thus if terms of order $(kr)^{-1}$ may be neglected,

$$\psi_P = \frac{ik}{4\pi} \int_{S} \frac{e^{-ikr}}{r} (1 + \cos\theta)\psi \, dS. \qquad (7.5)$$

This is the Kirchhoff diffraction formula which will be used to calculate the fields on the plates.

Let ψ_q be the field on one mirror after q reflections, and let ψ_{q+1} be the field on the other mirror after $q+1$ reflections. According to the Kirchhoff formula,

$$\psi_{q+1} = \frac{ik}{4\pi} \int_S \frac{e^{-ikr}}{r} (1+\cos\theta)\psi_q \, dS, \qquad (7.6)$$

where the integral is taken over the area of the first mirror.

Now suppose the configuration of the mirrors to be symmetrical, that is the mirrors and the fields over them are similar apart from facing in opposite directions. It does not then matter on which mirror the field is established, whereas if the system were not symmetrical, it would be necessary to consider two successive reflections, re-establishing the field on the initial mirror. With this simplification, and assuming that

$$\psi_q = v/\gamma^q,$$

$$\psi_{q+1} = v/\gamma^{q+1},$$

where γ, in general a complex quantity, is a product of an amplitude and a phase factor, the integral equation to determine v becomes

$$v = \frac{i\gamma k}{4\pi} \int_S \frac{e^{-ikr}}{r} (1+\cos\theta)v \, dS. \qquad (7.7)$$

The solution of equation (7.7) depends on being able to separate v into the product of factors that are functions of one variable only, that is

$$v = v_1(x_1)v_2(x_2),$$

where x_1 and x_2 are orthogonal coordinates over the surface of the mirror. The possibility of such a separation depends on the co-ordinate system used to express position over the mirror, and that in turn depends on the shape of the edge of the mirror. Separation can be effected in cylindrical co-ordinates, used with circular mirrors, and in Cartesian coordinates, used with rectangular mirrors, but in general it may not be possible to solve the equation by separating the variables and then a numerical solution is necessary. In the present example, cylindrical coordinates are used.

The geometry is shown in Fig. 7.1. The mirrors are separated by a distance d and positions on them are expressed by coordinates r_1, ϕ_1, r_2, ϕ_2, in the planes tangential to the two mirrors and perpendicular to the axis of the pair of mirrors. Mirror 1 is that over which the field is given, mirror 2 is that over which it is to be calculated.

The element of area on either mirror is $dS = r \, dr \, d\phi$ (neglecting the curvature of the mirror).

Let R be the distance between any point on one mirror and any point on the other; then

$$R^2 = (d-\Delta_1-\Delta_2)^2 + r_1^2 + r_2^2 - 2r_1 r_2 \cos(\phi_1-\phi_2), \qquad (7.8)$$

where Δ_i is the axial distance of a point on a mirror from the plane tangential to that mirror through its centre (Fig. 7.1).

If the mirrors are confocal spheres, the radius of curvature of each is d and

$$\Delta_i(2d-\Delta_i) = r_i^2,$$

or, approximately,

$$\Delta_i = r_i^2/2d. \qquad (7.9)$$

The result is exact for confocal paraboloids, for which the common focal length is $d/2$, for as indicated in Fig. 7.2,

$$(\tfrac{1}{2}d+\Delta)^2 = r^2 + (\tfrac{1}{2}d-\Delta)^2,$$

or

$$\Delta = r^2/2d. \qquad (7.10)$$

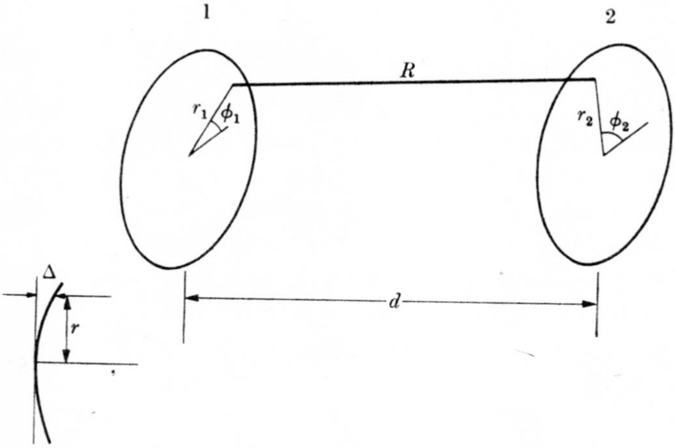

FIG. 7.1. Geometry of twin reflectors.

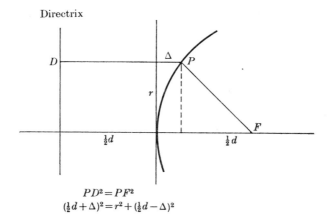

$$PD^2 = PF^2$$
$$(\tfrac{1}{2}d + \Delta)^2 = r^2 + (\tfrac{1}{2}d - \Delta)^2$$

Fig. 7.2. Geometry of parabolic reflector.

Thus exactly for paraboloids and approximately for spheres,

$$R^2 = \left(d - \frac{r_1^2 + r_2^2}{2d}\right)^2 + r_1^2 + r_2^2 - 2r_1 r_2 \cos(\phi_1 - \phi_2)$$

$$= d^2 + \left(\frac{r_1^2 + r_2^2}{2d}\right)^2 - 2r_1 r_2 \cos(\phi_1 - \phi_2)$$

$$\doteqdot d^2 - 2r_1 r_2 \cos(\phi_1 - \phi_2) \qquad \text{if } d/r \gg 1. \tag{7.11}$$

The last approximation is almost always justified, for it is found that the area of a laser beam is usually very small compared with the distance between the mirrors. Then

$$R \doteqdot d - r_1 r_2 \cos(\phi_1 - \phi_2),$$

and

$$v(r_2,\, \phi_2) = \left(\frac{ike^{-ikd}}{4\pi d}\right) \int\limits_{S} 2v(r_1,\, \phi_1)\exp\left\{\frac{ikr_1 r_2 \cos(\phi_1 - \phi_2)}{d}\right\} r_1 \, dr_1 \, d\phi_1, \tag{7.12}$$

where it has also been supposed that θ is very nearly zero so that $1 + \cos\theta = 2$ and R may be taken to be d in the denominator. The two approximations are of the same order. If the factor e^{-ikd} is absorbed into γ,

$$v(r_2,\, \phi_2) = \gamma \int\limits_{0}^{a} dr_1 \int\limits_{0}^{2\pi} d\phi_1 K(r_2,\, \phi_2;\, r_1,\, \phi_1) v(r_1,\, \phi_1) r_1. \tag{7.13}$$

This is the integral equation for v with circular spherical or paraboloidal mirrors. $K(r_2,\, \phi_2;\, r_1,\, \phi_1)$ is the *kernel* of the equation and, with the assumptions made above, is

$$\frac{i}{\lambda d}\exp\left\{ik\frac{r_1 r_2}{p}\cos(\phi_1-\phi_2)\right\}.$$

Suppose that

$$v(r,\ \phi)\ =\ S_n(r,\ \phi)\mathrm{e}^{-in\phi},$$

where n is an integer. Thus

$$S_n(r_2,\ \phi_2)\ =\ \gamma\mathrm{e}^{in\phi_2}\int\limits_0^a\mathrm{d}r_1\int\limits_0^{2\pi}\mathrm{d}\phi_1\frac{ir_1}{\lambda d}\times$$

$$\times\exp\left\{ik\frac{r_1 r_2}{d}\cos(\phi_1-\phi_2)\right\}S(r_1,\ \phi_1)\mathrm{e}^{-in\phi_1}.\quad(7.14)$$

But a standard result in the theory of Bessel functions is that

$$\int\limits_0^{2\pi}\exp\left\{ik\frac{r_1 r_2}{d}\cos(\phi_1-\phi_2)\right\}\mathrm{e}^{-in\phi_1}\,\mathrm{d}\phi_1\ =\ 2\pi\mathrm{e}^{in(\frac{1}{2}\pi-\phi_2)}J_n\left(\frac{kr_1 r_2}{d}\right),\quad(7.15)$$

where J_n is a Bessel function of the first kind.

Making the further simplification that S_n is independent of ϕ,

$$S_n(r_2)\ =\ 2\pi\gamma\int\limits_0^a\frac{i^{n+1}}{\lambda d}\,J_n\left(\frac{kr_1 r_2}{d}\right)r_1 S_n(r_1)\,\mathrm{d}r_1.\quad(7.16)$$

r_1 appears unsymmetrically in equation (7.16), so we try instead for a solution of the form $r^{\frac{1}{2}}S_n(r)$, for which the integral equation is

$$r_2^{\frac{1}{2}}S_n(r_2)\ =\ \gamma_n\int\limits_0^a K_n(r_1,\ r_2)[r_1^{\frac{1}{2}}S_n(r_1)]\,\mathrm{d}r_1,$$

where

$$K_n(r_1,\ r_2)\ =\ \frac{i^{n+1}k}{d}\,J_n\left(\frac{kr_1 r_2}{d}\right)(r_1 r_2)^{\frac{1}{2}},\quad(7.17)$$

and γ_n is an eigenvalue corresponding to the integer n.

We now use once more the fact that the beam of a laser is usually confined to a very small area of the mirrors so that the mirrors may be considered to be of infinite radius and the integral may be taken between 0 and ∞. In that case the integral equation is a form of *Hankel* transform (just as $g(y) = \int f(x)\ \mathrm{e}^{ixy}\ \mathrm{d}x$ is the Fourier transform of $f(x)$, so

$$g(y)\ =\ \int f(x)J_n(xy)(xy)^{\frac{1}{2}}\,\mathrm{d}x$$

is the Hankel transform of $f(x)$). $r^{\frac{1}{2}} S_n$ will then be a solution of the integral equation if it is self-reciprocal under the Hankel transformation (for comparison, e^{ikx} is self-reciprocal under the Fourier transform). Such self-reciprocal functions form complete orthogonal sets over the appropriate domain. The corresponding orthogonal property for the Fourier transform is that $\int \exp[ix(k_2 - k_1)] \, dx = 0$ unless $k_1 = k_2$.

Functions that are self-reciprocal under the Hankel transformation may be expressed in terms of Laguerre polynomials, $L_p^n(x^2)$, equal to

$$\sum_{m=}^{p} \binom{p+n}{p-m} \frac{(-x^2)^m}{m!},$$

where

$$\binom{p+n}{p-m} = \frac{p+n)!}{(p-m)!\,(n+m)!}, \quad \text{(Abramowitz and Stegun 1964)}.$$

For example,

$$L_0^0 = 1,$$
$$L_1^0 = 1 - x^2,$$
$$L_2^0 = 1 - 2x^2 + \tfrac{1}{2}x^4.$$

In terms of the Laguerre polynomials, the solutions that are self-reciprocal under the Hankel transform are

$$S_{np}(r) = (-1)^p \left(\frac{kr^2}{d}\right)^{\frac{1}{2}n} e^{-kr^2/2d} L_p^n\left(\frac{kr^2}{d}\right). \tag{7.18}$$

They contain the factor $(-1)^p$, whereas the kernel $K_n(r_1, r_2)$ contains the factor i^{n+1}; γ_n must therefore be proportional to i^{2p+n+1}. But γ is already proportional to e^{-ikd}; the eigenvalues are accordingly

$$\exp[-ikd + \tfrac{1}{2}\pi i(2p+n+1)].$$

Now the total phase shift in the two reflections from mirror 1 to mirror 2 and back again must be $2\pi s$, where s is an integer. Thus at resonance $4d/\lambda = 2s + 2p + n + 1$. λ^s is the order of the longitudinal mode and is ordinarily very large, between 10^5 and 10^6. p is the order of the radial mode and is usually small, as is n, the order of the azimuthal mode. The wavelength is therefore determined essentially by s, that is by the separation of the reflectors.

In the simplest case when p and n are zero, the field is proportional to $e^{-kr^2/2d}$ and the beam through the cavity is known as a Gaussian beam.

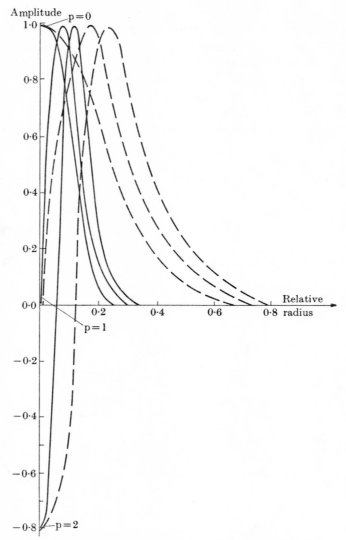

FIG. 7.3. Radial variation of field between confocal mirrors.
Full lines: $a^2k/d = 200$
Broken lines: $a^2k/d = 25$.

The general expression for the field variable v on one of the mirrors is

$$v = e^{-\mathrm{i}n\phi}e^{-kr^2/2d}\left(\frac{kr^2}{d}\right)^{\frac{1}{2}n}L_p^n\left(\frac{kr^2}{d}\right);$$

it is of the separated form

$$v = v_r(r).v_\phi(\phi).$$

If the field is axially symmetrical, that is if n is zero, then the field varies radially with a number of maxima and minima as indicated in Fig. 7.3. When p is 1, there are zeros at $x = 0$ and 1 and a maximum at $x = 3^{-\frac{1}{2}}$. When p is 2, there are zeros at $x^2 = 2 \pm 3^{\frac{1}{2}}$ and maxima at the centre and at $x^2 = 4 \pm 6^{\frac{1}{2}}$. There are somewhat similar radial variations when the fields have an azimuthal variation.

The foregoing calculations, which are on the lines of the work of Boyd and Gordon (1961) and of Boyd and Kogelnik (1962), indicate the mathematical methods to be used in studying the modes of a Fabry–Perot resonator, but they are in a number of ways incomplete. Boyd and Kogelnik (1962) have shown how to extend the results to systems in which the radii of curvature of the mirrors are unequal and in which the mirrors are not confocal. The major limitation of the calculations given above is that by allowing the integrations over the mirrors to go out to infinity, it is implied that the diffraction losses are negligible and so the calculations can give no estimate of those losses, which are none-theless of great importance in deciding whether a particular configura-tion is suitable for a laser and which modes will dominate in operation. Formally, the eigenvalues γ have unit moduli. If the integration is limited to a finite area, then different eigenfunctions must be used to solve the integral equations and the moduli of the eigenvalues will depend upon the range of integration. Since the intensity of the field is proportional to $|\gamma|^2$, the diffraction loss is $1 - |\gamma|^2$ after one complete reflection. For example, if the reflectors are square, the proper eigen-functions are spheroidal wave functions (Flammer 1957) and the diffraction losses are then as shown in Fig. 7.4. It will be seen that the

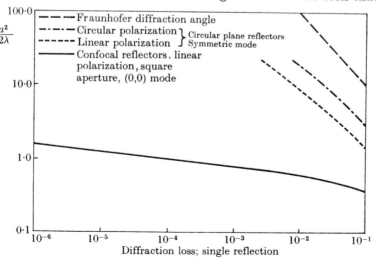

FIG. 7.4. Diffraction losses (Boyd and Gordon 1961).

losses increase rapidly with the order of the radial mode and therefore the mode of lowest order is the one most readily excited in a laser. The modes of higher order have the greater losses because the field distribution extends further out from the centre of the reflector. Plane parallel reflectors cannot be treated by the analytical methods, used for curved reflectors, but the integral equations have been solved numerically (Fox and Li 1961; Lotsch 1967, 1968).

Curved reflectors, especially in confocal configurations, have a number of advantages over plane parallel reflectors for a laser resonator. Diffraction losses increase rapidly with the radial or angular order of the mode whereas this is not so with plane parallel reflectors, and thus it is easier to operate a laser with confocal reflectors in one mode, that of lowest order, the others being suppressed by diffraction loses. The other great advantage is that, as with the spherical Fabry–Perot interferometer, it is much easier to adjust the curved reflectors than the plane ones.

Vector diffraction theory has been applied to the study of modes of a Fabry–Perot interferometer by Bergstein and Schuchter (1964).

8

THE DETERMINATION OF THE METRE

OVER a period of almost sixty years, the determination of the metre in terms of wavelengths of light has demanded the most exacting techniques of interferometry, not only because of the accuracy sought in the measurements but also because of the difficulties of relating the interferometric phenomena to the mechanical objects by which the metre was defined. At the time of the French Revolution, it was intended to define the metre to be the length of one ten-millionth of the arc of a quadrant of the Earth along a meridian, and a bar—the *Mètre des Archives*—was constructed having a length between its parallel ends intended to be equal to the unit so defined. Subsequent measurements showed that the correspondence was not exact and it was agreed internationally that the metre should be defined by the *Mètre des Archives* and not by the Earth, and that a new standard should be constructed, the International Prototype Metre, on which the metre was defined by the interval between two lines inscribed on the polished neutral surface of the bar. The International Prototype was adopted by international agreement in 1889, in the same year that A. A. Michelson and E. W. Morley indicated how a wavelength of light could be used as a standard of length and how it could be related to the International Prototype. Michelson's determination was carried out at the International Bureau of Weights and Measures in 1892 and 1893 and his account was published in 1895 (Michelson and Benoît 1895).

Michelson's studies were in two parts, the first the examination of the profiles of various lines, as already mentioned in Chapter 5, on the basis of which he selected the red line of cadmium to compare with the metre; and the second, that comparison. All the determinations of the metre on which the presently adopted relation between the wavelength of the orange line (605·8 nm) of krypton and the metre is based were made before single isotopes could be isolated, and therefore used the red line of cadmium, which of all those radiated by a natural mixture of isotopes has the narrowest profile. The width of the cadmium line is such that interference fringes cannot readily be observed over more than about 0·09 m and therefore somewhat elaborate means are necessary to make the comparison between such a length of path in an interferometer and the metre; when single isotopes became available, the procedures for the comparison could be somewhat simplified, but it was

considered that the discrepancies between the existing determinations
of the metre in terms of the cadmium line were in large measure due
to the uncertainties of the settings on the lines on the standard metre
rather than to the interferometric measurements and that it was not
necessary to redetermine the metre in terms of the krypton line but
simply to determine the ratio of the wavelengths of the two lines and on
the basis of that, to assign a value to the metre in terms of the krypton
wavelength.

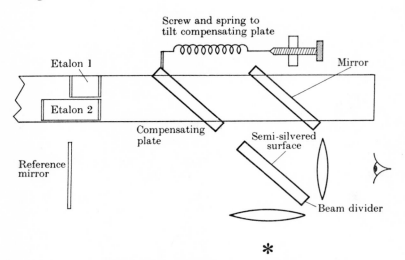

Fig. 8.1. Layout of Michelson's interferometer.

A diagram of Michelson's apparatus is shown in Fig. 8.1. It comprises
a bed having two very accurately worked sets of ways on one of which
rests the carriage bearing a reference mirror in one arm of the interferometer, while on the other set of ways there rest carriages bearing
special etalons, the design of which is shown in Fig. 8.2. Michelson used
nine etalons, the lengths of which were $0 \cdot 1 \times 2^{-p}$ m, p ranging from 0 to
8 so that the longest etalon was $0 \cdot 1$ m long and the shortest was
$0 \cdot 390625$ mm. The etalons were blocks of bronze on which were mounted
two mirrors as shown in Fig. 8.2; the mirrors could be adjusted to be
parallel.

Among the experimental techniques used by Michelson is one now
widely used for checking the straightness of ways. He placed on the
ways a carriage with a mirror which he observed with an autocollimation system and worked the ways until, as the carriage was moved
along, it remained perpendicular to the optical axis of the collimator.

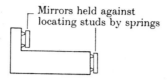

FIG. 8.2. Principle of Michelson's etalon.

Michelson's measurements were in three parts, the determination of
the number of wavelengths in the shortest etalon by direct counting,
the determination of the ratios of the etalons one to another, and the
comparison of the 10 cm etalon with a metre standard. It is a remarkable fact that the counts of fringes made by Michelson and Benoît in
these determinations are the only ones that have been made in all the
determinations of the metre until photoelectric fringe counting was
brought into use in recent years, and that our adopted wavelengths
depend on single counts made on two separate occasions. The counts
were made on circular fringes, and Michelson found it necessary to
arrange that the relative change of path difference during the count
was not too great, for otherwise the change of scale of the fringes led to
difficulties in making an unambiguous count. The arrangement was
as shown in Fig. 8.3. A second etalon (2), of which only one mirror was
used, was set up beside and to the rear of the shortest etalon (1), and the
reference mirror was then moved during the count from the position in
which it gave fringes in white light with one of the mirrors of the
shortest etalon to that in which it gave white fringes with the other

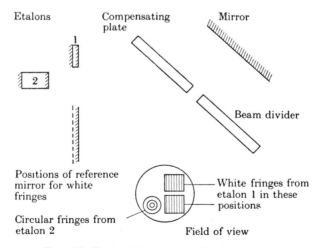

FIG. 8.3. System for counting circular fringes.

mirror of that etalon. The monochromatic fringes that were counted were those formed between the moving reference mirror and the stationary mirror of the second etalon (2), fringes corresponding to a path difference much greater than the separation of the mirrors on the shortest etalon. The field of view is shown in Fig. 8.3. In Michelson's interferometer, the compensator plate could be rotated by very small amounts to introduce small changes of path difference between the interfering beams, and the fractional part of the order of interference in the shortest etalon was determined by rotating the compensating plate. The etalons were first adjusted to give circular fringes on the auxiliary mirror and straight line fringes in white light on the front mirror of the shortest etalon. Those readings of the tilt of the compensating plate were noted for which the central white fringe was on a reference cross wire in the field and for which the centre of the ring pattern was dark. The reference mirror was then displaced while counting the circular fringes and at the end the compensator readings were again noted for which the central circular fringe was dark and for which the white fringe, now on the other mirror of the shortest etalon, was on the centre of the field. It seems that counts took a long time (each of the two observers counted 100 fringes at a time), partly because it was necessary to move the reference mirror very slowly and to readjust it for parallelism from time to time. The concordance between the fractional parts of the order of interference was therefore rather poor, no doubt because of changing temperature, but the order of interference was checked in two ways, through a repetition of the counts at the end of the whole determination of the metre, and secondly through checking the fractional parts of the orders of interference in four lines of cadmium, the relative wavelengths of which were known from observations with a Rowland diffraction grating.

The disposition of the interferometer for the comparison of etalons is shown in Fig. 8.4. The path differences between the front mirrors of the two etalons and the reference mirror were first made the same, as indicated by white light fringes, and the reference mirror was then moved back to give white fringes with the rear mirror of the shorter etalon. Next the shorter etalon was moved back until its front mirror gave white fringes with the reference mirror. If the longer etalon were exactly twice the length of the shorter, white fringes should be seen simultaneously on moving the reference mirror back to give white fringes with the rear mirror of the longer etalon. The small difference actually existing from the ideal condition was taken up by tilting the

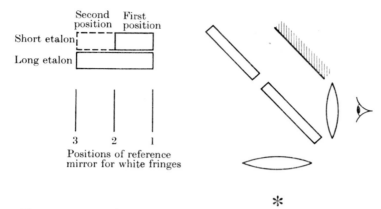

Fɪɢ. 8.4. Arrangements of interferometer for comparison of etalons.

compensating plate to give white fringes on the rear mirror of the shorter etalon. In this way the difference between the length of the longer etalon and twice the length of the shorter was found in terms of the tilt of the compensating plate, which was calibrated with fringes in the yellow light of sodium. Care was taken to have the white fringes on the different etalon mirrors fall as close as possible together in the field of view to minimize effects of the reference mirror being not truly flat. At each stage, circular fringes were established between each mirror of the etalon and the reference mirror, the excess fractional parts of the order of interference in four cadmium lines were measured, and the computed length of each etalon was adjusted to minimize the discrepancies between the observed and calculated fractions. The discrepancies were usually of the order of 0·05 fringe. The measurement of the excess fraction was of course most difficult for the 0·1 m etalon with which the fringe diameters were small and the fringes, especially in the blue light, not very distinct.

The 0·1 m etalon carried an outrigger on the end of which was engraved a line similar to that on an auxiliary metre line standard, also of bronze, set up on the interferometer. The 0·1 m etalon was set up so that the line was close to that on one end of the auxiliary line standard and the interval between them was measured with a micrometer microscope. The etalon was then moved back in ten steps, the front mirror on each occasion being brought into the same plane as the rear mirror on the previous step as shown by the white light fringes formed with the reference mirror. At the end of the ten steps, the line on the etalon was almost in line with the trace on the further end of the auxiliary standard, and the difference between them was measured with a micrometer microscope. The final stage of the whole determination was to compare the auxiliary metre with one of the fundamental line standards by the usual line standard procedures.

It is remarkable how close Michelson's result is to the mean of more recent work (Table 8.1, p. 163). Visual observations on two-beam interference systems are of restricted precision, but the metrological deficiencies of Michelson's procedure were a greater handicap. In the first place, all the etalons and the auxiliary metre were of bronze with a relatively high coefficient of expansion and, placed as they were in air, the measurements of temperature could be expected to be somewhat unreliable. Secondly, the geometry of the arrangement of the trace on an outrigger from the 0·1 m etalon is unsatisfactory. Michelson's scheme also demands exceptionally high stability for the supports of the etalons and auxiliary metre, which must not move when they are left nominally in a constant position. Lastly, Michelson ignored the effect of the humidity of the air in calculating refractive indices, so that his original results, subsequently corrected by Benoît, Fabry, and Perot (1913), were considerably in error.

A second determinaiton of the metre in terms of wavelengths was made by Benoît, Fabry, and Perot (1913) in 1905–6, using Fabry–Perot fringes in monochromatic light and fringes of superposition formed between two Fabry–Perot interferometers for multiplication. The shortest etalon was 0·0625 m long and successive etalons were 0·125, 0·25, 0·5, and 1 m long, so that at each stage a factor of two was involved. The form of each etalon is shown in Fig. 8.5. The optically worked glass plates were held in contact with a spacer in the form of a

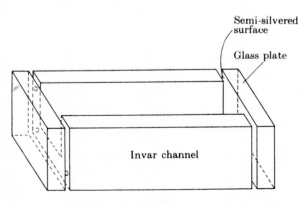

FIG. 8.5. Etalon of Benoît, Fabry, and Perot (1913).

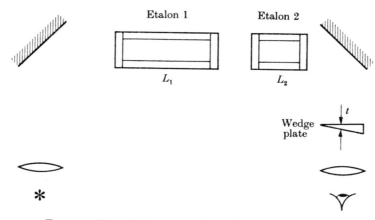

FIG. 8.6. White light system of Benoît, Fabry, and Perot.

channel made of invar. Invar was used for the etalons and for the
auxiliary metre line standard with which the longest etalon was
compared in order to reduce the effects of uncertain temperature
measurement when the etalons were in air. The longest etalon was
slightly less than 1 m long (the shorter etalons being in proportion) and
the glass plates for it carried traces ruled with diamonds on the upper
surfaces, so that when assembled on the spacer, the distance between
the traces was very close to 1 m.

The 0·0625 m etalon was too long for the order of interference to be
determined unambiguously from excess fractions and it was therefore
compared, by means of fringes in white light, with etalons that were
$\frac{1}{5}$, $\frac{1}{4}$, $\frac{1}{3}$, and $\frac{1}{2}$ of its length, these etalons being established on supports of
variable spacing. The orders of interference in the $\frac{1}{5}$, $\frac{1}{4}$, and $\frac{1}{3}$ spacings
could be found independently from the excess fractions in cadmium
and mercury radiations and those in the half-spacing and 0·0625 m were
then found from white light multiplication with a check from the excess
fractions. The white light system is shown in Fig. 8.6. The etalons are
adjusted to be parallel by autocollimation from the silvered plates, and
light that had passed through both etalons of the pair to be compared
was viewed through a compensator wedge. The purpose of the wedge
was to introduce an additional path difference equal to the discrepancy
between the (appropriately reflected) paths in the two etalons. Fringes
in white light were therefore seen on the wedge where

$$L_1 - 2L_2 = 2t,$$

where t is the local thickness of the wedge, L_1 is the length of one etalon, and L_2 that of the second. The thickness t was calibrated with wedge fringes formed in sodium light.

As with Michelson's determination, a key step in that of Benoît, Fabry, and Perot was the comparison between the longest etalon and the auxiliary metre line standard, which in this case involved the distance between the trace ruled on the horizontal upper surface of a block of glass and the effective optical reflecting surface on the vertical face at right angles to it. The sum of these distances for the two glass blocks was found by detaching the blocks from the 1 m etalon and mounting them in turn on shorter spacers to form interferometers with spacings of about 0·01 and 0·02 m. The optical separations l_1 and l_2 of the reflecting surfaces in the two arrangements were found interferometrically, while the distances between the traces ruled on the upper surfaces were compared by micrometer microscopes with the 0·01 m and 0·02 m intervals on a 0·06 m scale divided at 0·01 m intervals.

Let t be the difference between the trace separation and the interferometrically measured separations l_1 and l_2.

Let the interval between the traces on the interferometer plates at 1 cm separation be d_1: $d_1 = t + l_1$.

Let x_i be the position of a 0·01 m graduation line on the 0·06 m scale, measured from the zero line. A typical 1 cm interval is then $x_{i+1} - x_i$ and the micrometrically measured difference between it and d_1 is

$$x_{i+1} - x_i - d_1,$$

a small quantity which will be called y_{1i}. Similarly, measurements at the 2 cm spacing give small differences y_{2i}.

There are 6 intervals of 0·01 m on the scale and 5 of 0·02 m and so there are 6 observation equations of the first type and 5 of the second, as follows:

$$x_{i+1} - x_i - t = l_1 + y_{1i}, \quad \text{(6 equations)}$$

$$x_{i+2} - x_i - t = l_2 + y_{2i}. \quad \text{(5 equations)}$$

From the observation equations, normal equations were derived for the calculation of the x_i and t by the method of least squares. Having so obtained the constant t, the interval between the lines on the glass blocks was compared, by the normal methods using micrometer microscopes, with the auxiliary invar line standard, which itself was compared with one of the standards of the International Bureau of Weights and Measures. The interferometric measurements, like those of

Michelson, were made in air, but the humidity of the atmosphere was taken into account in calculating the refractive index.

A determination of the metre by Watanabe and Imaizumi (1928) was made with apparatus that was essentially a direct copy of that used by Benoît, Fabry, and Perot.

Stress has been laid on the methods used by Michelson and by Benoît, Fabry, and Perot to compare the optical separation of two mirrors, which was found interferometrically, with the separation of two traces on a line standard that defined the metre; and in considering current applications of interferometric methods, as well as in studying the historical determinations, it should be appreciated that the emphasis is entirely proper, for the real difficulties in applying interferometric techniques to metrology usually lie not in the interferometry but in relating the results of the interferometric measurements to quantities that are defined mechanically rather than optically (see, for example, Cook 1961, 1967). Thus it has been pointed out that a possible weakness of the work of Michelson lies in the requirement for very high stability in the support of the various etalons during movement of other parts of the apparatus, while in the determination of Benoît, Fabry, and Perot the relation of the position of the traces on the upper surfaces of the glass blocks of the 1 m etalon to the mean optical reflecting surfaces of those blocks required very careful control of the alignment of the blocks and etalon. A further disadvantage of these first determinations was the number of multiplications that they entailed. Suppose that n multiplications by a factor p are involved and that the standard deviation of the measurement of the shortest etalon in terms of the cadmium radiation is σ_1, that of each step of multiplication is σ_2 and that of the comparison with the metre line standard is σ_3; the standard deviation of the final result will then be expected to be

$$(n^2\sigma_1^2 + n\sigma_2^2 + \sigma_3^2)^{\frac{1}{2}}.$$

Of the three errors, that of the multiplication by fringes in white light is almost always much less than the others, while that of the determination of the shortest length is about 0·02 fringes or 6 nm in visual observations, and that of the line standard comparison would be about 50 nm. The expected error in Michelson's determination would thus be about 1·5 μm, σ_1 giving much the greatest contribution, while in the determination of Benoît, Fabry, and Perot, the resultant error would be expected to be 55 nm, the error of the comparison with the metre being now dominant. Clearly the number of multiplications should be kept as small as possible and the highest accuracy should be sought in the final comparison with the metre.

Sears and Barrell, in their determination (1932, 1934), paid great attention to these points, starting with an etalon of $\frac{1}{12}$ or $\frac{1}{9}$ of 1 m and proceeding by one stage of multiplication to an etalon of $\frac{1}{3}$ m and thence by a further one stage to the 1 m etalon. Their direct comparison was not with a line standard but with an end standard, a metal bar having plane ends polished to be optically flat and parallel, the length being defined by the mechanical separation of the faces. The problem still remained, of course, of comparing such a bar with the line standard by which the metre was defined. Sears and Barrell introduced a number of other improvements. They used a better design of cadmium lamp, which was much brighter than Michelson's, yet which they had shown gave the same wavelength, they worked in vacuum to avoid the uncertainty of the refractive index of air, they used a form of etalon at once more stable and more readily adjustable than that of Benoît, Fabry, and Perot, and they took advantage of these features of their etalons to employ a more convenient method for the white light comparisons.

The design of etalon introduced by Sears and Barrell was shown in Fig. 6.7. The spacer is an invar tube, the walls of which are thick enough for the ends to be lapped to be flat and parallel so that, after plating with chromium and final polishing, the glass mirrors could be attached by molecular adhesion. Close to the ends of the tube, collars are fitted through which are threaded four screwed rods; by adjusting nuts on these rods, the length of the etalon can be changed slightly and the ends can be made parallel. The etalon is very stoutly constructed and once adjusted, will remain in alignment over some years. The adjustments enabled the lengths of two etalons to be brought very closely into an integral relation. The optical arrangement of the apparatus is shown in Fig. 8.7. The three etalons are arranged in line with a telescope and the two shorter ones can be moved in turn out of line for the observation of the white light fringes. The order of interference in the shortest etalon was found from the excess fractional orders in radiations of natural krypton as well as of cadmium. The method for the comparison of the etalons by means of the fringes in white light involved tilting the one etalon of a pair so that its length projected on to the axis of the other bore to the length of the latter an exact integral relation. The principle was described in Chapter 6. In the apparatus of Sears and Barrell the axes of the shortest and the longest etalons were adjusted to be parallel

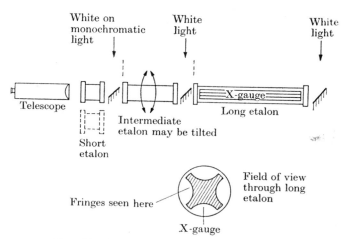

FIG. 8.7. Optical scheme of Sears and Barrell.

to the optical axis of the telescope, while the intermediate etalon was placed on a carriage that could be tilted. As will be seen by reference to Fig. 6.17, there are two positions of the relatively longer etalon for which the central white fringe lies on the optical axis of the telescope and the angle between these two positions of the intermediate etalon was measured in the comparisons, first with the shortest and then with the longest etalon. Sears and Barrell were able to use white fringes at multiplications of three and four.

In the previous determinations, the temperatures of the metal standards had been found with mercury-in-glass thermometers adjacent to the apparatus in a common air bath and calibrated against the hydrogen gas-thermometer scale of the International Bureau of Weights and Measures. Sears and Barrell took great care with the regulation of the temperature of the air in their apparatus and measured the temperature of the 1 m etalon with a platinum resistance thermometer wound along the outside of it; the thermometer was calibrated on the International Practical Scale of Temperature.

The 1 m etalon was of sufficient diameter for a 1 m end gauge of X-cross-section to be placed inside it and yet allow the observation of fringes in white light through each of the four channels between the X-gauge and the tube of the etalon. The length of the X-gauge was then found from interference fringes formed in the short gaps between the plane polished ends of the X-gauge and the glass plates of the 1 m etalon, and in this way the optical length of the X-gauge was determined in terms of the cadmium red line. In deriving the mechanical

length of the end gauge, corrections must be applied for the difference
between the mechanical surface and effective optical reflecting plane of
a polished metal surface (Rolt and Barrell 1929) and also for the fact
that the effective reflecting plane of the silvered glass plate on the 1-m
etalon is in different positions when it is used for the white light fringes
and when it is used for the monochromatic fringes between itself and
the ends of the X-gauge. Finally, the X-gauge must be compared with a
1 m line standard. A special composite gauge was used for that comparison: it consisted of an end gauge about 0·99 m long together with
two blocks each about 0·01 m long having flat sides on which traces
were ruled parallel to the plane polished faces of the end gauges. These
blocks could be wrung into optical contact with the 0·99 m gauge and
then formed a 1 m line standard. Alternatively, if only one of the 0·01 m
blocks was wrung on to the 0·99 m gauge, the combination formed a
1 m end gauge that could be compared optically with the X-gauge. By
attaching the 0·01 m blocks to the 0·99 m gauge in different combinations and arrangements, the unknown positions of the lines on the
0·01 m blocks could be eliminated from comparisons of the 1 m line
standard combinations with a reference line standard. The overall
accuracy cannot of course exceed the accuracy of the intercomparisons
of line standards, but the replacement of the intermediate stages by end
standard comparisons means that no other sources of error dominate
the final line standard errors.

At about the same time as Sears and Barrell, Kösters and Lampe
(1934) made determinations of 1 m end standards using the Kösters
interferometer described in Chapter 4; the end gauge was always in air,
the refractive index of which was measured interferometrically. Similar
measurements have been made in Russia (see Barrell 1946). The determinations of the metre in terms of the red line of natural cadmium are
summarized in Table 2. The original results have been adjusted to allow
for differences of temperature scales, of refractive index estimates, and
of the values assigned to the various copies of the metre on which the
results depend.

The practical use of interferometric methods often depends on
accurate estimates of the refractive index of air. The presently accepted
relation between the density of air and the refractive index depends to a
large extent on the work of Barrell and Sears (1939) undertaken in
conjunction with their determination of the metre. The accuracy of
refractive index determinations by interferometric means depends of
course on the path length, and if a simple Michelson or Fabry–Perot

TABLE 2

Determination of the metre: wavelength of the
Cd–red line (Barrell 1946)

Date	Observers	Published value (nm)	Wavelength in normal air (nm)
1892–3	Michelson and Benoît	643·84722	643·84691
1905–6	Benoît, Fabry, and Perot	696	703
1927	Watanabe and Imaizumi	685	682
1933	Sears and Barrell	711	713
1934–5	Sears and Barrell	709	709
1933	Kösters and Lampe	672	689
1934–5	Kösters and Lampe	685	690
1937	Kösters and Lampe	700	700
1940	Romanova, Varlick, Kartashev, and Bartarchukova	677	677

Mean value 643·84695 nm

interferometer is used, an upper limit is set by the visibility of fringes in the various lines for which it is desired to measure the refractive index. Barrell and Sears extended the path length by using fringes of superposition with two etalons each two-thirds of a metre long, of which one was evacuated while the other could be filled with air. The etalons were placed at a small angle, as in the determination of the metre, so that parallel fringes were seen in monochromatic light. The refractive index was found from the number of fringes passing the optical axis of the viewing telescope as the pressure in the one etalon was changed, allowance being made for the change of mechanical length of the etalon with pressure.

When it was agreed internationally that the metre should be defined in terms of the wavelength of an orange line (605·8 nm) of krypton-86 instead of by a line standard, it was decided that there was no point in making any direct determinations of the metre line standard in terms of the krypton wavelength, since the errors of the line standard comparisons would prevent any greater accuracy being attained than had been achieved in the comparisons with the red line of cadmium. Accurate comparisons of the cadmium and krypton wavelengths were made and the metre was redefined so that the existing relation between the cadmium red line and the metre was preserved. Some comparisons of copies of the metre with the krypton-86 standard line have subsequently been made and show a slight difference from the earlier work.

The main difference of procedure is in the use of photoelectric microscopes for setting on the lines of a line standard. Line standard comparisons with such instruments are much more reproducible than those made visually and, together with photoelectric observations of interference fringes, have led to greater precision in the interferometric measurement of a line standard (Baird, 1963, Baird and Howlett 1963). Using such apparatus, Hart and Baird (1961) found the line standard metre to be 0.2 μm longer than the value given by the adopted wavelength of the krypton standard (see also Hart and Sawabe 1968). The most up to date method for the determination of a line standard involves the electronic counting of fringes formed in the light from a gas laser (Rowley and Stanley 1965).

9

MULTIPLE-BEAM FIZEAU INTERFERENCE

THE fringes formed when the mirrors of a Michelson interferometer are set at a small angle are two-beam fringes with a sinusoidal distribution of intensity, and those formed in the analogous Fizeau wedge plate systems, such as are used in elementary interferometers used for the measurement of short gauges or the testing of optically worked surfaces, are also two-beam fringes in general, although the fringes are sometimes sharpened by increasing the reflectivity of one of the surfaces. If the surfaces of a wedge are made highly reflecting, as in the Fabry–Perot interferometer, the intensity distribution in the resulting fringes may, in suitable circumstances, follow the Airy function as with the Fabry–Perot interferometer, but the conditions for fringes to be observed are much more stringent than for the two-beam Fizeau fringes, because the geometry of reflection from highly reflecting inclined surfaces means that it is in general difficult for a large number of multiply reflected beams to interfere.

Consider two highly reflecting surfaces with a small angle θ between them, and let parallel light be incident on them in a direction making an angle χ with one of the plates. The beams emerging in the same direction as the incident beam after one, two, three . . . reflections within the wedge make angles $\chi+2\theta$, $\chi+4\theta$, $\chi+6\theta$, . . . with the normal to the reference surface (Fig. 9.1). If AC and BC are the reflecting surfaces and if CD_0 is the incident wave front, the wave fronts following the successive reflections are CD_1, CD_2, CD_3, . . . CD_n . . ; they all pass through C, the intersection of the wedge. CD_n makes an angle $\chi+2n\theta$ with AC. Let P be some field point having Cartesian coordinates x, y, with respect to axes of which one is AC and the other is CX perpendicular to AC. The resultant amplitude at P will be

$$A = a \sum r^n \exp(-ik\delta_n),$$

where a is the amplitude of the incident light, r is the amplitude reflection coefficient (assumed for simplicity to be the same for the two surfaces), and δ_n is the path difference between the nth reflected beam and the incident beam.

$$\delta_n = PM_n - PM_0$$

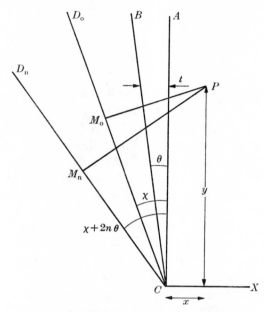

FIG. 9.1. Interference of beams reflected at a wedge.

and

$$PM_n - PM_0 = x\{\cos(\chi+2n\theta)-\cos\chi\}+y\{\sin(\chi+2n\theta)-\sin\chi\}.$$

Consider first a beam incident normally on AC, so that $\chi = 0$. Then

$$PM_n - PM_0 = x(\cos 2n\theta - 1)+y\sin 2n\theta.$$

If y is measured from C, then

$$y = t/\tan\theta,$$

where t is the thickness of the wedge, that is, the separation of the plates, at the point on the reference plate, AC, corresponding to P. Then

$$\delta_n = 2nt\left\{1-\frac{2n^2+1}{3}\theta^2\right\}-2n^2\theta^2 x+\ldots,$$

or, putting

$$4\pi t/\lambda = \psi,$$

$$\phi_n = k\delta_n = n\psi-n^2\frac{4\pi\theta^2 x}{\lambda}-\tfrac{2}{3}n^3\psi\theta^2.$$

In the neighbourhood of maximum intensity, $t \approx \tfrac{1}{2}N\lambda$, where N is an integer. Thus we may put

$$\psi = 2N\pi+\alpha,$$

where α is an angle less than 2π.   Therefore

$$\phi_n = 2nN\pi + n\alpha - \tfrac{2}{3}n^3\theta^2(2N\pi + \alpha),$$

assuming x to be zero (i.e., the fringes are supposed to be in focus on AC).

Suppose that the wedge angle θ is very small so that

$$\tfrac{2}{3}n^3\theta^2\alpha \ll \alpha.$$

The condition cannot of course be satisfied for all values of n but it will be supposed that there is a value of n beyond which the contributions from further reflected beams are negligible; the condition is then to be satisfied for that value of n.

In such circumstances,

$$\phi_n - 2nN\pi = n\alpha - \tfrac{4}{3}n^3\pi N\theta^2,$$

and the resulting intensity may be written as proportional to

$$|\sum r^n \exp\{-\mathrm{i}(n\alpha - n^3\beta)\}|^2,$$

where

$$\beta = \tfrac{4}{3}\pi N\theta^2.$$

The sum cannot be evaluated analytically, but by considering the Fourier components, it is easy to see the nature of the result. If β is zero, all the cosine components of $|\sum r^n e^{-\mathrm{i}n\alpha}|^2$ have their maxima when $\alpha = 0$ and are symmetrical about this ordinate. The sum is therefore symmetrical about that same ordinate—it is the Airy function (Fig. 9.2(a)). If β is not zero, the maxima of the successive cosine terms

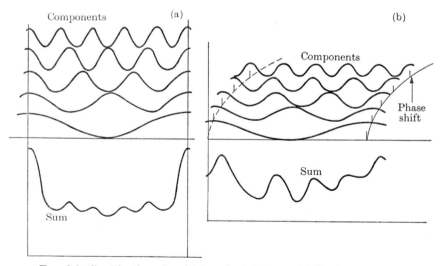

Fig. 9.2. Combination of multiply reflected beams (a) No phase shift.
(b) Extra phase shift.

are displaced more and more all in the same direction and, if β is very small, the sum is a single asymmetrical peak. With larger values of β secondary maxima may appear (Fig. 9.2(b)). In particular, if $n\alpha - n^3\beta$ should become equal to 2π while r^n is still significant, a secondary maximum will develop midway between the principal maxima. The details of the form of the intensity distribution accordingly depend on the reflectivity of the wedge surfaces and on the angle between the surfaces, as well as on the order of interference, N. To give an idea of the orders of magnitude involved, if θ is about 10^{-4}, N may reach 10^4 and the effective value of n may be 10 before significant secondary maxima might appear, but for the fringes to be effectively symmetrical, N would have to be no more than about 10^2.

If the light is not incident normally, that is if χ is not zero, then

$$\delta_n = 2nt \cos \chi \left\{ 1 - n\theta \tan \chi - \frac{2n^2+1}{3} \theta^2 \right\} \quad \text{(again for } x = 0\text{)}.$$

As before, write

$$t = \frac{\psi\lambda}{4\pi} = \frac{\lambda}{4\pi} (2N\pi + \alpha).$$

Then

$$k\delta_n = n(2N\pi + \alpha)\cos \chi \left\{ 1 - n\theta \tan \chi - \frac{2n^2+1}{3} \theta^2 \right\}$$

$$= (2Nn\pi + n\alpha - nN\pi\chi^2) \left\{ (1 - n\theta \tan \chi - \frac{2n^2+1}{3} \theta^2 \right\}$$

$$= 2Nn\pi + n\alpha - n(N\pi\chi^2 + 2\pi Nn\theta \tan \chi) - \tfrac{4}{3}n^3\theta^2 N\pi,$$

or

$$k\delta_n - 2Nn\pi = n\alpha - Nn\pi(\chi^2 + 2n\theta\chi) - \tfrac{4}{3}n^3\theta^2 N\pi,$$

which vanishes to first order when $\alpha = N\pi(\chi^2 + 2n\theta\chi)$.

The phase now includes a term proportional to n^2 as well as one proportional to n^3, and so there is a further contribution to the asymmetry of the fringes. If χ is not very small, the fringes are displaced (α equals $N\pi\chi^2$ instead of being zero for a maximum), while if the range of χ is large, the term in $\cos \chi$ contributes to the asymmetrical broadening of the fringes since $Nn\pi\chi^2$ always has the same sign whatever the value of χ. The general behaviour of the fringes in these conditions is indicated in Fig. 9.3. The asymmetry when the range of χ is large can be used to determine the direction in which the wedge is widening.

In the Fabry–Perot interferometer, where the plates are nominally parallel, the limitation on the effective number of reflections that are

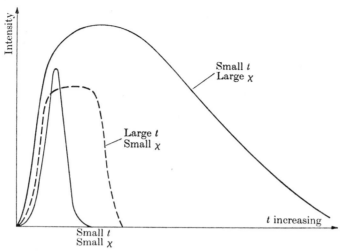

FIG. 9.3. Multiple-beam Fizeau fringes: off-normal incidence.

summed is set by the reflectivity of the coatings, but it is otherwise with
Fizeau fringes, the component beams of which diverge at considerable
angles in the higher orders. The aperture of the optical instrument
with which the fringes are viewed may then limit the number of beams
included in the summation. The Abbe theory of the microscope may
be used to analyse the situation (Fig. 9.4). Let C be the collimator lens
and M the objective of the microscope. Multiple reflections in the
wedge generate a series of beams that are brought to foci in the focal

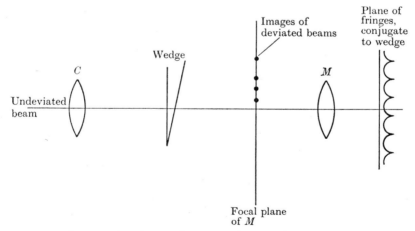

FIG. 9.4. Abbé analysis of multiple-beam Fizeau system.

plane of M, the positions of the spots corresponding to the directions of the beams. Images of the focal spots are then re-imaged to form the fringes on the plane conjugate to the wedge (where they are viewed in the eyepiece). As with ordinary Fizeau fringes, multiple-beam Fizeau fringes are localized, since with divergent and refocused beams there is a particular plane on which they can recombine. This is very similar to the treatment of the microscope with a periodic object but there is an

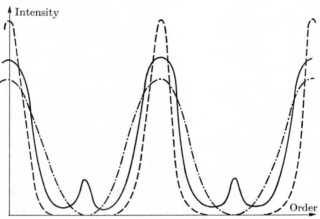

FIG. 9.5. Introduction of artefacts by restriction of aperture.
— — — —   many beams—Airy function
— · — · —   two beams—(cos)² function
————   three beams.

important difference: the successive diffracted beams from a periodic object are symmetrical in space about the zero-order beam but the successive reflected beams from a wedge are all on the one side of the undeviated beam.

Following the lines of the theory of the microscope, the effects of restricting the aperture of the microscope can be analysed. In particular, if only two or three beams are admitted, the corresponding cosine terms in the fringes will be seen separately as subsidiary maxima and minima. Some examples are shown in Fig. 9.5.

The conditions for sharp fringes without misleading artefacts can now be summarized. In the first place, the usual applications of this type of interference require that the fringes should be as sharp as possible; θ and t must thus both be very small. Generally, $\frac{4}{3}\pi n^3 N \theta^2$ should be less than π for a suitably large value of n. But in addition $n^3\theta^2$ must be less than $\frac{3}{2}$; thus, if the largest value of n is taken to be 60, θ must be less than $3\cdot10^{-3}$ and then t should be less than 250 nm.

Next, the aperture of the microscope must be sufficiently large: again if 60 beams are to be added and θ is 10^{-3}, the aperture, which must be greater than $2n\theta$, must be at least $0\cdot12$ rad.

Lastly, the range of χ should be small, unless it is made deliberately large as a means of identifying the direction in which the wedge widens, and the incident light must be carefully collimated to avoid a general displacement of the fringes along the wedge.

A further cause of artefacts has been studied by Tolansky (1944a). Light reflected at the semi-silvered surfaces is partially polarized and, if the phase shift on reflection is different for the two directions of polarization, two sets of fringes will be seen when the angle of incidence is great enough—about 30°.

So far the phases have been evaluated at the plane $x = 0$, that is, on the front face of the wedge, the case of most practical importance because if fringes are formed on that plane, they and the surface of the wedge may be viewed simultaneously in the microscope. It is, however, possible to obtain fringes in positions corresponding to other planes. The general expression for the phase on a plane for which x is not zero, is

$$\phi_n = n\psi - n^2 4\pi\theta^2 x/\lambda - 2n^3\psi\theta^2/3.$$

Now let

$$x = p\lambda/2\theta^2 \ (p = 0, 1, 2, \ldots),$$

so that $\Delta\phi_n$, the difference of phase from the value on the front of the wedge, is

$$2pn^2\pi,$$

which is a multiple of 2π. The distribution of the phases of the successive beams is then the same on all planes for which $x = p\lambda/2\theta^2$.

The spacing of the planes is considerable, for example if λ is 5000 Å and θ is 10^{-4}, the planes are separated by 25 m.

The fringes on the displaced planes have been observed (Brossel 1947) but do not appear to have been put to practical use.

Multiple-beam Fizeau fringes have so far been assumed to be formed in monochromatic light and in general there is a stringent condition on the extent of the spectrum of the light that will allow clear fringes to be seen. An arrangement similar to the channelled spectra obtained with a Fabry–Perot interferometer enables fringes to be observed with white

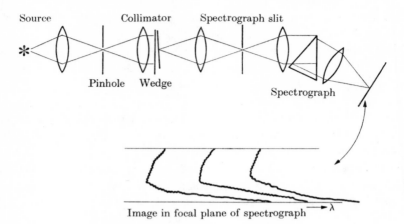

Source   Collimator   Spectrograph slit

Pinhole   Wedge

Spectrograph

Image in focal plane of spectrograph ⟶ λ

FIG. 9.6. Fringes of equal chromatic order.

light (Fig. 9.6). Loci of constant t/λ may be drawn on a wedge and if
the wavelength is fixed, as when the fringes are viewed in monochromatic light, the observed fringes are loci of constant t. But now
let the wedge be illuminated with white light and be imaged on the slit
of a spectrograph. The portion of the surface defined by the slit will
then be imaged in different colours in the focal plane of the spectrograph
and bright fringes will be seen superposed on that image wherever
$t/\lambda = \frac{1}{2}n$, n being an integer. They are known as *fringes of equal chromatic order* and are useful in studying the details of the topography of
a wedge.

The applications of multiple-beam Fizeau fringes have been extensively developed by S. Tolansky (for example, Tolansky 1944b, 1945)
and are described in detail in his book (1948). They depend on the fact
that the fringes are very sharp if the surfaces are close together, nearly
parallel, and have a very high reflectivity, so that in favourable circumstances differences of the separation of the wedge of only a few Ångströms
can be detected. Thus they have been used to study the structure of
crystal surfaces, the form of optically worked surfaces, and the thicknesses of thin films. In such a studies the surface to be examined is
coated with a uniform layer of silver of high reflectivity and an optically
flat surface coated with a silver film having a very high reflectivity
is supported above it. Silver is used for the coatings because, of all
metals, it has the highest reflectivity for the least absorption. The
separation of the two surfaces is carefully adjusted to be as small as
possible and to vary as slowly as possible across the area being studied.

The interferometer will be illuminated with monochromatic light incident at right angles to the comparison surface and will be viewed with a microscope focused on the comparison surface; because the structures that are studied this way are usually of small lateral extent the microscope will have a high power and a large aperture.

The roughness of a surface can be derived in a statistical way from the width of the fringes when the structure is too fine to resolve. If the relative increase in the width of the fringes is b, the r.m.s. roughness of the surface is about $b\lambda$. The fringes may also be used to observe very small movements of one of the surfaces. Slow movements may be resolved in time by a suitable detector or, if the movements are too small or too fast, the amplitudes may be inferred, like the roughness of a surface, from the broadening of the fringes. Multiple-beam interference fringes have been used in this way to study the patterns of the modes of acoustical vibrations of crystals, in particular of quartz crystals at frequencies of the order of a few megahertz for which the amplitudes are much less than 1 μm.

Multiple-beam Fizeau fringes have been used to study the variation with wavelength of the phase shift on reflection from a metal surface (Chapter 6). They are also convenient for some spectroscopic applications, because the fringe spacing can be adjusted over a wide range independently of the width of the fringes by altering the wedge angle. Burgess and Cooper (1965) have used such an interferometer to study the pressure shifts in lines emitted from a plasma source; by means of a

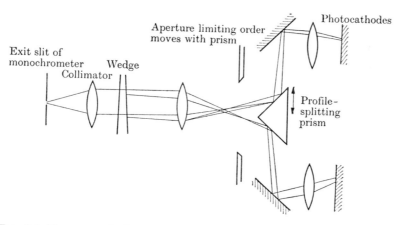

Fig. 9.7. Measurement of spectrum line shift with multiple-beam Fizeau fringes (Burgess and Cooper 1965).

double-beam system (Fig. 9.7) they were able to measure the consequent displacements of a fringe along the wedge, displacements that could be made relatively large by keeping the wedge angle small. Because the fringes are very narrow, the amount of light transmitted is low and multiple-beam Fizeau fringes are only useful for the study of very bright sources.

10

THE GENERAL THEORY OF SPECTROMETERS

A SPECTRUM is the distribution of energy radiated from a source, considered as a function of frequency or wavelength, and detailed specifications of spectra are fundamental to most major topics of physics and chemistry as well as to many applications in engineering. Spectroscopy is almost the most important method of study in modern physical science, embracing as it does not only the traditional studies of optical spectra of atoms and molecules with their extensions ranging from X-rays to microwaves, but including nuclear spectroscopy and the spectroscopy of astronomical radio sources as well as mechanical and acoustical spectroscopy over periods ranging from many minutes (or even days) in geophysics to less than a microsecond in solid-state physics. In many instances spectrometers depend on interference phenomena, in fact, this is almost always true where the wavelike character of the radiation is dominant and the velocity of the waves is independent, or nearly independent, of frequency. The other major technique of spectroscopy, the measurement of the velocity with which energy is transmitted, is applicable to waves in highly dispersive media (such as the Earth) or to radiation in the form of particles with significant rest mass for which the velocity depends upon energy. This chapter is concerned with the spectroscopic applications of interferometers with particular reference to optical systems.

All optical spectrometers are in fact interferometers. Apart from the obvious interferometer systems, the diffraction grating is an interferometer, depending as it does on the interference between light diffracted from different lines on the grating, while the prism is akin to a diffraction grating in which the number of lines has been increased while the spacing has been reduced so that the system becomes continuous. Most interferometric spectrometers use the transforming property of an interferometer in such a way that the distribution of energy with respect to frequency, the spectrum, is transformed into one with respect to direction, for instance with respect to the base of a prism or the normal to a diffraction grating, but it is also possible to have a distribution with respect to path difference, as in the Fabry–Perot and Michelson interferometers. In a simple system, the transformed distribution (or interferogram) approximates to a delta function if the spectrum is a delta function, and for many purposes this is the easiest to interpret. Such systems are not the most powerful and when the most discriminating studies are to be made, systems giving more complex transforms must be employed, in particular, Fourier transform spectrometers may be used. A Fourier transform interferogram may be transformed numerically to give a spectrum or it may be used directly, for in some circumstances the parameters of the Fourier transform of a spectrum are as directly, or possibly more directly, related to the state of a physical system as those of the spectrum.

A spectrum is defined by dividing a range of frequency into a number of elements and specifying the total energy emitted or absorbed over each element. Evidently, the greater the subdivision, the smaller the total energy within each part, the smaller the signal-to-noise ratio in the detector, and the less the accuracy of measurement. In general, therefore, high photometric accuracy in the definition of a spectrum has to be balanced against high precision in the definition of the frequency of an element of the spectrum. At the same time, the fineness with which the range of frequency can be subdivided is limited by instrumental properties, usually diffraction at some controlling aperture of the optical system, and so the energy from a delta-function spectrum is spread out over a finite range of angle in the interferogram. The main purpose of this chapter is to show how these considerations may be discussed in a systematic way for different types of instrument. The traditional problem is spectroscopy is that of *resolving power*, namely the power of resolving two close components of a spectrum, and it will be discussed on the lines first laid down by Jacquinot (1958). Somewhat different considerations are involved if attention is restricted to a narrow range of frequency, as in the measurement of the wavelength of an isolated line; this problem also will be discussed. The main emphasis of the arguments is upon factors that determine signal-to-noise ratio, but they are not the only ones that should be considered in choosing an instrument for a specific problem. Inherent defects of instruments may, for example, produce systematic errors in measurements that may be at least as significant as the random errors arising from noise.

Apart from possible systematic errors, there are four basic factors involved in the selection of a spectrometer: the resolving power, the range, the time taken for a measurement, and the transmissivity of the optical system.

Let $\delta\nu$ be the smallest distinguishable interval of frequency, as set for example by diffraction at the controlling aperture. The *resolving power* at the frequency ν is defined to be

$$\mathcal{R} = \nu/\delta\nu. \tag{10.1}$$

In many instruments, $\mathcal{R}$ is equal to the maximum order of interference N to within a factor of order unity, that is

$$\mathcal{R} \approx \frac{\partial\Delta}{\partial\lambda}, \tag{10.1a}$$

where Δ is a path difference equal to $N\lambda$.

Thus, for the diffraction grating used in the first order, let ψ be the phase shift between successive lines, which for normal incidence is equal to

$$\frac{2\pi}{\lambda} d \sin \theta,$$

where θ is the angle of deviation.

The intensity distribution in the interferogram is

$$I = I_0 \frac{\sin^2 \frac{1}{2}(N+1)\psi}{\sin^2 \frac{1}{2}\psi},$$

where N is the total number of lines in the grating, and so at a phase angle $2N\pi + \delta\psi$ the intensity is

$$\frac{\sin^2 \frac{1}{2}(N+1)\delta\psi}{\sin^2 \frac{1}{2}\delta\psi}.$$

The value of $\delta\psi$ at half the maximum intensity is given by

$$\sin^2 \tfrac{1}{2}(N+1)\delta\psi = \tfrac{1}{2}(N+1)^2 \sin^2 \tfrac{1}{2}\delta\psi$$

or

$$\delta\psi = (3!)^{\frac{1}{2}}/(N+1).$$

Hence

$$\delta\left(\frac{2\pi}{\lambda} d \sin \theta\right) = \frac{(3!)^{\frac{1}{2}}}{N+1}.$$

The width at half intensity is twice the value given by this formula and so

$$\mathcal{R} = \frac{\nu}{\delta\nu} = \frac{\lambda}{\delta\lambda} = \frac{\pi}{(3!)^{\frac{1}{2}}} \cdot \frac{(N+1)d \sin \theta}{\lambda}. \tag{10.2}$$

The maximum order of interference is

$$\lambda^{-1}(N+1)d \sin \theta$$

and the numerical factor in the expression for the resolving power is

$$\pi/(3!)^{\frac{1}{2}} \quad \text{or about } 1\cdot3.$$

The half-intensity points for the response curve of the Fabry–Perot interferometer occur where the product kl differs from the value at the peak by

$$\delta(kl) = \pm\frac{1}{\rho^{\frac{1}{2}}}, \qquad \left[\rho = \frac{4R}{(1-R)^2}\right],$$

that is,

$$l.\delta k = \rho^{-\frac{1}{2}}. \tag{10.3}$$

The order of interference for a single reflection, Δ_1, is kl/π and so, if $\delta\nu$ is the overall width a half amplitude,

$$\frac{\nu}{\delta\nu} = \tfrac{1}{2}\pi\rho^{\frac{1}{2}}\Delta_1. \tag{10.4}$$

$\rho^{\frac{1}{2}}$ may be considered to be the effective number of reflections between the plates, so that the maximum order of interference is $\rho^{\frac{1}{2}}\Delta_1$ and the numerical factor in the expression for the resolving power is $\tfrac{1}{2}\pi$.

If the maximum path difference used with a Michelson interferometer is X, the Fourier transform of the interferogram obtained with a delta-function spectrum is

$$\frac{\sin k'X}{k'X} .$$

The first minimum occurs at $k'X = \pi$ and the width at half intensity is given by

$$\delta k = 2\pi/X.$$

Thus

$$\frac{\nu}{\delta\nu} = \frac{\lambda}{X},$$

the maximum order of interference, and the numerical factor is 1.

An important characteristic of a spectrometer is the range M, that is the maximum number of spectral elements $\delta\nu$ that can be scanned without confusion. For a prism, there is no restriction set by the inherent characteristics of the device, although there are practical limitations set by the absorption of the material of the prism. Notionally, however, the range M may be taken to be infinite. The range of a grating instrument is set by the interval between successive orders, namely

$$\Delta\nu = c/d \sin\theta,$$

so that

$$M = \Delta\nu/\delta\nu = (3!)^{\frac{1}{2}}(N+1)/\pi. \tag{10.5}$$

The Fabry–Perot interferometer has a range corresponding to the interval between successive maxima, so that

$$M = \pi\rho^{\frac{1}{2}}. \tag{10.6}$$

For the Michelson interferometer, sampling theory shows that the maximum observable wave number is equal to $1/d_{min}$, where d_{min} is the least step in path difference made in scanning the interferogram. Thus

$$M = \frac{1}{d_{min}\delta\lambda} = X \quad \text{(in wave numbers)}. \tag{10.7}$$

In general, the greater the resolving power of a spectrometer, the less the range. If a detailed study is to be made of some particular feature of a spectrum, a restricted range is no handicap, but for an overall survey of a complex spectrum, a large range is necessary and then resolving power has to be sacrificed.

The third significant parameter of a spectrometer is the time T taken to observe the M elements of the range. The elements may be observed simultaneously, as in a photographic instrument, or sequentially, as is usual with photoelectric instruments. T is set by the photometric accuracy that is desired for it depends on the signal-to-noise ratio at the detector; the greater this ratio, the less the time for a given accuracy.

Finally, there is the transmissivity of the instrument, determined by such quantities as the aperture of the system or absorption in optical components; it may be defined by the least brightness B of an element that can be detected, given specified range, resolving power, and time of observation.

Jacquinot (1958) introduced the idea of a *factor of merit*, $\mathcal{M}$, a combination of $\mathcal{R}$, M, T, and B that enables spectrometer performances to be compared for given signal-to-noise ratio. Consider a spectrum scanned element by element; the signal-to-noise ratio, S/N, fixes the time required for the measurement of a single element when the photometric accuracy has been specified:

S/N is proportional to (time for measurement of a single element)$^{\frac{1}{2}}$

or

$$S/N \propto (T/M)^{\frac{1}{2}}. \tag{10.8}$$

A modification is required for the Michelson interferometer with which the *interferogram* is scanned element by element.

Let Ω be the solid angle within which light is accepted by the instrument, so that the flux transmitted for each element of brightness B is

$$B\Omega.$$

If photon noise is the dominant noise component,

$$S/N \propto (B\Omega)^{\frac{1}{2}}.$$ (10.9)

If receiver noise dominates, the signal S is proportional to $B\Omega$ and if the receiver area can be made small enough that it just subtends the solid angle Ω, the noise is proportional to $\Omega^{\frac{1}{2}}$ and

$$S/N \propto B\Omega^{\frac{1}{2}}.$$ (10.9a)

On the other hand, if the receiver area much exceeds the minimum (and optimum) value, then N is independent of Ω and

$$S/N \propto B\Omega.$$ (10.9b)

A fundamental factor in the comparison of spectrometers is that there is a relation between the resolving power $\mathscr{R}$ and the solid angle Ω which is characteristic of the type of instrument.

Let Σ be a characteristic area of the instrument, that of the grating for a diffraction grating, or that of the plates for a Fabry–Perot interferometer. The general result is that

$$\Omega = Q\Sigma/R,$$ (10.10)

where Q is a factor that, to an order of magnitude, characterizes the type of instrument.

Consider a grating operating in the pth order:

$$2\pi d \sin \theta = p\lambda.$$

Then

$$2\pi d \cos \theta . \delta\theta = p\delta\lambda = p\lambda/\mathscr{R},$$

so that

$$\delta\theta = \frac{1}{\mathscr{R}} \tan \theta.$$

Let the length of the slit be β. The solid angle corresponding to the element of wavelength $2\delta\lambda$ is then

$$2\beta \, \delta\theta.$$

Hence

$$\Omega/\Sigma = 2\beta \, \delta\theta = \frac{2\beta \tan \theta}{\mathscr{R}}$$

and

$$Q = 2\beta \tan \theta,$$ (10.11)

which is equal to β to within a factor of order unity. A similar result applies to any dispersive instrument in which the elements of the spectrum are isolated by a narrow slit.

If a Fabry–Perot or Michelson interferometer is used photoelectrically with an isolating aperture of angular radius α, the maximum possible value of α is such that the range of phase over α is π, that is

$$\tfrac{1}{2}k_0 l \alpha_{\max}^2 = \pi \qquad \text{or} \qquad \alpha_{\max}^2 = 2\pi/k_0 l.$$

Now

$$\Omega/\Sigma = \alpha^2 \text{ and } \mathscr{R} = k_0 l, \text{ and therefore } Q_{\max} = 2\pi. \qquad (10.12)$$

This important result is one of the main reasons for the superiority of the Michelson and Fabry–Perot interferometers over almost all other spectroscopic instruments. It corresponds to the fact that they have an axis of symmetry, whereas all other instruments are at the most symmetrical about a plane. It must be emphasized that not all interferometers have axial symmetry, for example, multiple-beam Fizeau systems, the Fabry–Perot used off-axis, and the Lummer–Gehrcke plate all have slits to isolate the spectral elements and all have lower transmissivities.

The ratio $2\pi/\beta$ between the transmissivities of instruments with axial symmetries and those with planar symmetries can be very large, for β rarely exceeds $5 \cdot 10^{-3}$, fairly stringent limits being set by aberrations of imaging systems. The ratio is therefore usually 10^3 at least.

The advantage is not always as great as indicated here. In the first place, an interferometer has usually to be used in series with a prism or grating spectrometer (although of much lower resolving power) to isolate a convenient range of spectrum. Secondly, by using a grating (echelle) at a very high angle of deviation, the resolution for a given slit width is increased (Shafer, McGill, and Droppleman 1964).

Figures of merit, $\mathscr{M}$, may now be defined in the extreme cases in which photon noise dominates or receiver noise dominates. In the first,

$$\mathscr{M}_p = \mathscr{R}M/TB, \qquad (10.13)$$

while in the second

$$\mathscr{M}_r = \mathscr{R}M/TB^2. \qquad (10.13a)$$

In general, some intermediate definition may be appropriate.

B is the brightness at the receiver, that is to say

$$\tau B_s,$$

where B_s is the source brightness and τ is a factor that allows for absorption and scattering within the interferometer. The minimum source brightness to give a prescribed photometric accuracy is therefore inversely proportional to τ.

This time of observation has so far been discussed as though the spectrum is scanned sequentially so that if t is the time for the observation of one spectral element, the time T to scan over the range of the instrument is Mt. Some instruments use a number of detectors so that a number of elements may be observed simultaneously (multi-slit instruments); if q elements are observed simultaneously,

$$T = Mt/q.$$

In photographic observation, all elements are observed at the same time, q is the same as M, and T is equal to t.

In simultaneous observations with dispersive instruments, each spectral element is observed separately, although perhaps at the same time as another. It is different for the Fourier transform spectrometer. The mean signal observed is equal to the sum of the signals from the total range of the instrument; if S_D is the signal from a dispersive instrument and S_T that from a Fourier transform instrument of the same range M,

$$S_T \simeq M S_D.$$

If receiver noise dominates, as is usual in infra-red spectroscopy, the signal-to-noise ratio for a Fourier transform instrument is M times greater than for a dispersive instrument. If, however, photon noise dominates, as is usually the case in the visible and certainly so in the ultra-violet, the noise is proportional to $M_1^{\frac{1}{2}}$, where M_1 is the total range admitted, which may be greater than the range M to be studied. The time of observation, which is proportional to N^2, is thus proportional to M_1 and the ratio of the time of observation with a Fourier transform instrument to that with a dispersive instrument will be M_1/M, which is not less than 1. There is thus no signal-to-noise advantage in using a Fourier transform instrument if photon noise predominates. This is the situation in radio astronomy and, while Fourier transform methods of spectroscopy have been used in radio astronomy (Blum 1960), they have no signal-to-noise advantage over methods using sharp filters. That is not of course to say that there is no place for Fourier transform methods in these ranges of frequency, for there are many special problems which can be best treated by taking advantage of other features of Fourier transform spectroscopy, but it is certainly true that in these ranges Fourier transform methods are not suitable for general surveys of a spectrum, whereas there are ranges in the infra-red where they may still be preferred even for such surveys (Chapter 5).

The relative factors of merit of different classes of instrument may now be summarized as in Table 3, in which G is the reciprocal of the factor $\beta/2\pi$ that expresses the solid angle disadvantage of instruments without axial symmetry.

The foregoing is a very general account of the factors that affect the performances of different instruments, in which no account has been taken of specific features of the observations to be made. If attention is confined to a specific type of study, a more precise account can be given. Such an analysis has been made for wavelength measurements

TABLE 3

Figures of merit for spectrometers

	Photon noise limit	Detector noise limit
Grating, echelon, echelle	τ	τ^2
Fabry–Perot on axis	τG	$\tau^2 G$
Michelson	$\tau G M/M'$	$\tau^2 M G$

$G = 2\pi/\beta$; τ = transmission factor (see Jacquinot 1958).

(Hanes 1959, 1963). The accuracy of wavelength measurements is determined by the precision of setting on some feature of the response of a spectrometer. In elementary systems, it may be a setting on the peak of the response, in more elaborate ones it may be to the maxima of the derivative of the response, or to a feature of the integral of the response, such as the median. The position of a response curve can be defined in a number of ways depending on the instrumental function of the spectrometer, the profile of the spectrum line, and the characteristics of the noise. In this discussion a particular procedure of observation is considered, but it is not difficult to extend the analysis to any other procedure, providing only that it is well defined.

The precision $\mathscr{P}$ of a measurement of wave number may be defined to be

$$k/\kappa,$$

where κ is the r.m.s. fluctuation in the derived wave number arising from the noise on the signal when a specific procedure of setting on the response is adopted; the definition of precision is thus dependent on the setting procedure. In highly developed methods of setting, $\mathscr{P}$ may be as much as 1000 times $\mathscr{R}$.

Consider a procedure in which part of the response is selected by an aperture in front of the detector and the aperture is switched between two positions (1 and 2) separated by about the width of the response curve. The position of the response curve may then be defined to be the mean of the two positions of the aperture when the fluxes through them are equal. The procedure, which lends itself well to synchronous detection, can give very favourable signal-to-noise ratios (Fig. 10.1).

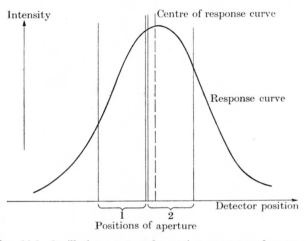

FIG. 10.1. Oscillating aperture for setting on centre of response.

Let v be the width of the response (it is the operational sum of the slit width s and line width w) and let the width of each aperture be $w/2$. Also let the two positions of the apertures just touch. This specification is adopted for simplicity, but small departures from it will not alter numerical values very greatly. Let the total number of photons emerging from the spectrometer in time t within the particular spectrum line be N, so that the number passing through each position of the aperture will be $N/2$. (That is really the specification of the aperture, which is supposed to be such that the condition is fulfilled.) The fluctuation in the number of photons passing either aperture is $(N/2)^{\frac{1}{2}}$ and in the difference between the two numbers, it is $N/2$.

The number of photons per unit wave number emerging from the spectrometer in time t is $2N/v$, if v is, as usual, the width at half intensity. Thus

$$\delta N = 2\frac{N}{v} \cdot \delta k, \tag{10.14}$$

and if δN has a fluctuation $N^{\frac{1}{2}}$ the corresponding fluctuation in k is

$$v/2N^{\frac{1}{2}}$$

and the precision is

$$2N^{\frac{1}{2}}k/v.$$

Now N and v are not independent. Let B_s be the brightness of the source so that the number of photons incident on the spectrometer is

$$2\pi B_s/hck.$$

If the quantity $QS\tau/\mathcal{R}$ is called the *luminosity* $\mathcal{L}$ (for Q, see eqn (10.10)), the number N of photons emerging in time t from the spectrometer within the width v at half intensity will be

$$\frac{2\pi B_s}{hck}\frac{\mathcal{L}}{2}t,$$

and therefore

$$\mathcal{P} = \left[\frac{2Q\tau}{hc}StB_s\frac{s}{v^2}\right]^{\frac{1}{2}}$$

in the ideal case where the quantum efficiency of the detector is 1. If the quantum efficiency (including the factor τ) is θ, less than 1,

$$\mathcal{P} = \left[\frac{2Q}{hc}St\theta B_s\frac{s}{v^2}\right]^{\frac{1}{2}}. \tag{10.15}$$

The width v is that of the overall response of the spectrometer to the particular line of the spectrum being measured, the response being the convolution of the instrumental function with a half width s (slit width) and the line profile with a half width w (line width). Symbolically,

$$v = s\oplus w.$$

Thus

$$\mathcal{P} = \left[\frac{2Q}{hc}St\theta B_s\frac{s}{(s\oplus w)^2}\right]^{\frac{1}{2}}. \tag{10.16}$$

The slit width of a prism spectrometer is much greater than the width of any line of which the wavelength would be measured very accurately. Thus

$$s = w\oplus s$$

and it is found that, for a prism with a base of about 0·2 m square, $\mathcal{P}$, which is proportional to $s^{-\frac{1}{2}}$, will be about 4×10^8, taking the quantum efficiency to be 5 per cent, a value that is less than that of many photocathodes but that allows for other losses in the instrument, that is, it includes the transmission factor τ.

In estimating $\mathscr{P}$, B_s has been taken to be 3×10^{-1} Wm^{-2} s^{-1}, which is that of the standard line of krypton-86 at 605·8 nm, the time of observation t has been taken to be 1 s and the angular height of the slit has been taken to be 3×10^{-2} rad. The same values are adopted for a grating instrument having a grating 0·2 m square. If the angle of diffraction is 30°, $\mathscr{R}$ will not be greater than 10^6 and for a line width w about 10^{-6}, $s \oplus w$ will be approximately s. $\mathscr{P}$ is then estimated to be 4×10^9.

With the limited resolving power of the prism and grating, the width v is fixed by the instrumental width s and the ratio $s/(s \oplus w)^2$ is $1/s$. With a Fabry–Perot interferometer the path difference can be chosen to give the value of s that makes $s/(s \oplus w)^2$ a maximum; this occurs when s is about equal to w and the maximum value is $1/2w$, that is it is determined by the properties of the line and not by those of the instrument. There is another consequence: at such long path differences that the width v is determined by the line width w and not by the finesse of the plates, it is possible to increase the light transmitted by the instrument by reducing the reflectivity of the plates, and it has been shown that the highest precision in wavelength measurements is obtained with reflectivities of no more than 60–70 per cent, appreciably less than the greatest attainable (Smith 1960).

The precision of a Fabry–Perot interferometer, in the condition where it is limited by the line width, is

$$\mathscr{P} = 4\cdot1 \times 10^{12}\left[St\theta \, \frac{B_s}{w} \right]^{\frac{1}{2}}.$$

Considering again the krypton-86 standard line, for which the half-width in wave numbers is 1·4 m^{-1}, and taking S to be the area of plates 4 cm in diameter, $\mathscr{P}$ is about $1\cdot5 \times 10^{10}$, a value much greater than that for a prism or grating of larger area S.

While the instrumental width of a Fabry–Perot interferometer can readily be made less than that of the line width of a conventional gas discharge source, the line width of a gas laser is much less than that of any practical interferometer, so that $s/(s \oplus w)^2$ is again $1/s$. Suppose, first, that the separation of the plates of the interferometer is small enough that the angular radius of the isolating aperature may be allowed to be greater than the semi-angular spread of the laser beam; if the latter is ψ and the plate separation is l, the condition is

$$kl < \psi^2/\pi.$$

In that case, the noise (which is no longer $N^{\frac{1}{2}}$, but some function $f(N)$, for the correlated laser light) and the number of photons are both independent of the path difference, and the precision is proportional to $s^{-\frac{1}{2}}$, that is to $l^{\frac{1}{2}}$: the greater the separation of the plates, the greater the precision of measurements.

If, on the other hand, the path length is so great that

$$kl > \psi^2/\pi,$$

the condition that the phase shift across the semi-aperture α must be less than π restricts α to be less than ψ, the number N is then proportional to α^2, that is to $1/l$, and since $f(N)$ behaves roughly like $N^{\frac{1}{2}}$, the precision will be independent of path difference. Thus the maximum useful path difference for wavelength measurements on lasers is about

$$\psi^2/k\pi.$$

The Michelson interferometer always gives sinusoidal fringes with an isolated line, but the visibility of the fringes depends on the line width and the path difference, and the precision of a measurement of wavelength is limited by the maximum path difference at which fringes can be observed in the presence of noise. Let the aperture have a width equivalent to half a fringe. If the path difference is l, the luminosity $\mathscr{L}$ is

$$\pi^2 S/kl.$$

If the fringe visibility is V, the relative intensities in the two positions of the scanning aperture are as $(1+V)/(1-V)$ and

$$\delta N = 4\pi N l V \, \mathrm{d}k,$$

so that

$$\mathscr{P} = 8\pi N^{\frac{1}{2}} kl V$$

$$= \left[\frac{8\pi}{hc} St\theta B_s l V^2\right]^{\frac{1}{2}}.$$

If the profile is dominated by Doppler broadening,

$$V = \exp[-\pi^2 l^2 w^2/\ln 2],$$

and the maximum value of $I V^2$ is $0\cdot32/w$ and occurs when $l = 0\cdot54/w$. V is then $0\cdot78$.

The precision of wavelength measurements with the Michelson is thus given by the same formula as for the Fabry–Perot:

$$\mathscr{P} = 4\cdot5 \times 10^{12}[St\theta B_s/w]^{\frac{1}{2}},$$

and for the krypton-86 standard line, the optimum value of path difference is 19 cm.

For wavelength measurements, as for other purposes, it must be emphasized that the choice of instrument does not depend solely on the precision attainable in making settings but that, in particular, it is very important to consider possible systematic errors. Systematic errors of wavelength measurements are in general less and are more readily determined for the Fabry–Perot and Michelson interferometers than for other spectrometers.

11

ANGULAR INTERFEROMETERS

THE interferometers so far discussed effect a transformation from the frequency into the time domain; those considered in this chapter effect a transformation from one spatial domain into a reciprocal spatial domain. The two types of transformation cannot strictly be separated, for a source distribution is a function both of spatial variables and of frequency, and any interferometer involves both transformations. In most practical cases the two may be separated to first order although if high accuracy is required, the effects of the subsidiary transformation upon the overall coherence of the interference phenomenon must be calculated. Thus the viewing aperture of a Michelson interferometer must be kept small and the spectrum of radiation falling on an angular interferometer must be restricted if the fringes are to be sharp.

Radio interferometers present some of the simplest and also some of the most instructive examples of angular interferometers (a general account has been given by Bracewell, 1958). Consider the system shown in Fig. 11.1. P is a point in a source, R_1 and R_2 are receivers, $R_1R_2 = 2d$, and R is the mid-point of R_1R_2. PR makes an angle θ with the plane normal to R_1R_2; dS is an element of the area of the source projected on to a plane normal to PR. A detector is placed at D and is connected to the receivers through equal transmission lines so that the phase lags in DR_1 and DR_2 are equal. Omitting the constant phase, the complex amplitude at D due to the element dS is

$$A \, dS\{\exp(-ikPR_1)+\exp(-ikPR_2)\},$$

a factor proportional to PR^{-2} having also been suppressed.

The amplitude is thus

$$A \, dS \, \exp(-ikPR_2)[1+\exp\{-ik(PR_1-PR_2)\}]. \tag{11.1}$$

Now
$$PR_1^2 = PR^2+d^2+2d.PR \sin \theta,$$
$$PR_2^2 = PR^2+d^2-2d.PR \sin \theta,$$

and so
$$PR_1^2-PR_2^2 = 4dPR \sin \theta,$$
$$PR_1-PR_2 \simeq 2d \sin \theta,$$

since
$$PR_1 \simeq PR_2 \simeq PR.$$

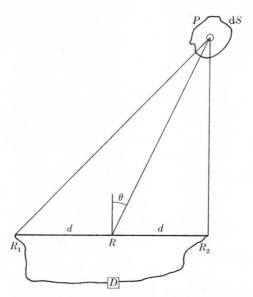

FIG. 11.1. Elementary radio interferometer.

The amplitude is thus

$$A \, \mathrm{d}Se^{-ikPR}[1 + e^{-2ikd \sin \theta}]$$

and the intensity is proportional to

$$2[1 + \cos(2kd \sin \theta)]. \tag{11.2}$$

The mutual coherence function corresponding to the area dS is

$$\mathrm{d}\gamma = \mathrm{d}Se^{-2ikd \sin \theta}, \tag{11.3}$$

and if the source lies wholly within the aerial beam width (it is not resolved) the mutual coherence function integrated over the whole projected area of the source and over the receiver bandwidth B is

$$\gamma = \frac{1}{I} \int_B \mathrm{d}k \int_S I_k(\theta, \phi) e^{-2ikd \sin \theta} \, \mathrm{d}\theta \, \mathrm{d}\phi. \tag{11.3a}$$

The angular position of the element of the projected area of the source is defined by the two angles θ and ϕ; θ is in the plane containing the receivers while ϕ lies in the plane normal to the line of the receivers. The phase factor is independent of ϕ and so the integration with respect to ϕ may be performed. If $I_k(\theta)$ is the intensity of the source integrated along a strip perpendicular to the projection of R_1R_2 on the source and

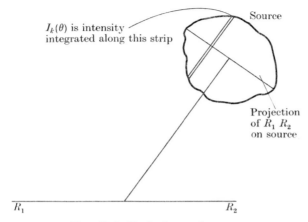

$I_k(\theta)$ is intensity integrated along this strip

Source

Projection of $R_1 R_2$ on source

R_1

R_2

FIG. 11.2. Equivalent strip source.

divided by the total intensity I (Fig. 11.2), the mutual coherence function becomes

$$\gamma = \int_B dk \int_{-\frac{1}{2}\pi}^{+\frac{1}{2}\pi} d\theta I_k(\theta) e^{-2ikd \sin \theta}. \tag{11.4}$$

If the angular spread of the source is small enough for it to be meaningful to express the intensity as a function of the deviation from some central direction (θ_0, ϕ_0) the source is said to be *compact*, an idea corresponding to the quasi-monochromatic source in the frequency description. Then, just as it is meaningful to speak of the frequency of a quasi-monochromatic source, it is meaningful to speak of the position of a compact source; the mutual coherence function may be written as

$$\gamma = e^{-2ikd \sin \theta_0} \int_B dk \int_{-\frac{1}{2}\pi}^{+\frac{1}{2}\pi} d\theta' I_k(\theta') \exp\{2ikd(\sin \theta - \sin \theta_0)\};$$

since $\theta' = \theta - \theta_0$ is small

$$\sin \theta - \sin \theta_0 \approx \theta' \cos \theta_0$$

and

$$\gamma = e^{-2 kd \sin \theta_0} \int_B dk \int_{-\frac{1}{2}\pi}^{+\frac{1}{2}\pi} d\theta' I_k(\theta') e^{-2ikd \cos \theta_0 \cdot \theta'} \tag{11.4a}$$

The interferometer response is accordingly a cosinusoidal function of path difference d, of which the periodicity gives the direction of the source θ_0 and the complex amplitude gives the angular distribution of the source.

It was supposed that the source was not resolved by the receivers so that the integrations with respect to angle were taken over the whole extent of the source. It is possible in radio astronomy for the aerial beam-width to be narrow enough to resolve the source, in which case the integration should extend over the polar diagram of the aerial. The interferometer will then not give much greater information than the aerials alone, just as there is not much point in examining with a Michelson interferometer the spectrum of a source isolated by a monochromator with a range less than the width of the spectrum. In those circumstances, the dominant factor in the Fourier transform would be the transmission function of the monochromator while in the radio astronomical case the dominant factor would be the angular response of the receiver.

Suppose that the distances from the receivers to the detector are not equal so that the total path difference is

$$PR_1 - PR_2 + R_1D - R_2D = 2d\sin\theta + \Delta;$$

the fringes from a point source at a single frequency then vary as

$$2[1 + \cos(2kd\sin\theta + k\Delta)]. \tag{11.5}$$

The fringes may be scanned either by letting θ vary with the rotation of the earth or by changing Δ. If the interferometer is to be used to find θ_0, the position of a source, then Δ must be well known. For a given intensity in the fringe pattern, variations of θ and Δ are related by

$$\delta\Delta = -2d\cos\theta\,\delta\theta, \tag{11.6}$$

an equation which specifies the allowable differences in the path lengths from receivers to detector for a specified uncertainty in angular position.

Thus if $\delta\theta$ is to be less than $10''$, or $5 \cdot 10^{-5}$ rad, for sources near the zenith ($\theta = 0$) $\delta\Delta$ must be less than $10^{-4}d$.

Suppose for instance that d is 1000λ and that λ is 3 m. $\delta\Delta$ must not exceed $0 \cdot 3$ m. The limits are much more stringent for sources away from the zenith. It may be noticed that the fringes occur at an angular spacing of $\lambda/2d\cos\theta$, that is $1 \cdot 5 \times 10^{-3}$ rad or $5'$ in this example.

The Michelson stellar interferometer (Michelson 1890, 1920, Anderson 1920, Michelson and Pease 1921, Pease 1931) is exactly analogous to the radio interferometer (Fig. 11.3). The two mirrors M_1 and M_2 form

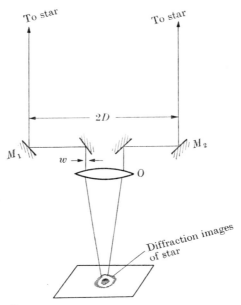

FIG. 11.3. Michelson stellar interferometer.

coincident images of the star S at the focus of the objective O. Each image is a diffraction image corresponding to the width of the entrance slit w, which in practice is much less than the aperture of the objective. The star is not resolved and the intensity at any point in the diffraction image is the integral over the whole star, just as in the radio interferometer with a source that is not resolved the detector output is the integral over the whole source. The fringes are observed differently, however. In the radio interferometer they are scanned in the time domain by letting θ or Δ vary with time, but in the optical interferometer as devised by Michelson they are spread out in space because the path difference varies over the diffraction image. Since the path difference of the beams from the two mirrors is, by the fundamental property of a lens, zero from the face of the lens to the focal plane, the path difference from the star to a point in the focal plane is $2D \sin \theta$, where $2D$ is the separation of the entrance slits. Different values of θ correspond to different coordinates in the focal plane (in this case $\theta = 0$ defines the optical axis of the objective) and so the diffraction image is crossed by fringes of which the visibility as a function of D gives the Fourier transform of $I_k(\theta)$. The spacing of the fringes, $\delta\theta$, is given by

$$2D \cos \theta \; \delta\theta = 2\{(n+1) - n\}\pi\lambda, \tag{11.7}$$

that is
$$\delta\theta \; = \; \pi\lambda/D \cos\theta.$$

It should be noted that the radio and optical interferometers are essentially similar in that the system is sensitive to sources in an area of the sky appreciably larger than a typical source and that the sensitive area is determined by the diffraction properties of the interferometer, by the width of the entrance slits in the optical interferometer and by the beam pattern of the receivers in the radio interferometer. Within this diffraction-limited area, the angular filter represented by the fringes is determined by the geometrical arrangement of the interferometer. A minor difference is that the optical interferometer is kept pointing at the star by an equatorial mounting and the fringe pattern is not scanned by letting the source drift in front of the interferometer.

The main disadvantage of the interferometer as devised by Michelson is that the fringe spacing is inversely proportional to the spacing $2D$, so that the fringes become very difficult to observe at large path differences. For example, if $2D = 20$ m, the fringes are spaced at 5×10^{-3} arc seconds or $0 \cdot 25$ μm at a focal length of 10 m. Further, the arrangement of the fringes is not very convenient for photoelectric observation.

H. A. Gebbie and R. Q. Twiss have accordingly devised a version of the Michelson interferometer in which the fringes are observed at one particular value of θ, that is, at one point in the field of view; they may then be observed photoelectrically as indicated in Fig. 11.4. As

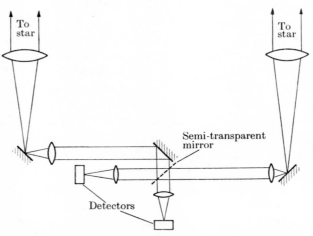

FIG. 11.4. Photoelectric stellar interferometer (Gebbie and Twiss.)

mentioned earlier, the bandwidth must be restricted, and the fringes are observed through a spectrometer with a pass band of about 0·1 nm. The beams from the two telescopes fall upon a semi-reflecting plate which combines the beams in such a way that the intensity of one of the emergent beams is

$$I(1 + V \cos \Psi'),$$

while that of the other is

$$I(1 - V \cos \Psi') \quad \text{(see Chapter 4)}.$$

I is the intensity of the light, V is the visibility of the fringes, and Ψ' is $2kD \sin \theta$.

Photomultipliers measure the intensities of the separate emergent beams; the sum of the photomultiplier outputs is proportional to I and the difference to $IV \cos \Psi'$. Thus $V \cos \Psi'$ may be found, in practice as the ratio of counts of photons in the different channels.

Scintillation, and in particular different path lengths in the atmosphere outside the separate telescopes, gives rise to large fluctuations in Ψ' and Gebbie and Twiss have provided elaborate means for measuring and eliminating scintillation fluctuations electronically. Most of the variations in refractive index occur within 10 m of the ground and so the telescopes are enclosed in sealed tubes extending that distance beyond the objective lenses.

The measurement of diameters of stars has been reviewed by Brown (1968).

Fringe geometry of radio interferometers

The fringe maxima formed with a two-beam interferometer lie in directions that make an angle θ with the line joining the receivers (the axis of the interferometer), where

$$2kd \sin \theta = n\pi, \tag{11.8}$$

n being an integer.

As the Earth rotates, the axis of the interferometer rotates about the polar axis of the Earth; if the axis lies in the east–west direction, it will be perpendicular to the polar axis. The general position is shown in Fig. 11.5. N is the North Pole and P is the horizontal plane at the interferometer. l is the latitude of the site. The interferometer axis II' makes an angle α with the east–west direction.

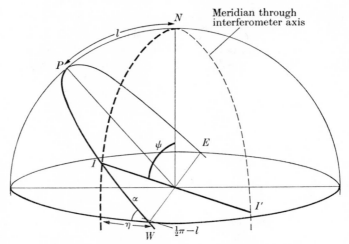

Fig. 11.5. Interferometer in relation to celestial sphere.

ψ, the angle between the polar axis and the interferometer axis, is given by

$$\cos \psi = \sin \alpha \cos l. \tag{11.9}$$

The longitude of the projection of the axis on the celestial sphere differs from that of the east–west direction by the angle η, given by

$$\sin \eta = \sin \alpha \sin l. \tag{11.10}$$

Sources move in the sky around the polar axis in small circles of angular radius equal to the declination δ.

The relation between the path of a source S and the interferometer fringes is shown in Fig. 11.6: $I_1 I_2$ is the interferometer axis and the

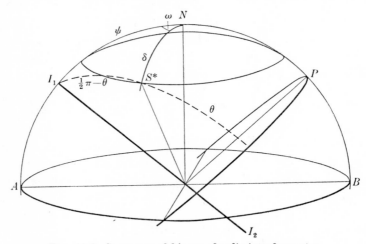

Fig. 11.6. Geometry of fringes of radio interferometer.

great circle I_1NI_2 meets the equator in AB. The interferometer equator, the plane normal to I_1I_2, meets ANB in P.

S^* is the position of the source in a fringe maximum. I_1S^* equals $(\frac{1}{2}\pi-\theta)$ while NS^* equals δ and NI_1 is ψ. If ω is the angle ANS^*,

$$\cos \omega = \frac{\sin \theta}{\sin \delta \sin \psi} - \cot \delta \cot \psi. \tag{11.11}$$

Eqn (11.11) gives the difference between the hour angle of the source and the hour angle of I; the latter is derived from the angle η. Hence

$$-\sin \omega \,.\, \delta\omega = \frac{\delta(\sin \theta)}{\sin \delta \sin \psi}.$$

Let $\delta(\sin \theta)$ be the difference between successive fringes, that is

$$\delta(\sin\theta) = \pi/2kd;$$

hence

$$\delta\omega = \frac{-\pi}{2kd} \frac{1}{\sin \omega \sin \delta \sin \psi}. \tag{11.12}$$

The time interval between fringe maxima is given by

$$\delta t = -\frac{\pi}{2kd\varpi} \frac{1}{\sin \omega \sin \delta \sin \psi}, \tag{11.13}$$

where ϖ is the angular spin velocity of the Earth.

In this formula, ψ is a property of the interferometer alone, δ of the source alone, while ω is a property of both. To find the co-ordinates of a source, ω must first be determined by finding the time at which the source passes through a particular fringe of the interferometer. The fringe pattern lies within the envelope of the aerial polar diagram and it is usually easy to identify the most intense fringe at the centre of the polar diagram. The hour-angle measurements must in general be calibrated by observations of sources of known hour angle. Then with ω and ψ known, δ may be calculated from δt.

The relation of source positions to the fringe geometry may be seen in Fig. 11.7, drawn for a nearly east–west interferometer (see Bracewell 1962). The fringe maxima lie on small circles about II', the intersection of the interferometer axis on the celestial sphere, while the source rotates in a small circle about the north pole N. A is the projection of the envelope of the aerial polar diagram on the celestial sphere. The small circles of the source and fringes are fixed on the celestial sphere but the envelope A may be moved over the sky by steering the aerials until the desired source lies within A.

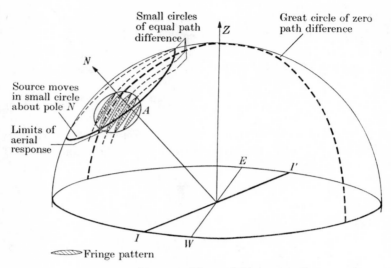

FIG. 11.7. Source position and fringe geometry.

The first applications of the two-beam interferometer were in radar and in the sea interferometer of McCready, Pawsey, and Payne-Scott (1947), in each of which the surface of the sea was used as a horizontal mirror to reflect a second ray into a single aerial placed above the sea in an arrangement exactly similar to Lloyd's single-mirror optical inter-ferometer (Fig. 11.8). The central fringe is not bright but dark on account of the phase shift of π on reflection at the surface of the sea, but refraction in the troposphere further alters the position of the central fringe. Because the axis of the interferometer is vertical, the

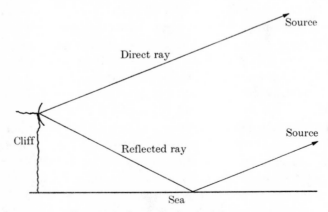

FIG. 11.8. Sea reflection interferometer.

angle ψ in Fig. 11.5 is equal to the latitude of the site and the system is most effective in low latitudes—at the poles the interferometer axis would be parallel to the polar axis, the fringes would lie on small circles concentric with the paths of sources in the sky, and so sources would not cross the fringe pattern as the Earth rotated.

There are advantages in making one aerial larger than the other. The envelope of the fringe pattern will then have a width corresponding to the diffraction pattern of the large, rather than the small aerial, while the small aerial, being more portable, can be taken to greater

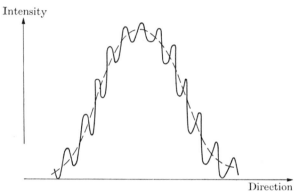

Fig. 11.9. Interference pattern between two beams with large and small aerial.

separations than could a second large aerial. The fringe modulation is proportional to the ratio of the area of the small aerial to that of the large one (the ratio ρ of Chapter 3), (Fig. 11.9). The high directivity of the large aerial enables the central fringe to be more readily identified than would be possible with two smaller aerials.

The fringe maxima of a two-beam interferometer occur whenever the phase angle $k(2d \sin \theta + \Delta)$ is a multiple of 2π, and in the systems so far considered the angle varies on account of the rotation of the Earth. That is in some ways inconvenient because the rate at which fringes are traversed is low and changes with the position of the source; more effective methods of detection are possible if the fringes are traversed rapidly at a known rate, for then the signals may be passed through a filter tuned sharply to the corresponding frequency and the signal-to-noise ratio may be improved. Payne-Scott and Little (1950, 1951) accordingly developed an interferometer in which the path difference Δ is varied rapidly at a steady rate by mechanically or electrically changing the length of the cable between one of the receivers and the

14

detector. Suppose that $\Delta = -\Omega t$. The mutual coherence function is then

$$\gamma = \int\int I_k(\theta)\exp\{-ik(2d \sin \theta - \Omega t)\} \, dk \, d\theta$$

$$= \exp\{-ik(2d \sin \theta_0 - \Omega t)\} \int\int I_k(\theta')\exp\{-2ikd \cos \theta_0 . \theta'\} \, dk \, d\theta'.$$

$$1(11.4)$$

Thus γ varies with speed $k\Omega$, the phase of the variation giving θ_0 while the amplitude of the variation gives the Fourier transform of $I_k(\theta')$.

The response of an interferometer to a source giving fringes of visibility V when the diffraction pattern of the aerials is represented by $R(\theta)$, is

$$R(\theta)\{1 + V \cos(2kd \sin \theta + \Delta)\}, \tag{11.15}$$

a function of which the mean value over a few fringes is $R(\theta)$. In searching for faint sources, changes in the mean value due to instabilities in the electrical circuits or from other causes can obscure the desired signals. If a phase shift of π is introduced into one of the arms of the interferometer, the resultant signal is

$$R(\theta)\{1 - V \cos(2kd \sin \theta + \Delta)\}, \tag{11.15a}$$

and if the additional phase is switched between 0 and π it will be possible to detect and record the difference between the two fringe signals, namely

$$2R(\theta)V \cos(2kd \sin \theta + \Delta), \tag{11.16}$$

for it is the amplitude of the square-wave signal at the switching frequency (Ryle 1952). Again, with a system tuned sharply to the switching frequency, the signal-to-noise ratio is improved. The same idea was used by Fellgett (1958) in an infra-red stellar interferometer, but there, by proper choice of the beam divider properties, the two signals may be observed simultaneously on two photo-detectors. The system used by Gebbie and Twiss in their version of the Michelson stellar interferometer (see p. 194) is identical.

The principle of the two-aerial interferometer has recently been extended in a most powerful manner. In the original form the signals from two aerials V_1 and V_2 are correlated in a receiver the output of which is $V_1^* V_2$ or some related quantity. It is not, however, necessary to perform the correlation that way, and the same result would be obtained if the signals V_1 and V_2 were recorded and the correlation performed on a computer. V_1 and V_2 are, of course, functions of time and must therefore be recorded in the same time scale if the correlation is to be calculated correctly. One procedure is to generate at each aerial reference signals having the same frequency, and to record on magnetic tape the (audio-frequency) differences between V_1 and V_2 and the reference signals. The two reference frequencies are derived from atomic frequency standards so that the ratio of the one to the other is well known. The phases must also be known and can be determined to a few microseconds by time-signal comparison techniques. Beyond that, however, the phase difference can be allowed to vary in calculating the correlation, and that difference adopted that gives the maximum correlation. If the aerials are looking at a very small source, a small quasar, for example, then the fringe visibility will be almost 1, the correlation or $|V_1^* V_2|$ will be quite high, and the best phase difference between the reference signals can be established to better than 1 μs. In fact, different systems of time signals can be compared better by this means than in any other way.

Having established the phase difference of the reference signals, the visibility of the fringes is found from the variation of $V_1^* V_2$ with the rotation of the Earth. Long-distance interferometers have been set up with aerials at pairs of sites separated by continental or intercontinental distances (see Broten, Locke, Legge, McLeish, Richards, Chisholm, Gush, Yen, and Galt 1967; Gubbay and Robertson 1967; Burke, Moran, Barrett, Rydbeck, Hansson, Rogers, Ball, and Cudaback 1968) and with them, angular sizes of quasars and galactic hydroxyl sources have been estimated. It has been shown that some sources have diameters less than $0''\cdot0006$ (for a general review, see Cohen, Jauncey, Kellerman, and Clark 1968).

Two-dimensional systems

While the angular interferometer in one dimension is the simplest and corresponds exactly to the spectroscopic interferometer, a direction is in general determined by two angles and there is a corresponding two-dimensional Fourier transform.

Let the position of an element R of an array of receivers in the local horizontal plane be given by the Cartesian coordinates x, y, and let the direction of a source, in the sky be given by the direction cosines, ξ, η, ζ, relative to the same axes in the local horizontal plane together with the local vertical. Then the cosine of the angle ψ between the direction of the source and the direction of the element of the aerial from the origin of coordinates is

$$\cos \psi = (\xi x + \eta y)(x^2 + y^2)^{-\frac{1}{2}}. \qquad \text{(Fig. 11.10)} \qquad (11.17)$$

Suppose that all elements are connected to a detector at the centre O of the array by cables of the same length so that the path difference between a signal received at the centre element and one received from the element at (x, y) is the projection of the line OR upon the direction of the source, that is

$$OR \cos \psi,$$

or

$$\xi x + \eta y.$$

If the surface brightness of the source is $I(\xi, \eta)$, its two dimensional Fourier transform is

$$\mathscr{I}(x, h) = \iint I(\xi, \eta) e^{-ik(\xi x + \eta y)} \, d\xi \, d\eta. \qquad (11.18)$$

If the source is compact in the neighbourhood of a point with direction cosines (ξ_0, η_0, ζ_0), the Fourier transform may, in the same way as for one-dimensional transforms, be written as

$$\mathscr{I}(x, y) = e^{-ik(\xi_0 x + \eta_0 y)} \iint I(\xi', \eta') e^{-ik(\xi' x + y' y)} \, d\xi' \, d\eta', \qquad (11.19)$$

where $\xi' = \xi - \xi_0, \ldots$.

One aerial array for determining two-dimensional Fourier transforms is the Mills Cross (Mills and Little 1953), consisting of two long aerial arrays at right angles, each array comprising a large number of receivers. Let d be the distance between receivers. Consider a point source in the

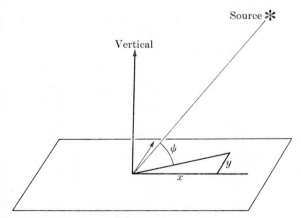

FIG. 11.10. Geometry of two-dimensional Fourier transform.

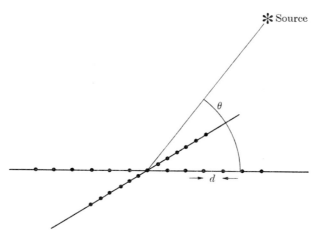

FIG. 11.11. Mills Cross.

vertical plane passing through one array and in a direction making an angle θ with the vertical (Fig. 11.11). The phase difference ψ between signals received at one receiver and the next is

$$kd \sin \theta,$$

and, just as for a diffraction grating, the response of an array of N elements is

$$\mathscr{A}(\theta, \phi) \cdot \frac{\sin^2 \frac{1}{2}(N+1)\psi}{\sin^2 \frac{1}{2}\psi},$$

where $\mathscr{A}(\theta, \phi)$ is the angular response of a single receiver.

Now let two arrays be set up at right angles along the directions of the coordinate axes. Let the phase differences between successive elements be ψ_1 in the one array and ψ_2 in the other. Then

$$\psi_1 = kd_1\xi, \qquad \psi_2 = kd_2\eta,$$

for a point source with direction cosines (ξ, η, ζ).

If V_1 and V_2 are the outputs of the two arrays for a source $I(\xi, \eta)$,

$$
\begin{aligned}
V_1(\xi, \eta) &= \iint I(\xi, \eta) \frac{\sin^2 \frac{1}{2}(N+1)\psi_1}{\sin^2 \frac{1}{2}\psi_1}\, d\xi\, d\eta, \\
V_2(\xi, \eta) &= \iint I(\xi, \eta) \frac{\sin^2 \frac{1}{2}(N+1)\psi_2}{\sin^2 \frac{1}{2}\psi_2}\, d\xi\, d\eta;
\end{aligned}
\tag{11.20}
$$

the factor $\mathscr{A}$ has been omitted since it will usually be constant over the source.

In the Mills Cross, the outputs V_1 and V_2 are alternately added and subtracted by the insertion or removal of a suitable length of cable between the detector and one or other of the arrays. When added, the power from the combined arrays is

$$(V_1^* + V_2^*)(V_1 + V_2) \ldots (= A) \tag{11.21}$$

and when subtracted the power is

$$(V_1^* - V_2^*)(V_1 - {}_2V) \ldots (= S). \tag{11.21a}$$

The difference signal $(A - S)$, at the switching frequency, is

$$2(V_1^* V_2 + V_2^* V_1), \tag{11.22}$$

so that the response to a point source is proportional to

$$\frac{\sin^2 \tfrac{1}{2}(N+1)\psi_1}{\sin^2 \tfrac{1}{2}\psi_1} \cdot \frac{\sin^2 \tfrac{1}{2}(N+1)\psi_2}{\sin^2 \tfrac{1}{2}\psi_2}. \tag{11.23}$$

Now the diffraction pattern of a complete square array of side $D = Nd$ would be

$$\frac{\sin^2 \tfrac{1}{2}N\psi_1}{\tfrac{1}{4} \cdot N^2 \psi_1^2} \cdot \frac{\sin^2 \tfrac{1}{2}N\psi_2}{\tfrac{1}{4}N^2 \psi_2^2}. \tag{11.24}$$

The ratio of the output of the Mills Cross to the diffraction pattern of the rectangular array is thus equal to

$$\frac{\psi_1^2}{4 \sin^2 \tfrac{1}{2}\psi_1} \cdot \frac{\psi_2^2}{4 \sin^2 \tfrac{1}{2}\psi_2}, \tag{11.25}$$

multiplied by a factor depending on the areas of the arrays, and it will be seen that the resolution of the two patterns is effectively the same but that the side lobes of the cross are larger than for the complete rectangle and that the sensitivity of the cross is less in the ratio of the areas of the arrays. The latter disadvantage may be overcome by making more observations, but the side-lobe disadvantage can only be alleviated by making observations at more positions of the aerials, for the restriction of the path differences between the aerials to those on the two perpendicular arrays means that certain of the Fourier components of the response of the complete rectangle are absent from that of the cross.

Aperture synthesis

Ryle and his collaborators (Ryle and Hewish 1960, Ryle and Neville 1962) have shown how the response of a complete receiver may be built up from a succession of interferometric observations, so enabling results that would otherwise only be obtained with very large aerials to be matched with much less expensive equipment.

The fundamental property of a parabolic reflector is that radiation crossing the plane of the aperture is reflected to the focus with a phase shift that is independent of the position at which a ray crosses the plane of the aperture. If the direction cosines of a source are ξ, η, ζ then the phase of a ray crossing the aperture at a point with coordinates (x, y) will be $k(\xi x + \eta y)$ at the aperture and will be greater by a constant at the focus. The power received at the focus will therefore be

$$\int_A \mathrm{d}x\,\mathrm{d}y \int_S \mathrm{d}\xi\,\mathrm{d}\eta I(\xi,\,\eta)\exp\{-2ik(x\xi+y\eta)\}, \qquad (11.26)$$

where the integrations extend over the aperture A and the source S. Thus the power is

$$\int_A \mathscr{I}(x,\,y)\,\mathrm{d}x\,\mathrm{d}y, \qquad (11.27)$$

where

$$\mathscr{I}(x,\,y) = \int_S I(\xi,\,\eta)\exp\{-2ik(x\xi+y\eta)\}\,\mathrm{d}\xi\,\mathrm{d}\eta, \qquad (11.27\mathrm{a})$$

the two-dimensional Fourier transform of $I(x,\,y)$.

Now consider an array of discrete aerials, placed on a grid of unit dimensions x_1, y_1 and having N elements in the x-direction and M in the y-direction. The power received at a common detector can then, by proper adjustment of the lengths of the cables joining the aerials to the detector, be made equal to

$$\sum_n \sum_m \mathscr{I}(nx_1,\,my_2), \qquad (11.28)$$

a result that corresponds to that for a paraboloid. If, however, the terms of the sum could be obtained one by one and subsequently added, it would be possible to reconstruct the response of a paraboloid from the response of a pair of aerials at different spacings. A pair of aerials is needed because the phase of a signal from a single aerial is arbitrary, and, to be able to combine the signal with that from other aerials, some reference is necessary. In the paraboloid, the important quantity is the phase difference from the ray reflected from the centre of the paraboloid, and in the system of discrete aerials the same difference is obtained if observations are made with two aerials simultaneously. Consider two aerials with relative numerical coordinates (n_0, m_0), (n, m). The sum of the amplitudes of the signals from the two aerials will be

$$A(\xi,\,\eta)[\exp\{-ik(n_0x_1\xi+m_0y_1\eta)\}+ \exp\{-ik(nx_1\xi+my_1\eta)\}],$$

that is

$$A(\xi,\ \eta)\exp\{-ik(n_0x_1\xi+m_0y_1\eta)\}[1+\exp\{-ik(\nu x_1\xi+\mu y_1\eta)\}],\quad (11.29)$$

where
$$\nu = n-n_0,\qquad \mu = m-m_0.$$

The power is thus
$$2[I+\mathscr{I}(\nu,\ \mu)],\qquad (11.30)$$

where
$$I = \int_S I(\xi,\ \eta)\ \mathrm{d}\xi\ \mathrm{d}\eta$$

and
$$\mathscr{I}(\nu,\ \mu) = \int_S I(\xi,\ \eta)\cos\{2k(\nu x_1\xi+\mu y_1\eta)\}\ \mathrm{d}\xi\ \mathrm{d}\eta.$$

Then by choosing different values of n, m, the Fourier components corresponding to all the spacings νx_1, μy_1 in the array representing the complete paraboloid can be obtained. With the Fourier components known, the power that would be received at the focus of the aperture built up of the whole range of spacings may be obtained by numerical addition of the Fourier transforms multiplied by the proper phase factors so that the numerical summation is equivalent to the integral of equation (11.27). The summation must be carried with proper weighting. The number of spacings in the aperture with $\nu = 1$ is $M(N-1)$, where M and N are the greatest values of μ and ν respectively, the number with $\nu = 2$ is $Mn(N-1)/2$, and so on. The formula for the total power at the focus of the equivalent paraboloid is therefore

$$MNI+M\sum_{\nu=1}^{N-1}\binom{N-1}{\nu}\mathscr{I}(\nu,\ 0)+N\sum_{r=1}^{M-1}\binom{M-1}{\mu}\mathscr{I}(0,\ \mu).\quad (11.31)$$

The diffraction pattern of a large paraboloid is very narrow, so that the whole aerial must be steered to look at sources one at a time. The signal-to-noise ratio for observations on one source will be proportional to the square root of the area of the aperture, that is to $(MN)^{\frac{1}{2}}$, and so the time for an observation of specified uncertainty will be proportional to $1/(MN)^{\frac{1}{2}}$. With the same factors of proportionality, the signal-to-noise ratio for observations with one aerial pair will be unity and the time taken for observations at all spacings will also be unity. But the data obtained in this time will be sufficient to enable all sources lying within the diffraction pattern of a single aerial, that is within a solid angle $(MN)^{\frac{1}{2}}$ times greater than the pattern of the complete paraboloid, to be determined; the observation time for a single source is therefore effectively the same as for the complete paraboloid.

By combining the Fourier components in different ways, it is possible to reconstruct a pencil-beam instrument or an interferometer.

The largest aperture synthesis instrument at Cambridge consists of three aerials in line with a maximum spacing of about 1 mile. As the Earth rotates, all the aerial positions corresponding to those on a ring of diameter equal to the spacing between the aerials are traced out, and by setting the aerials at different spacings from day to day, the complete aperture of a paraboloid 1 mile in diameter can be reconstructed. The Cambridge instrument has been used for a study of radio sources over the whole sky visible from Cambridge (see, for example, Kenderdine, Ryle, and Pooley 1966; Pooley and Kenderdine 1968; Pooley 1969). The technique has been extended to reflections of radar pulses from the Moon, making use of the Doppler shift due to the rotation of the Moon to establish a correspondence between the frequency of the reflected signal and position on the Moon (Thomson and Ponsonby 1968), and it is the basis of sideways looking radar.

Determination of the distribution of polarization in a source

In the foregoing treatment, it has been assumed that radiation from a source is unpolarized, but most astronomical sources show some degree of polarization, and the study of the degree of polarization and its distribution in the source may throw considerable light on the mechanism of radiation. Interferometers have therefore been devised which are sensitive to polarization.

Consider the correlation of the voltages generated in two linearly polarized aerials (Fig. 11.12). Take arbitrary axes x, y in the plane containing the aerials and perpendicular to the direction of the source. Consider a point source, and let the electric field components at one of the aerials (1, say) be E_x, E_y; they may be written as

$$\mathrm{Re}\{E \cos \theta e^{i(\omega t - \chi)}\}$$

and

$$\mathrm{Re}\{E \sin \theta e^{i(\omega t + \phi - \chi)}\},$$

respectively, where χ is the phase angle measured from the point midway between the two aerials, ω is the angular frequency, and E, θ, and ϕ are parameters describing the polarization (Chapter 2).

This form represents elliptically polarized radiation.

Suppose the direction of polarization of the aerial makes an angle θ_1 with the x-axis. The voltage induced in the aerial will be proportional to

$$E_y \cos \theta_1 + E_x \sin \theta_1,$$

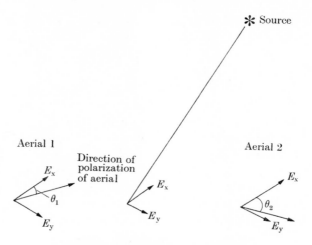

E_x, E_y: field components in arbitrary
perpendicular directions in plane
normal direction of source

FIG. 11.12. Interferometer for determination of polarization.

that is to

$$\text{Re } V_1,$$

where V_1, the complex voltage, is

$$E \cos \theta \cos \theta_1 e^{i(\omega t - \chi)} + E \sin \theta \sin \theta_1 e^{i(\omega t + \phi - \chi)}. \qquad (11.32)$$

Similarly, the voltage induced in aerial 2 is proportional to $\text{Re } V_2$ with

$$V_2 = E \cos \theta \cos \theta_2 e^{i(\omega t + \chi)} + E \sin \theta \sin \theta_2 e^{i(\omega t + \phi + \chi)}, \qquad (11.32a)$$

χ now appearing with the positive sign.

The output of a correlating detector will be proportional to

$$\tfrac{1}{2}[V_1^* V_2 + V_1 V_2^*],$$

that is to

$$|E|^2[(\cos^2\theta \cos \theta_1 \cos \theta_2 + \sin^2\theta \sin \theta_1 \sin \theta_2)\cos 2\chi +$$

$$+ \cos \theta \sin \theta \cos \theta_1 \sin \theta_2 \cos(2\chi + \phi) +$$

$$+ \cos \theta \sin \theta \cos \theta_2 \sin \theta_1 \cos (2\chi - \phi)]. \qquad (11.33)$$

Now in terms of the Stokes parameters (Chapter 2),

$$E^2 \cos^2\theta = |E_x|^2 = \tfrac{1}{2}(I+Q)$$
$$E^2 \sin^2\theta = |E_y|^2 = \tfrac{1}{2}(I-Q)$$
$$E^2 \cos\theta \sin\theta \cos\phi = |E_x|\,|E_y|\cos\phi = \tfrac{1}{2}U \qquad (11.34)$$
$$\cdot \quad E^2 \cos\theta \sin\theta \sin\phi = |E_x|\,|E_y|\sin\phi = \tfrac{1}{2}V.$$

The output of the correlator is thus proportional to

$$\{\tfrac{1}{2}(I+Q)\cos\theta_1\cos\theta_2+\tfrac{1}{2}(I-Q)\sin\theta_1\sin\theta_2\}\cos 2\chi+$$
$$+\tfrac{1}{2}U\sin(\theta_1+\theta_2)\cos 2\chi+\tfrac{1}{2}V\sin(\theta_1-\theta_2)\sin 2\chi$$
$$= \{\tfrac{1}{2}I\cos(\theta_1-\theta_2)+\tfrac{1}{2}Q\cos(\theta_1+\theta_2)+\tfrac{1}{2}U\sin(\theta_1+\theta_2)\}\cos 2\chi+$$
$$+\tfrac{1}{2}V\sin(\theta_1-\theta_2)\sin 2\chi. \quad (11.35)$$

The expression (11.35) is the real part of

$$R = \tfrac{1}{2}e^{-2i\chi}F(I, Q, U, V),$$

the *response* of the interferometer (Morris, Radhakrishnan, and Seielstad 1964), where

$$F(I, Q, U, V) = I\cos(\theta_1-\theta_2)+Q\cos(\theta_1+\theta_2) +$$
$$+U\sin(\theta_1+\theta_2)+iV\sin(\theta_1-\theta_2).$$

In this expression, I, Q, U, and V are properties of the source, χ depends on the spacing of the aerials, and the factors involving θ_1 and θ_2 depend on the polarization of the aerials.

Now consider a compact source with distribution of Stokes parameters.

Suppose the centre of the source to lie in a direction making an angle ψ_0 with the plane normal to the base line of the interferometer and suppose an element of the source lies at ψ' from the centre.

If the separation of the aerials is $2D$ and the wavelength is λ,

$$\chi = \frac{2\pi D}{\lambda}\sin(\psi_0+\psi')$$
$$= \chi_0+\chi',$$

where

$$\chi_0 = \frac{2\pi D}{\lambda}\sin\psi_0$$

and

$$\chi' = \psi'\frac{2\pi D}{\lambda}\cos\psi_0,$$

since

$$\psi' \ll \pi.$$

The response of the interferometer to the source is accordingly

$$\tfrac{1}{2}\int e^{-2i(\chi_0+\chi')} F(I, Q, U, V) \, d\Omega = \tfrac{1}{2} e^{-2i\chi_0} \int e^{-2i\chi'} F(I, Q, U, V) \, d\Omega,$$
$$(11.36)$$

where $d\Omega$ is an element of solid angle in the direction of the source.

But
$$\int e^{-2i\chi'} I \, d\Omega$$

is just the complex Fourier transform of I, and so the complex response to a distributed source is obtained from that to a point source by replacing each of the Stokes parameters by its complex Fourier transform.

Aerials in general are not linearly polarized and the foregoing discussion can be extended to deal with elliptically polarized aerials (see Morris, Radhakrishnan, and Seielstad 1964). It is evident that by choosing suitable aerial configurations, the distributions of the source parameters can be found (see also Ko 1967, Conway and Kronberg 1969).

Alignment interferometers

The basic interferometer discussed above consists of two receivers used to observe a natural source of arbitrary intensity distribution. The earliest, and for long the only, angular interferometers were those in which an artificial source was constructed from an illuminated aperture; it was with such devices as Young's double slit that interference effects were early demonstrated.

The geometry of a general double-slit interferometer is shown in Fig. 11.13. Let Cartesian coordinates be taken in planes parallel to the planes of the double slit and of the screen, and let (x, y) be coordinates in the plane of the source slit, (x_1, y_1), (x_2, y_2) in the plane of the double slit measured from the respective centres of the slits, and (ξ, η) in the plane of the screen. Let the origins of the (x, y) and (ξ, η) coordinate systems lie on a common normal to the screen and let the distances of the mid-points of the slits from the same normal be s_1 and s_2. Let the distance of the source slit from the plane of the double slits be d and that of the screen from the double slits be D. Let the distances d_1 and d_2 be distances between arbitrary points in the source slit and the double slits and let the distances D_1 and D_2 be the distances between the same points in the double slits and an arbitrary point on the screen. The path difference between light reaching the screen from some point in the

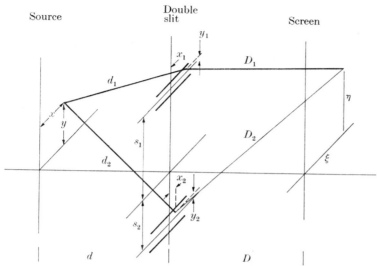

FIG. 11.13. Geometry of two-slit interferometer.

source slit by paths through the separate slits of the double slit is then

$$\Delta = d_1 + D_1 - (d_2 + D_2).$$

Now

$$d_1^2 = d^2 + (x_1 - x)^2 + (s_1 + y_1 - y)^2,$$
$$d_2^2 = d^2 + (x_2 - x)^2 + (s_2 + y_2 - y)^2,$$
$$D_1^2 = D^2 + (\xi - x_1)^2 + (\eta - s_1 - y_1)^2,$$
$$D_2^2 = D^2 + (\xi - x_2)^2 + (\eta - s_2 - y_2)^2,$$

so

$$\Delta = \frac{1}{2d}\{x_1^2 - x_2^2 - 2x(x_1 - x_2)\} +$$

$$+ \frac{1}{2d}\{y_1^2 - y_2^2 + 2y_1 s_1 + 2y_2 s_2 - 2y(s_1 + s_2) + s_1^2 - s_2^2 - 2y(y_1 - y_2)\} +$$

$$+ \frac{1}{2D}\{x_1^2 - x_2^2 - 2\xi(x_1 - x_2)\} +$$

$$+ \frac{1}{2D}\{-2\eta(s_1 + s_2) + y_1^2 - y_2^2 + 2s_1 y_1 + 2s_2 y_2 - 2\eta(y_1 - y_2) + s_1^2 - s_2^2\},$$

provided $\xi, \eta, s_1, s_2, x, y, x_1, y, x_2, y_2 \ll d, D,$ (11.37)

If geometrical factors in the amplitudes of the waves reaching the screen are ignored, the coherence function Γ for light falling on the screen is

$$\iiint\!\!\iiint e^{-ik\Delta}\, dx\, dy\, dx_1\, dy_1\, dx_2\, dy_2. \tag{11.38}$$

If

$$\Delta = \Delta_0 + \Delta_x + \Delta_y,$$

where Δ_x is a function of the x-coordinates, Δ_y is a function of the y-coordinates, and Δ_0 is independent of x and y, then

$$\Gamma = e^{-ik\Delta_0}\iiint e^{-ik\Delta_x}\,dx\,dx_1\,dx_2\iiint e^{-ik\Delta_y}\,dy\,dy_1\,dy_2. \quad (11.39)$$

Now

$$\Delta_0 = \frac{-\eta}{D}(s_1+s_2)+\tfrac{1}{2}(s_1^2-s_2^2)\left(\frac{1}{d}+\frac{1}{D}\right),$$

$$\Delta_x = \tfrac{1}{2}(x_1-x_2)\left\{\frac{x_1+x_2-2x}{d}+\frac{x_1+x_2-2\xi}{D}\right\},$$

$$\Delta_y = \tfrac{1}{2}(y_1-y_2)\left\{\frac{y_1+y_2-2y+s_1-s_2}{d}+\frac{y_1+y_2-2\eta+s_1+s_2}{D}\right\}+$$

$$+\tfrac{1}{2}(s_1+s_2)\left\{(y_1+y_2)\left(\frac{1}{d}+\frac{1}{D}\right)-\frac{2y}{d}\right\}.$$

Let

$$I_x = \iiint \exp(-ik\,\Delta_x)\,dx\,dx_1\,dx_2.$$

Put

$$x_1-x_2 = X_1,$$
$$x_1+x_2 = X_2.$$

Then

$$dx_1\,dx_2 = J\,dX_1\,dX_2,$$

where

$$J = \left|\frac{\partial x_i}{\partial X_j}\right| = 2.$$

If the limits of x_1 and x_2 are the lengths of the slits $\pm l_1$, $\pm l_2$ respectively, the limits of X_1, X_2 are each $\pm L$, where $L = l_1+l_2$.

Let the limits of x be likewise $\pm l$.

Hence

$$I_x = 2\int_{-L}^{+L}dX_1\int_{-L}^{+L}dX_2\int_{-l}^{+l}dx\,\exp\left\{-\tfrac{1}{2}ikX_1\left(\frac{X_2-x}{d}+\frac{X_2-2\xi}{D}\right)\right\}$$

$$= 4l\int_{-L}^{+L}dX_1\int_{-L}^{+L}dX_2\,\exp\left\{-\tfrac{1}{2}ikX_1X_2\left(\frac{1}{d}+\frac{1}{D}\right)\right\}\times$$

$$\times\exp\{ikX_1\xi/D\}\cdot\frac{\sin(kX_1l/d)}{(kX_1l/d)}$$

$$= 4lL\int_{-L}^{+L}dX_1\,\exp\{ikX_1\xi/D\}\frac{\sin(kX_1l/d)}{(kX_1l/d)}\cdot\frac{\sin\left\{kX_1L\left(\frac{1}{d}+\frac{1}{D}\right)\right\}}{\left\{kX_1L\left(\frac{1}{d}+\frac{1}{D}\right)\right\}}.$$

$$(11.40)$$

For convenience, write

$$A = kl/d, \qquad B = kL\left(\frac{1}{d}+\frac{1}{D}\right),$$

so that

$$I_x = 4lL\int_{-L}^{+L} dX_1 \exp\left\{\frac{ikX_1\xi}{D}\right\} \cdot \frac{\sin AX_1}{AX_1} \cdot \frac{\sin BX_1}{BX_1}. \qquad (11.40\text{a})$$

Similarly

$$I_y = 4wW\int_{-W}^{+W} dY_1 \exp\left[-\tfrac{1}{2}ikY_1\left\{(s_1-s_2)\left(\frac{1}{d}+\frac{1}{D}\right)-\frac{2\eta}{D}\right\}\right]\times$$

$$\times \frac{\sin A'(Y+s_1+s_2)}{A'(Y+s_1+s_2)} \cdot \frac{\sin B'(Y+s_1+s_2)}{B'(Y+s_1+s_2)}, \qquad (11.41)$$

where the limits of y, y_1, and y_2 are the width of the slits, respectively $\pm w$, $\pm w_1$, and $\pm w_2$, $W = w_1+w_2$, and

$$A' = kw/d,$$

$$B' = kW\left(\frac{1}{d}+\frac{1}{d}\right).$$

It will be supposed in the subsequent discussion that A, B, A', B' are all very small so that the functions $\sin AX_1/AX_1$ and so on, may be taken to be 1 under the integral signs. This is necessary for sharp fringes to be seen and is justified since in general ξ, η, the variable co-ordinates on the screen, will be much greater than L and W. For convenience, put s_1 equal to s_2. Then Γ is proportional to

$$e^{-ik\Delta_0}\int_{-L}^{+L} dX_1 \exp\left(\frac{ikX_1\xi}{D}\right) \int_{-W}^{+W} dY_1 \exp\left(\frac{ikY_1\eta}{D}\right),$$

that is to

$$e^{-ik\Delta_0}\frac{\sin(kL\xi/D)}{(kL\xi/D)}\frac{\sin(kW\eta/D)}{(kW\eta/D)}. \qquad (11.42)$$

This expression shows that there are bright fringes whenever $k\Delta_0$ increases by 2π, that is, when $k\eta(s_1+s_2)/D = 2n\pi$; the fringes are straight lines parallel to the slits instead of being hyperbolae as in the elementary theory of a double pinhole interferometer. The visibility of monochromatic fringes falls off with distance from the centre of the pattern like the product

$$\frac{\sin(kL\xi/D)}{(kL\xi/D)} \cdot \frac{\sin(kW\eta/D)}{(kW\eta/D)}. \qquad (11.43)$$

If the light is not monochromatic, we restrict attention to the centre of the pattern and suppose that this product may be taken as 1 when integrating with respect to k. In these circumstances the mutual coherence becomes proportional to

$$e^{-ik_0\Delta_0} \int_{-\infty}^{+\infty} I(k)e^{-ik'\Delta_0} \, dk', \qquad (k = k_0 + k'), \qquad (11.44)$$

and is very small except for the few central fringes if the light is not quasi-monochromatic.

Double-slit interferometers are used for the alignment of optical systems and have found important applications in engineering (van Heel 1950, 1961 see also, Danjon 1955). If a line is defined by the centre of the source slit and the mid-point of the double slits, then the central bright fringe formed in white light always falls on that line. The precision with which the central fringe can be located depends on the spacing of the fringes, which is proportional to $D/(s_1+s_2)$. Thus, for a given separation of the slits, the precision is inversely proportional to the distance from the slits, while the angular precision is constant; if it is supposed that 1/20 of a fringe may be distinguished, the angular precision is

$$\lambda/20(s_1+s_2);$$

for example, for slits with a separation of 0·01 m and using light with a mean wavelength of 500 nm, the angular precision would be $0''·5$.

Two slits give parallel fringes and so can only be used to align with respect to a plane; if two pairs of slits are used at right angles to each other and with a common mid-point, the fringes will turn into a series of spots on a rectangular grid and then may be used for alignment with respect to an axis. More complex patterns have been devised for such purposes. In general, the fringe pattern formed in monochromatic light is the spatial Fourier transform of the pattern of the slits.

It is the extension of this idea that is the basis of the method of X-ray diffraction for the analysis of crystal structure. The only difference from the multiple-slit interference systems is that instead of light being diffracted from slits to a range of directions over which interference can take place, the X-rays are scattered from the electrons in the crystal.

In Fig. 11.14, P is a scattering centre, and S is a point on a screen. Let the locations of these points be specified by the respective vectors $\mathbf{r}_i$ and $\mathbf{R}$ drawn from some arbitrary origin. Let $\mathbf{k}$ be the wave vector

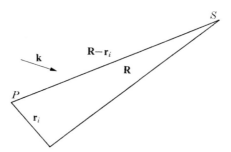

FIG. 11.14. X-ray diffraction.

of the radiation incident on the crystal. The phase of radiation arriving at S after scattering at P is $\mathbf{k} \cdot (\mathbf{R} - \mathbf{r}_i)$. If a_i is the amplitude of the radiation scattered from the ith centre, the amplitude of the resultant at S is

$$\sum_i a_i \exp[\mathrm{i}\mathbf{k} \cdot (\mathbf{R} - \mathbf{r}_i)] = \mathrm{e}^{\mathrm{i}\mathbf{k} \cdot \mathbf{R}} \sum_l a_i \exp(-\mathrm{i}\mathbf{k} \cdot \mathbf{r}_i). \qquad (11.45)$$

Since the scatterers are in a regular lattice, the vector $\mathbf{r}_i$ may be written as $p_i\boldsymbol{\rho}$, where p_i is an integer and $\boldsymbol{\rho}$ is an elementary vector. Thus the scattered intensity at S is

$$\left| \sum_{i,\boldsymbol{\rho}} a_i \exp(-\mathrm{i}p_i\mathbf{k} \cdot \boldsymbol{\rho}) \right|^2, \qquad (11.46)$$

an expression that is the three-dimensional equivalent of the grating formula and that has sharply peaked maxima in any direction for which

$$\mathbf{k} \cdot \boldsymbol{\rho} = 2n\pi.$$

The pattern of spots on the screen thus consists of infinite series of spots in directions corresponding to each elementary vector of the lattice and represent the Fourier transform of the elementary vectors of the lattice.

The size of the spots formed by interference from a single crystal is determined by the size of the crystal, the thermal motion of the atoms, the collimation of the radiation, and the width of the spectrum. The size of the crystal determines the number of terms in the sum (11.46); this is usually so great that the corresponding spread of the spot is much less than that from the other causes. X-ray beams can only be collimated by a series of slits so that there is usually an angular spread of about 1 in 10^2 in the beam and compared to this the effect of the finite spectrum of the radiation can also usually be ignored. The finite

range of angle and spectrum can be combined as a range of the vector
k and thus of the scalar product **k . ρ**; the complete expression for the
intensity of a spot is accordingly

$$\left| \sum_i a_i \int d\mathbf{k} \, \exp(-ip_i \mathbf{k} \cdot \boldsymbol{\rho}) \right|^2.$$

If a crystal is rotated about an arbitrary axis, a series of spots will
appear on the screen in any direction for which

$$\mathbf{k} \cdot \boldsymbol{\rho} = 2\pi n;$$

all such directions lie on cones about the vector **k**, one for each value of
n and **ρ**. If therefore a crystal is rotated so that it comes to lie successively in all possible orientations, the spots will spread out to cover
the cones. A more practical way of realizing this scheme is to use a
powder of small crystals of random orientation; the diffraction pattern
then formed is known as a powder photograph. Similar patterns may
be obtained with beams of electrons, which, so far as interference
phenomena are concerned, behave as electromagnetic radiation.

12

OPTICAL BEATS AND
TRANSIENT PHENOMENA

Optical beats

WHILE, in general, as pointed out in Chapter 1, beats between optical signals cannot be observed, there are special circumstances in which it is possible to detect them and they are proving a powerful means of studying the behaviour of gas lasers. They can only be detected if the sources are highly monochromatic; in that case it may also be possible to observe interference between light from different sources.

Consider two beams of light incident on a plane photocathode P. Using the notation of Chapter 2, the intensity at $\mathbf{r}$ on P is

$$I(\mathbf{r}, t) = |K_1|^2 = |K_1|^2 I_1(\mathbf{r}_1, t-t_1) + |K_2|^2 I_2(\mathbf{r}_2, t-t_2) +$$
$$+ 2\mathrm{Re}\{K_1^* K_2 V^*(\mathbf{r}_1, t-t_1) V(\mathbf{r}_2, t-t_2)\}. \quad (12.1)$$

As before, I_1 and I_2 are the intensities at points $\mathbf{r}_1$ and $\mathbf{r}_2$ on some other plane P_0 and V is the complex analytical signal on P_0.

If the signals at the two points of P_0 come from independent sources, the ensemble average of the interference term, $V^* V_2$ is zero; the terms

$$K_1 V(\mathbf{r}_1, t-t_1) \quad \text{and} \quad K_2 V(\mathbf{r}_2, t-t_2)$$

may therefore be replaced by

$$[I, (t)]^{\frac{1}{2}} e^{2\pi i \nu_1 t + i\phi_1} \quad \text{and} \quad [I_2(t)]^{\frac{1}{2}} e^{2\pi i \nu_2 t + i\phi_2}$$

respectively. It is supposed that the sources are both quasi-monochromatic with centre frequencies ν_1 and ν_2 respectively, and that the intensities I_1 and I_2 and the phase angles, ϕ_1 and ϕ_2, vary slowly.

Then

$$I(\mathbf{r}, t) = I_1(t-t_1) + I_2(t-t_2) +$$
$$+ 2[I_1(t-t_1) . I_2(t-t_2)]^{\frac{1}{2}} \times$$
$$\times \cos[2\pi(\nu_2-\nu_1)t + 2\pi(\nu_1 t_1 - \nu_2 t_2) + \phi_2(t-t_2) - \phi_1(t-t_1)]. \quad (12.2)$$

Here $\phi_1(t-t_1)$ and $\phi_2(t-t_2)$ denote the values of ϕ_1 and ϕ_2 at $(t-t_1)$ and $(t-t_2)$ respectively.

This expression has now to be integrated over the area of the photocathode to give a response R:

$$R = \alpha \int_S I(\mathbf{r}, t) \, d\mathbf{r}.$$

S is the area of the photocathode and α is the quantum efficiency. We wish to examine the time variation of this response and the way that it depends on the optical properties of the system.

Assume that P_0 is a long distance from P so that the wave fronts at P are effectively plane. Let the wave fronts be inclined at angles θ_1 and θ_2 to P (Fig. 12.1) and suppose, for simplicity, that the intersections

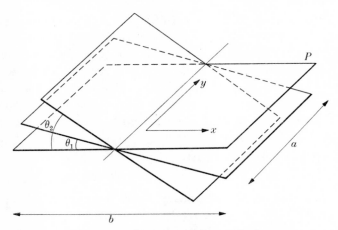

FIG. 12.1. Geometry of photocathodes.

of the wave fronts with each other and with P are collinear. Take coordinates y and x in the plane P in directions respectively parallel to and at right angles to the line of intersection; then if, for illustration, the photocathode is taken to be rectangular with dimensions a and b respectively,

$$R(t) = \alpha b \int_0^a I(x, t)\, dx, \qquad (12.3)$$

while the responses from the two separate beams will be

$$R_1(t) = \alpha b \int_0^a I_1(x, t)\, dx \quad \text{and} \quad R_2(t) = \alpha b \int_0^a I_2(x, t)\, dx.$$
$$\tag{12.3a}$$

Put

$$t_1 = \tau_1 + \frac{x}{c} \sin \theta_1 \quad \text{and} \quad t_2 = \tau_2 + \frac{x}{c} \sin \theta_2,$$

and assume that $(a/c) \sin \theta_1$ and $(a/c) \sin \theta_2$ are much less than the coherence times of the two sources. Then I_1, I_2 and ϕ_1, ϕ_2 may be considered to be constant across the photocathode and

$$R_1 = \alpha a b I_1, \qquad R_2 = \alpha a b I_2, \qquad (12.4)$$

while in the integral

$$\int_0^a dx[I_1(t-t_1) \cdot I_2(t-t_2)]^{\frac{1}{2}} \times$$

$$\times \cos[2\pi(\nu_2-\nu_1)t+2\pi(\nu_1 t_1-\nu_2 t_2)+\phi_2(t-t_2)+\phi_1(t-t_1)]$$

it is necessary to consider only the variation of the cosine term over the photocathode.

Now

$$\nu_1 t_1-\nu_2 t_2 = \nu_1\left(\tau_1+\frac{x}{c}\sin\theta_1\right)+\nu_2\left(\tau_2+\frac{x}{c}\sin\theta_2\right)$$

$$= \nu_1\tau_1-\nu_2\tau_2+\frac{x}{c}(\nu_1\sin\theta_1-\nu_2\sin\theta_2),$$

and so

$$2\pi(\nu_2-\nu_1)t+2\pi(\nu_1 t_1-\nu_2 t_2)+\phi_2-\phi_1 = \Phi+\frac{2\pi x}{c}(\nu_1\sin\theta_1-\nu_2\sin\theta_2),$$

where

$$\Phi = 2\pi\{(\nu_2-\nu_1)t+\nu_1\tau_1-\nu_2\tau_2\}+\phi_2-\phi_1 \text{ is independent of } x\,.$$

ϕ_1 and ϕ_2 are taken to be constant since they vary slowly and $(a/c)\sin\theta_1$ and $(a/c)\sin\theta_2$ are much less than the coherence times.

Let $\kappa = 2\pi/c(\nu_1\sin\theta_1-\nu_2\sin\theta_2)$. Then the integral

$$\int_0^a \cos(\Phi+\kappa x)\,dx$$

is equal to

$$-\frac{\cos\Phi}{\kappa}\sin\kappa a-\frac{\sin\Phi}{\kappa}(\cos\kappa a-1)$$

or

$$\frac{\sin\frac{1}{2}\kappa a}{\frac{1}{2}\kappa}[-\cos\Phi\cos\tfrac{1}{2}\kappa a+\sin\Phi\sin\tfrac{1}{2}\kappa a] \quad \text{for} \quad \kappa a \ll 1.$$

Hence

$$R(t) = R_1(t)+R_2(t)+2[R_1(t)\cdot R_2(t)]^{\frac{1}{2}}\frac{\sin\psi}{\psi}\cos(\Phi+\psi), \quad (12.6)$$

where

$$\psi = \tfrac{1}{2}\kappa a = \frac{\pi a}{c}(\nu_1\sin\theta_1-\nu_2\sin\theta_2).$$

The interpretation of this formula is that R varies with the beat frequency $(\nu_2 - \nu_1)$ and that the amplitude of the modulation is

$$2\,\frac{\sin \psi}{\psi}\left\{\left(\frac{R_1}{R_2}\right)^{\frac{1}{2}} + \left(\frac{R_2}{R_1}\right)^{\frac{1}{2}}\right\}^{-1}.$$

Thus, as for two-beam interferometers, the intensities of the two beams should be nearly equal for the greatest modulation. The angle ψ must also be much less than 1, that is to say

$$\frac{a}{c}(\sin \theta_1 - \sin \theta_2) \ll \nu_1, \nu_2.$$

The wave fronts from the sources should therefore be very closely parallel; the conditions for obtaining beats are the same as for obtaining good fringes in the Michelson interferometer: the intensities should be equal and the beams closely parallel. In addition, the light times across the photocathode must be very much less than the coherence times of the sources. Evidently, beats will be most readily detected with two lasers, for the coherence times are long and the sources are highly monochromatic so that the range of beat frequency will not be great. Such beats are extensively used to study the behaviour of gas lasers, the width of the line, drifts of frequency, effects of acoustic vibration, and so on, and form a powerful means of investigation. Beat frequencies are typically of the order of 1 MHz.

Beats may also be used for high resolution spectroscopy (see van Bueren 1969). If one source is a highly monochromatic laser and the other the source to be studied, a spectrum analysis of the beats will give the spectrum of the source under investigation relative to the laser frequency. It is easiest if the laser frequency is nominally the same as the centre frequency of the spectrum being studied; the method is therefore restricted at present to very few lines, especially since the depth of modulation will be much reduced if the second spectrum is from an incoherent source. Furthermore, the noise on the highly degenerate light from a gas laser is very much less than that on the non-degenerate light from a gas discharge lamp. Nonetheless, it has proved possible to detect beats between two incoherent sources, namely, two Zeeman components from a mercury discharge lamp (Forrester, Gudmunsen, and Johnson 1955); frequencies are of the order of 100 MHz.

The practical uses of beats are in studies with light from gas lasers, which are continuous sources. It is also possible to observe beats with light from pulsed lasers but it is much more difficult because the beats appear only during the short time when the two lasers are radiating simultaneously.

Interference between separate lasers

In order to observe beats, the response of the detector was resolved in time but integrated over the area of the detector. To investigate whether it is possible to see interference fringes between two independent sources, we study the integration of the response with respect to time, coupled with resolution in space.

If the detector integrates for a time T, the output as a function of position is

$$R(x, t, T) = \alpha \int_t^{t+T} I(x, t')\, \mathrm{d}t', \qquad (12.7)$$

where

$$I(x, t') = I_1(t' - t_1) + I_2(t' - t_2) + 2(I_1 I_2)^{\frac{1}{2}} \times$$
$$\times \cos[2\pi(\nu_2 - \nu_1)t' + 2\pi(\nu_1 t_1 - \nu_2 t_2) + \phi_2(t' - t_2) - \phi_1(t' - t_1)]. \quad (12.8)$$

As before, we set

$$\alpha \int_t^{t+T} I_1(t' - t_1)\, \mathrm{d}t' = R_1(t, T);$$

$$t_1 = \tau_1 + \frac{x}{c}\sin\theta_1, \qquad t_2 = \tau_2 + \frac{x}{c}\sin\theta_2.$$

The argument of the cosine term then becomes

$$2\pi(\nu_2 - \nu_1)t' + 2\pi(\nu_1\tau_1 - \nu_2\tau_2) +$$

$$+ \frac{2\pi x}{c}(\nu_2\sin\theta_2 - \nu_1\sin\theta_1) + \phi_2(t' - t_2) - \phi_1(t' - t_1)$$
$$= 2\pi(\nu_2 - \nu_1)t' + \Psi(x), \quad (12.9)$$

where now the part Ψ, independent of t, is separated out.

The integral

$$\int_t^{t+T} \cos\{2\pi(\nu_2 - \nu_1)t' + \Psi(x)\}\, \mathrm{d}t'$$

is equal to

$$T \times \frac{\sin\{\pi(\nu_2 - \nu_1)T\}}{\pi(\nu_2 - \nu_1)T}\cos\{2\pi(\nu_2 - \nu_1)(t + \tfrac{1}{2}T) + \Psi(x)\}, \quad (12.10)$$

and the intensity therefore varies in space like

$$\cos(Kx + \text{const.}),$$

where

$$K = \frac{2\pi}{c} (\nu_1 \sin \theta_1 - \nu_2 \sin \theta_2).$$

The maxima of the fringes occur at intervals of $c/\nu(\theta_1 - \theta_2)$ if ν_2 is very close to ν_1 and θ_1 and θ_2 are both small.

The visibility of the fringes is

$$2 \frac{\sin \pi(\nu_2 - \nu_1)T}{\pi(\nu_2 - \nu_1)} \cdot \left\{ \left(\frac{R_1}{R_2}\right)^{\frac{1}{2}} + \left(\frac{R_2}{R_1}\right)^{\frac{1}{2}} \right\}^{-1}.$$

It is again necessary that the intensities of the two interfering beams should be nearly the same. The permissible integration time is determined by the factor

$$\frac{\sin \pi(\nu_2 - \nu_1)T}{\pi(\nu_2 - \nu_1)T};$$

evidently, T must be much less than $1/\pi |\nu_2 - \nu_1|$. The frequencies radiated by two independent laser sources will usually differ by some tens of megahertz and T must therefore be much less than 1μs if fringes are to be recorded. Fringes have been observed (Magyar and Mandel 1963, 1964) by arranging for the light from two pulsed solid-state lasers to interfere on the photocathode of an image intensifier and having the image intensifier operate simultaneously with the two lasers (Fig. 12.2).

The positions of the fringes depend on the phase angles

$$\phi_1, \; \phi_2, \; 2\pi(\nu_1\tau_1 - \nu_2\tau_2), \quad \text{and} \quad 2\pi(\nu_1 - \nu_2)(t + \tfrac{1}{2}T),$$

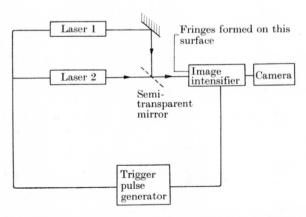

FIG. 12.2. Interference fringes between light from two lasers.

which are arbitrary; the positions therefore vary from one laser pulse to the next and the fringes formed in one pulse must be recorded separately from those in another.

The fringes cannot be seen in incoherent light, for apart from the much poorer signal-to-noise ratio as compared with degenerate light, the arbitrary phases, which are nearly constant within one laser pulse but which vary from one pulse to the next, take all values in incoherent light, smearing out the fringes completely.

13

INTENSITY INTERFEROMETERS

MOST astronomical sources have extremely small angular dimensions. Very few stars have been resolved in the visible and while radio sources within the galaxy are in general much larger than stars, radio wavelengths are also much greater than those of visible light and it is difficult to set up radio telescopes or interferometers of sufficient size to resolve sources less than some 5′ in diameter. The size of a source is of prime importance in astrophysics; the absolute intensity of radiation from a star, a necessary datum in studying stellar structure, cannot be found without knowing the size of the star, and, similarly, the absolute intensities of radiation from many of the small and strange radio sources, such as quasars and regions in which stimulated emission from molecules takes place, can be found only if the size is known. In addition, many sources are not single and there is great interest in resolving them into their components. Observations of very small sources, with diameters much less than 0·1″, are thus of great importance in astronomy. Interferometers with that resolution require path differences of more than 10^8 wavelengths. A. A. Michelson (1920) made a stellar interferometer with a path difference of some 10^7 wavelengths, and H. A. Gebbie and R. Q. Twiss are endeavouring to extend the technique to longer path differences with photoelectric recording of the fringes (Chapter 11), but it will be difficult to have a base line of more than 10^8 wavelengths and there are likely to be severe problems in making an instrument than can observe an arbitrary star. About 1952, R. Hanbury Brown and his colleagues saw that it was possible to derive the modulus of the mutual coherence function from observations in which the phase difference between the two interfering beams of radiation was not preserved, and they constructed a radio interferometer on this principle. Subsequently, Brown and Twiss (1956b, 1957a; b, Brown 1960) demonstrated the same principle for an optical interferometer. It seemed at first that intensity interferometry, as it was called, would be of most use in radio astronomy, but it has since become possible to set up radio links that preserve relative phase over very great distances so that 'conventional' interferometers can now be constructed with base lines up to 200 km (Elgaroy, Morris, and Rowson 1962), and more recently (see Chapter 11) the correlation of aerial signals through atomic-standard reference signals has enabled base lines to be extended to some 5000 km, corresponding to about $2 \cdot 5 \times 10^6$ wavelengths at $0 \cdot 21$ m. The need for intensity interferometers in radio astronomy has therefore diminished, but meanwhile Hanbury Brown has constructed a large optical interferometer for stellar observations and it now seems that here may be the most important application of intensity interferometers, for it is in optical observations that the greatest advantage in resolution is apparent over interferometers that preserve phase. Intensity interferometers may be applied to spectroscopic measurements as well as to angular measurements, but advances in the mechanical and optical design of long path interferometers as well as the application of optical beat observations to spectroscopy mean that there is no advantage to be had in the use of intensity interferometers.

In interference phenomena as usually understood, there is a single detector at which the combined electromagnetic signal is rectified and the correlated components of the two interfering signals are picked out. The detector thus combines two functions, that of *correlation* or producing a signal related to the correlated components, and that of *detection*, or producing a signal with non-zero mean from a signal that is zero in the mean. The correlation function depends on the phase relation between the two interfering signals. In intensity interferometry, the operations of detection and correlation are separated, the correlator being preceded by separate detectors for the two interfering signals.

Classical theory

Although the main applications of intensity interferometers are now in visual observations, it is easiest to explain the principles of the method in terms of the radio observations. The following discussion is based on the description of Brown and Twiss (1954). Consider an interferometer as shown in Fig. 13.1. Let A and B be the aerials and let the centre of the source be in the direction making the angle θ_0 with AB. The actual source must be replaced by the equivalent linear source (Chapter 11) lying in the plane that contains AB and the centre of the source. In this plane, let the y-axis join the centre of AB to the centre of the source and let the x-axis be perpendicular to it. If l is the projection of AB on the y-axis, the coordinates of the receivers are $(-\frac{1}{2}l \tan \theta_0, -\frac{1}{2}l)$ and $(\frac{1}{2}l \tan \theta_0, \frac{1}{2}l)$ respectively, where

$$l = AB \cos \theta_0.$$

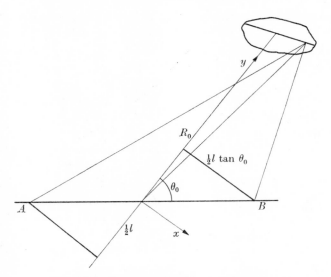

FIG. 13.1. Geometry of stellar interferometer.

The output from a portion of a radio source in the direction θ is a random signal that may be represented by a series of Fourier components of random phase, namely

$$\sum_{r=0}^{\infty} \frac{a_r(\theta)}{R} \cos\{2\pi rt/T - \phi_r(\theta)\}_{t-R/c}.$$

In this expression T is the time over which an observation is made, R is the distance from the source to the aerials, and $\phi_r(\theta)$ is a phase which lies between 0 and 2π, being distributed uniformly over this range so that there is no correlation between radiation from different regions (different values of θ), nor between radiation at different frequencies (different values of r). $a_r(\theta)$ is proportional to

$$[2p_r(\theta)\, d\theta/T]^{\frac{1}{2}},$$

where $p_r(\theta)\, d\theta$ is the power radiated from a region of angular width $d\theta$ at the frequency r/T.

It will be assumed in discussing the principles of the method for radio sources that noise in the receiver may be neglected, although detector noise dominates the behaviour of the optical interferometer.

The voltages induced in the aerials are the sums of components of different frequencies coming from different parts of the source. The voltages applied to the detectors may therefore be written as

$$V_1(t) = \int d\theta_p A \sum_{r=0}^{\infty} \frac{a_r(\theta_p)}{R_{1p}} \cos\left\{\frac{2\pi r}{T}\left(t - \frac{R_{1p}}{c}\right) - \phi_r(\theta_p) - \psi\right\}$$

$$V_2(t) = \int d\theta_q A \sum_{s=0}^{\infty} \frac{a_s(\theta_q)}{R_{2q}} \cos\left\{\frac{2\pi s}{T}\left(t - \frac{R_{2q}}{c}\right) - \phi_s(\theta_q) - \psi\right\}, \qquad (13.1)$$

where for simplicity it has been supposed that the channels are identical and have characteristics that are constant over the bandwidth of the system so that the factor A and the phase shift ψ are constants and the same for the two channels. The more general case has been analysed by Brown and Twiss (1954). The range of integration with respect to angle is of course the same in both expressions but it is desirable to distinguish the angular coordinates in the two. The distances R_{1p} and R_{2q} are given by

$$R_{1p} = [R_0^2 + \tfrac{1}{4}l^2 + R_0 l \tan\theta_0 - R_0 l\theta_p]^{\frac{1}{2}}$$
$$R_{2q} = [R_0^2 + \tfrac{1}{4}l^2 - R_0 l \tan\theta_0 + R_0 l\theta_q]^{\frac{1}{2}}. \qquad \text{(Fig. 13.1)} \qquad (13.2)$$

The output of one of the detectors, which is proportional to $|V_1|^2$, will be given by

$$D_1(t) = \int d\theta_p \int d\theta_{p'} A^2 \sum_{r,s=0}^{\infty} \frac{a_r(\theta_p)a_s(\theta_{p'})}{R_{1p}R_{1p'}} F(r-s) \times$$

$$\times \cos\left[\frac{2\pi t}{T}(r-s) - \frac{rR_{1p} - sR_{1p'}}{c} - \phi_{1r}(\theta_p) + \phi_{1s}(\theta_{p'})\right]. \qquad (13.3)$$

The form of this expression arises as follows. $|V_1|^2$ includes all products of terms with different r and s in the expression for V_1 and each product of the cosine terms can be expressed as the sum of a term with the frequency $2\pi(r-s)/T$ and one with the frequency $2\pi(r+s)/T$. The detector is followed by a filter with a low-frequency response $F(r-s)$, which cuts out the high-frequency terms with frequencies $2\pi(r+s)/T$. A further simplification has been made in writing down the detector output, in that it has been assumed that any phase shift in the detector and filter is independent of frequency.

The other detector gives a similar output and the two are combined in a correlator circuit to give an output proportional to

$$D_1(t).D_2(t-\tau),$$

where τ is a constant delay time that may, for example, compensate for a difference in the times of arrivals of the signals at the aerials. On multiplying cosine terms in the expressions for the detector outputs, and rewriting any product as the sum of terms with arguments that are the sum and difference of the original arguments, it will be seen that the only terms in the output of the correlator that have a non-zero average value in time are those for which the two terms of a product have the same value of $(r-s)$. Such terms are proportional to

$$\cos\left[\begin{array}{c} \dfrac{2\pi}{cT}\{r(R_{1p}-R_{2q})-s(R_{1p'}-R_{2q'})\}+ \\ +\phi_{1r}(\theta_p)-\phi_{1r}(\theta_q)-\phi_{1s}(\theta_{p'})+\phi_{1s}(\theta_{q'})+ \\ +\dfrac{2\pi}{T}(r-s)\tau \end{array}\right].$$

We require the average value of $D_1(t).D_2(t-\tau)$ as T approaches infinity. Making use of the fact that the radiation properties of the source may be considered to be stationary in time, the average can be found by replacing the discrete frequencies $2\pi r/T$, $2\pi s/T$, by frequencies with continuous range, ω, ω', equal to $2\pi r/T$, $2\pi s/T$ respectively, and by integrating with respect to ω, ω'. Since the phase angles $\phi_{1r}(\theta_p)\ldots$ are random, the only terms that contribute to the integrals are those for which $\theta_p = \theta_{p'}$, $\theta_q = \theta_{q'}$. Since to first order

$$R_{1p}-R_{2p} = l\tan\theta_0 - l\theta_p,$$

$$D_1(t).D_2(t-\tau) = A^4 F^2 \int d\theta_p \int d\theta_q \int d\omega \int d\omega' P(\omega, \theta_p) P(\omega',\theta_q) \times$$

$$\times \cos\left[-\frac{l}{c}(\omega\theta_p - \omega'\theta_q) - (\omega-\omega')\tau\right]. \quad (13.4)$$

Here $P(\omega, \theta_p)$ is the power received in bandwidth $d\omega$ and angle $d\theta$. In carrying out the final integrations with respect to frequency, it is supposed that the receiver bandwidth is b_R so that the integrand vanishes for

$$|\omega-\omega_0| > b_R,$$

while the bandwidth of the correlator is b_C so that the integrand vanishes when $\omega-\omega'$ lies outside that range.

$P(\omega, \theta_p)$ will be assumed constant over the receiver bandwidth and will be replaced by $P(\omega_0, \theta_p)$. The correlator output may then be written as proportional to

$$\int_{-\frac{1}{2}\alpha}^{+\frac{1}{2}\alpha} P(\omega_0, \theta_p)\,d\theta_p \int_{-\frac{1}{2}\alpha}^{+\frac{1}{2}\alpha} P(\omega_0, \theta_q)\,d\theta_q \cos\frac{\omega_0 l}{c}(\theta_p - \theta_q), \quad (13.5)$$

where the source lies within the angular range $\pm\frac{1}{2}\alpha$.

The expression (13.5) will now be shown to be equal to Michelson's fringe visibility, the key result in the application of intensity interferometry.

Since

$$\cos \frac{\omega_0 l}{c}(\theta_p - \theta_q) = \cos \frac{\omega_0 l}{c}\theta_p . \cos \frac{\omega_0 l}{c}\theta_q + \sin \frac{\omega_0 l}{c}\theta_p \sin \frac{\omega_0 l}{c}\theta_q,$$

the double integral is equal to

$$\int_{-\frac{1}{2}\alpha}^{+\frac{1}{2}\alpha} P(\omega_0, \theta_p)\cos \frac{\omega_0 l}{c}\theta_p \, d\theta_p \int_{-\frac{1}{2}\alpha}^{+\frac{1}{2}\alpha} P(\omega_0, \theta_q)\cos \frac{\omega_0 l}{c}\theta_q \, d\theta_q +$$

$$+ \int_{-\frac{1}{2}\alpha}^{+\frac{1}{2}\alpha} P(\omega_0, \theta_p)\sin \frac{\omega_0 l}{c} \, d\theta_p \int_{-\frac{1}{2}\alpha}^{+\frac{1}{2}\alpha} P(\omega_0, \theta_q)\sin \frac{\omega_0 l}{c}\theta_q \, d\theta_q. \quad (13.6)$$

But

$$\int_{-\frac{1}{2}\alpha}^{+\frac{1}{2}\alpha} P(\omega_0, \theta_p)\cos \frac{\omega_0 l}{c}\theta_p \, d\theta_p$$

and

$$+$$
$$\int_{+\frac{1}{2}\alpha} P(\omega_0, \theta_q)\cos \frac{\omega_0 l}{c}\theta_q \, d\theta_q$$

are the same since the variables θ_p and θ_q run over the same source and range. If α is large enough to include the whole of the source, each integral is the cosine Fourier transform of P, T_c, say. Similarly, each of the other pair of integrals is equal to the sine transform T_s. Thus the correlator response is proportional to

$$T_c^2 + T_s^2.$$

When normalized to unity at $l = 0$, this is just the same as the fringe visibility in the sense of Michelson. The intensity interferometer can thus, just like visibility measurements, enable an equivalent symmetrical model of a source to be constructed, but cannot provide any information about asymmetry.

A detailed discussion of the limitations and possibilities involved in deriving an intensity distribution from an intensity interferogram has been given by Bates (1969).

Quantum effects

The theory just outlined applies to classical fields and is thus applicable to radio waves. If the quantum nature of the optical field is accepted, the theory should be stated in terms of the correlations of fluctuations of the photoelectrons emitted from a photocathode. It can then be shown (Brown and Twiss 1956a, 1957a) that because of correlation effects between photons, the noise in the stream of electrons emitted from a single photocathode is somewhat greater than the counting noise of the electrons (after allowing for the quantum efficiency being less than unity), and also, the correlation between the fluctuations at separate photocathodes is, just as in the classical case, proportional to the visibility of the equivalent two-beam interference fringes.

Correlations between intensity fluctuations involve fourth-order moments of field variables.

The correlated part of the fluctuations of the optical intensities at two receivers has to be sought in the presence of noise from the photoelectric effect at each. The ratio of signal to noise is very much less than for conventional interferometric measurements and has to be discussed in some detail in order to determine the conditions for practical application of intensity interferometry.

The quantum theory of the emission and absorption of photons (which are bosons) shows (see Chapter 2) that the probability of the absorption of a photon and the emission of a photoelectron in an interval $(t \rightarrow t + dt)$ and at a site with coordinate x is equal to

$$P(t)\, dt = \alpha I_a(x, t)\, dt,$$

where α is the efficiency of the quantum detector and I_a is the intensity averaged over a few cycles of the incident light, thus excluding time intervals that are much less than the reciprocal of the frequency.

To obtain the probability that n electrons are emitted in a time T, consider T to be divided into elements dt so small that the probability of two electrons being emitted in any interval (which is proportional to dt^2) is negligible. The probability of n electrons being emitted is then equal to the probability of one being emitted in each of n elements and of none being emitted in the remainder. The probability of one electron being emitted at some time in the interval $(t \rightarrow t + T)$ is

$$\alpha \int_t^{t+T} I_a(x, t')\, dt',$$

so that the probability of n being emitted is

$$\left[\alpha \int_t^{t+T} I_a(x, t')\, dt' \right]^n .$$

The probability of no electrons being emitted in one of the remaining $N - n = T/dt - n$ elements is

$$1 - \frac{\alpha \int_t^{t+T} I_a \, dt'}{N - n}$$

and the probability of no electrons being emitted in each of them is

$$\left(1 - \frac{\alpha \int_t^{t+T} I_a \, dt'}{N - n} \right)^{N-n} = \exp\left\{ -\alpha \int_t^{t+T} I_a \, dt' \right\}.$$

Since the electrons are indistinguishable, the overall probability of the emission of just n electrons, $P_n(t, T)$, is

$$\frac{1}{n!} \left[\alpha \int_t^{t+T} I_a(t') \, dt' \right]^n \exp\left\{ -\alpha \int_t^{t+T} I_a(t') \, dt' \right\}. \tag{13.7}$$

The average number of electrons emitted in a time T, $\langle n_T \rangle$, is

$$\left\langle \sum_{n=0}^{\infty} n P_n(t, T) \right\rangle$$

or, putting

$$\alpha \int_t^{t+T} I_a(t') \, dt' = \xi,$$

$$\langle n_T \rangle = \sum_{n=0}^{\infty} \frac{n}{n!} \xi^n e^{-\xi} = \xi e^{-\xi} \sum_{p=0}^{\infty} \frac{\xi^p}{p!}, \qquad \text{where } p = n - 1.$$

Hence

$$\langle n_T \rangle = \xi = \alpha \left\langle \int_t^{t+T} I_a(t') \, dt' \right\rangle, \tag{13.8}$$

that is, $\alpha T \langle I_a \rangle$ for a stationary process.

With the same substitution of ξ, the average value of the square of the number of electrons emitted is

$$\langle n_T^2 \rangle = \sum_{n=0}^{\infty} \frac{n^2}{n!} \xi^n e^{-\xi}$$

$$= \sum_{n=0}^{\infty} \frac{1}{(n-1)!} \xi^n e^{-\xi} + \sum_{n=0}^{\infty} \frac{1}{(n-2)!} \xi^n e^{-\xi}$$

$$= \xi e^{-\xi} \sum_{p=0}^{\infty} \frac{\xi^p}{p!} + \xi^2 e^{-\xi} \sum_{q=0}^{\infty} \frac{\xi^q}{q!}, \tag{13.9}$$

where

$$p = n - 1 \quad \text{and} \quad q = n - 2.$$

Thus

$$\langle n_T^2 \rangle = \langle n_T \rangle + \xi^2.$$

But ξ^2 is the probability that two electrons will be emitted sometime in the interval of length T, and is

$$\alpha^2 \int_0^T \int_0^T \langle I_a(t+\mu).I_a(t+\nu) \rangle \, \mathrm{d}\mu \, \mathrm{d}\nu.$$

Hence

$$\langle n_T^2 \rangle = \langle n_T \rangle + \alpha^2 \int_0^T \int_0^T \langle I_a(t+\mu).I_a(t+\nu) \rangle \, \mathrm{d}\mu \, \mathrm{d}\nu$$

$$= \langle n_T \rangle + \alpha^2 \int_0^T \int_0^T \mathscr{R}_{ii}(x_1, x_1, \mu-\nu) \, \mathrm{d}\mu \, \mathrm{d}\nu. \tag{13.10}$$

$\mathscr{R}_{ij}$ is the average value of the product of the instantaneous intensities at two photocathodes labelled i and j. When the photocathodes are identical, $i = j$, and in addition the spatial co-ordinates, summarized in x_1, are the same. For a statistically stationary system, $\mathscr{R}_{ij}$ depends only on the time interval between two instants and not on the absolute time. Hence

$$\langle I_a(t+\mu).I_a(t+\nu) \rangle$$

can be written as

$$\mathscr{R}_{ii}(x_1, x_1, \mu-\nu).$$

Thus

$$\langle n_T^2 \rangle = \langle n_T \rangle + \alpha^2 \int_{-T}^{+T} (T - |\tau'|) \, \mathscr{R}_{ii}(x_1, x_1, \tau') \, \mathrm{d}\tau'. \tag{13.11}$$

Likewise, the average value of the product of the numbers of electrons emitted from each of two separate detectors is

$$\langle n_1, n_2 \rangle = \alpha^2 \int_{-T}^{+T} (T - |\tau'|) \, \mathscr{R}_{ij}(x_1, x_2, \tau') \, \mathrm{d}\tau'. \tag{13.11a}$$

The mean square fluctuation of the number of electrons emitted from a single photocathode is

$$\langle (n_T - \langle n_T \rangle)^2 \rangle = \langle n_T^2 \rangle - 2\langle n_T \langle n_T \rangle \rangle + \langle n_T \rangle^2$$

$$= \langle n_T^2 \rangle - \langle n_T \rangle^2$$

$$= \langle n_T \rangle + \alpha^2 \int_{-T}^{+T} (T - |\tau'|) \, \mathscr{R}_{ii} \, \mathrm{d}\tau' - \alpha^2 T^2 I_a^2. \tag{13.12}$$

In this expression, the random noise term N is $\langle n_T \rangle$ while the term due to coherence in the optical signal is of order $(\alpha^2 T \tau_c I_a^2)$, where τ_c is the coherence time. The ratio of coherence signal to noise is thus of order γn_B, where n_B is the number of photoelectrons per unit bandwidth of the radiation and γ is the quantum efficiency. The product is very much less than unity for starlight and for thermal laboratory sources (though not necessarily for lasers) and it is therefore hopeless to attempt to detect in the signal from a single photocathode a part dependent on the coherence of the radiation.

It is only in cross-correlation experiments, in which two photo-detectors are used, that it is possible to isolate a signal dependent on the coherence of the radiation.

Practical interferometers

The results of a detailed analysis of an intensity interferometer may be summarized as follows.

The time average of the correlation between the fluctuations in the outputs of two photomultipliers, which are in general not identical, is given by the formula

$$\overline{c(d)} = \Delta_\nu \Gamma_\nu^2(d) i_1 i_2 \frac{\sigma}{B_0} \epsilon b_\nu \frac{|F_{\text{max}}|^2}{G_1 G_2} . \qquad (13.13)$$

d is the separation of the centres of the two receivers and i_1 and i_2 are the d.c. components of the output currents of the two photomultipliers. ϵ is the efficiency of the correlator circuits.

B_0 is the optical bandwidth, defined as

$$\frac{\left[\int_0^\infty \gamma_1(\nu)\alpha_1(\nu)n_1(\nu)\, \mathrm{d}\nu . \int_0^\infty \gamma_2(\nu)\alpha_2(\nu)n_2(\nu)\, \mathrm{d}\nu \right]^{\frac{1}{2}}}{\gamma(\nu_0)\alpha(\nu_0)n(\nu_0)} ,$$

where $\alpha_i(\nu)$ is the quantum efficiency of cathode i for light of frequency ν, $\gamma_i(\nu)$ is the transmission coefficient of the optical system i, and $n_i(\nu)$ is the number of photons received per unit area, per unit time, and in unit bandwidth from the source. ν_0 is the mid-band frequency of the light falling on the cathodes and

$$\gamma(\nu_0)\alpha(\nu_0)n(\nu_0) = [\gamma_1(\nu_0)\alpha_1(\nu_0)n_1(\nu_0).\gamma_2(\nu_0)\alpha_2(\nu_0)n_2(\nu_0)]^{\frac{1}{2}}.$$

σ is the cross-spectral density defined as

$$\int_0^\infty \gamma_1(\nu)\alpha_1(\nu)n_1(\nu)\gamma_2(\nu)\alpha_2(\nu)n_2(\nu)\, \mathrm{d}\nu / B_0 \gamma^2(\nu_0)\alpha^2(\nu_0)n^2(\nu_0).$$

$F_i(f)$ is the gain of an electrical channel, including the photomultiplier, at the frequency f, and the cross-correlation bandwidth b_v is defined as

$$\tfrac{1}{2}\int_0^\infty \{F_1(f)F_2^*(f)+F_1^*(f)F_2(f)\}\ \mathrm{d}f/|F_{\max}|^2.$$

$|F_{\max}|^2$ is the maximum value of

$$\tfrac{1}{2}[F_1(f)F_2^*(f)+F_1^*(f)F_2(f)],$$

and G_1 and G_2 are the d.c. gains of the photomultipliers:

$$G_i = \frac{i}{eA}\int_0^\infty \gamma_i(v)\alpha_i(v)n_i(v)\ \mathrm{d}v,$$

e being the electronic charge and A the area of the cathode.

The correlation is reduced by the product of the partial coherence and correlation factors, Δ_v and $\Gamma_v^2(d)$ respectively. The former (Brown and Twiss 1957b) takes account of the possibility that the incident light may not be coherent over the apertures of the two receivers; it will be significantly less than unity for stars of large angular diameter observed with large mirrors to collect the light. The factor $\Gamma_v^2(d)$ is the Michelson visibility.

The interferometer at Narrabri has been described by Brown (1964) and by Brown, Davis, and Allen (1964, 1967). In it the photomultipliers are placed at the foci of two reflectors each about 6·5 m in diameter. The reflectors do not have to do more than concentrate the light from a star within the area of a photocathode and it was therefore possible to make them of a mosaic of spherical mirrors each about 0·38 m across. The correlated signal is greater the smaller the optical bandwidth and the bandwidth is therefore limited by interference filters placed in front of the cathodes. The filters must have uniform properties over their areas and be closely matched. The nominal wavelength is about 440 nm, at which the quantum efficiency is about 20 per cent. The reflectors are placed on a circular railway track and can be moved as the Earth rotates so that they stay at the same separation and at the same astronomical position angle.

The heart of the correlator is an electrical multiplying circuit that multiplies the fluctuations of the anode currents of the photomultipliers. To overcome problems of stability in the various electrical circuits, the phases of the currents are switched at 5 kHz and also at intervals of 10 s. The integrator following the multiplier is similarly switched. The integral of the product of the fluctuations is recorded every 10 s. The mean photocurrents are also recorded.

Because the ratio of signal to noise is in general low, significant results can only be obtained by observing for very long periods. Table 4, given

TABLE 4

Comparison of predicted and observed
signal-to-noise ratio

Star	Bolometric magnitude	Signal-to-noise ratio	
		Predicted	Observed
αCMa	−1·46	20 ± 4	16·0 ± 1·1
αLyr	0·00	5 ± 1	4·0 ± 0·3
αPsA	+1·24	1·5 ± 0·3	1·2 ± 0·1
αGru	+1·63	1·2 ± 0·2	0·9 ± 0.1

by Brown, Davis, and Allen (1967), shows the observed signal-to-noise ratios for an observing time of 100s and for the reflectors very close together. The results are compared with the calculated values for the particular stars and it will be seen that, in general, the observed ratio is about 20 per cent less than the calculated value. Just as with the Michelson interferometer, the results can be normalized and the various constant factors determined by observations with the reflectors close together. In general, observing times much longer than 100 s are needed and are mostly about 10 h, though, by observing on a number of nights, total times of up to 46 h have been used.

In all, observations on 15 stars have been reported (Brown, Davis, Allen, and Rome 1967). The wavelengths were close to 440 nm, the factor Δ_ν varied from 0·880 to 0·998, and the maximum base line, at which the correlation first fell to zero, ranged from 15 to nearly 160 m. The greatest angular diameter was $6·5'' \times 10^{-3}$ and the least was $0·7'' \times 10^{-3}$. Brown (1968) has reviewed the methods for the measurement of the diameters of stars.

Effects of scintillation

An important property of intensity interferometry relating to astronomical applications is that the results are insensitive to phase changes in the path such as give rise to scintillations. Consider light incident on two detectors A' and B' along two parallel paths AA' and BB', where A and B are above the atmosphere, and suppose that phase shifts ϕ_A and ϕ_B are introduced in the two paths. It is supposed that the phase shifts are the same for all Fourier components, implying that the path length varies only slowly with frequency, or that the light is quasimonochromatic.

Let
$$\mathscr{R}_{AB}(\tau) = \langle V_A(t+\tau)V_A^*(t+\tau)V_B(t+\tau)V_B^*(t+\tau)\rangle$$

and suppose that $\Gamma_{AB}(\tau)$ is not zero.

Before entering the atmosphere, let the complex signals be

$$V_j(t, \tau) = \int_0^\infty v_j(T, \omega)e^{-i\omega t}\,d\omega,$$

where $j = A, B$. After passing through the atmosphere, the signals will be

$$V_j'(t, \tau) = e^{-i\phi_j}\int_0^\infty v_j(T, \omega)e^{-i\omega t}\,d\omega.$$

Thus (see Chapter 2)

$$\Gamma_{A'B'}(\tau) = \Gamma_{AB}e^{-i(\phi_A-\phi_B)}$$

and if, as is generally the case, ϕ_A and ϕ_B have random fluctuations,

$$\overline{\Gamma_{A'B'}(\tau)} = 0.$$

Thus the second-order correlation is destroyed, but the products that enter the fourth-order moments, namely $V_A'V_A'^*$ and $V_B'V_B'^*$, are independent of ϕ_A and ϕ_B, and accordingly $\mathscr{R}_{A'B'}$ is equal to $\mathscr{R}_{AB}$ so that the response of an intensity interferometer, depending as it does on $\mathscr{R}$ (p. 232) is unaffected by scintillation.

It should be noted that the joint statistics of the light at A' and B' are not Gaussian because while $\Gamma_{A'B'}$ may vanish (or more generally be a function of ϕ_A and ϕ_B), $\mathscr{R}_{A'B'}$ is unaffected, whereas for Gaussian statistics, $\Gamma_{A'B'}$ and $\mathscr{R}_{A'B'}$ vanish together, $\mathscr{R}_{A'B'}$ being determined if $\Gamma_{A'B'}$ is known.

APPENDIX 1

COMMUTATION RELATIONS FOR VARIABLES
OF THE ELECTROMAGNETIC FIELD

As in the text, let $\alpha_\nu = \tau a_\nu$, $\beta_\nu = \tau b_\nu$, where a_ν, the variable for one sense of polarization, is $(p_\nu - 2\pi i\nu q_\nu)$ and b_ν, that for the other sense, is $(p_\nu + 2\pi i\nu q_\nu)$.

Then

$$\alpha_\nu^* \alpha_{\nu'} - \alpha_{\nu'} \alpha_\nu^* = \tau^2 (a_\nu^* a_{\nu'} - a_{\nu'} a_\nu^*)$$

$$= \frac{\tau^2}{\pi k_\nu^2} [(p_\nu + 2\pi i\nu q_\nu)(p_{\nu'} - 2\pi i\nu' q_{\nu'}) - (p_{\nu'} - 2\pi i\nu' q_{\nu'})(p_\nu + 2\pi i\nu q_\nu)]$$

$$= \frac{\tau^2}{\pi k_\nu^2} \left[\begin{array}{l} p_\nu p_{\nu'} - p_\nu p_\nu + 4\pi^2 \nu\nu'(q_\nu q_{\nu'} - q_{\nu'} q_\nu) + \\ + 2\pi i\nu(q_\nu p_{\nu'} - p_{\nu'} q_\nu) - 2\pi i\nu'(p_\nu q_{\nu'} - q_{\nu'} p_\nu) \end{array} \right].$$

The momenta and co-ordinates for different frequencies separately commute:

$$p_\nu p_{\nu'} - p_\nu p_\nu = 0,$$

$$q_\nu q_{\nu'} - q_{\nu'} q_\nu = 0.$$

Momenta and co-ordinates for different frequencies also commute jointly, but for the same frequency

$$q_\nu p_\nu - p_\nu q_\nu = ih/2\pi.$$

Hence

$$\alpha_\nu^* \alpha_{\nu'} - \alpha_{\nu'} \alpha_\nu^* = -\frac{4\tau^2 \nu h}{k_\nu^2}$$

if $\nu = \nu'$ and is otherwise zero.

The relations given in the text follow if

$$\tau = \frac{1}{2} \left(\frac{k\nu'}{hc} \right)^{\frac{1}{2}}.$$

APPENDIX 2

THE WAVE EQUATION FOR THE COHERENCE FUNCTION

IF the averages of the products of the field variables do not depend on the absolute value of the time, the mutual coherence function depends only on the difference between the times at the two points:

$$\Gamma(\mathbf{r}_1, \mathbf{r}_2, t_1, t_2) = \Gamma(\mathbf{r}_1, \mathbf{r}_2, \tau),$$

where

$$\tau = t_2 - t_1.$$

Now $\Gamma(\mathbf{r}_1, \mathbf{r}_2, t_1, t_2)$ is the ensemble average

$$\langle V_1^*(\mathbf{r}_1, t_1) . V_2(\mathbf{r}_2, t_2) \rangle_e.$$

V obeys the wave equation:

$$\nabla^2 V = -\frac{1}{c^2} \frac{\partial^2 V}{\partial t^2}.$$

V_1 is a function of $(\mathbf{r}_1, t_1)$ but not of $(\mathbf{r}_2, t_2)$. Thus if ∇_1^2 is the Laplacian with respect to the co-ordinates $\mathbf{r}_1$,

$$\nabla_1^2 V_1 = -\frac{1}{c^2} \frac{\partial^2 V_1}{\partial t_1^2}.$$

Similarly,

$$\nabla_2^2 V_2 = -\frac{1}{c^2} \frac{\partial^2 V_2}{\partial t_2^2}.$$

Using the fact that V_1 is independent of $(\mathbf{r}_2, t_2)$ and V_2 of $(\mathbf{r}_1, t_1)$, it follows that

$$\nabla_1^2 \Gamma(\mathbf{r}_1, \mathbf{r}_2, t_1, t_2) = \langle [\nabla_1^2 V_1^*(\mathbf{r}_1, t_1)] . V_2(\mathbf{r}_2, t_2) \rangle$$

$$= -\frac{1}{c^2} \left\langle \left[\frac{\partial^2}{\partial t_1^2} V_1^*(\mathbf{r}_1, t_1) \right] . V_2(\mathbf{r}_2, t_2) \right\rangle$$

$$= -\frac{1}{c^2} \frac{\partial^2}{\partial t_1^2} \Gamma(\mathbf{r}_1, \mathbf{r}_2, t_1, t_2).$$

Similarly

$$\nabla_2^2 \Gamma(\mathbf{r}_1, \mathbf{r}_2, t_1, t_2) = -\frac{1}{c^2} \frac{\partial^2}{\partial t_2^2} \Gamma(\mathbf{r}_1, \mathbf{r}_2, t_1, t_2).$$

Now

$$\Gamma(\mathbf{r}_1, \mathbf{r}_2, \tau) = \lim_{T \to \infty} \frac{1}{2T} \int_{-T}^{+T} \Gamma(\mathbf{r}_1, \mathbf{r}_2, t_1, t_1 + \tau) \, \mathrm{d}t_1.$$

Thus

$$\frac{\partial^2 \Gamma}{\partial \tau^2} (\mathbf{r}_1, \mathbf{r}_2, \tau) = \frac{\partial^2 \Gamma}{\partial t_2^2} (\mathbf{r}_1, \mathbf{r}_2, t_1, t_2)$$

and so

$$\nabla_2^2 \Gamma(\mathbf{r}_1, \mathbf{r}_2, \tau) = -\frac{1}{c^2} \frac{\partial^2 \Gamma}{\partial t_2^2}(\mathbf{r}_1, \mathbf{r}_2, t_1, t_2) = -\frac{1}{c^2} \frac{\partial^2 \Gamma}{\partial \tau^2}(\mathbf{r}_1, \mathbf{r}_2, \tau).$$

Similarly

$$\nabla_1^2 \Gamma(\mathbf{r}_1, \mathbf{r}_2, \tau) = -\frac{1}{c^2} \frac{\partial^2 \Gamma}{\partial \tau^2}.$$

Wolf (1955) first derived this result by considering the Fourier integral for Γ.

Observe, from this result, $\nabla_1^2 \Gamma = \nabla_2^2 \Gamma$.

REFERENCES

ABRAMOWITZ, M. and STEGUN, IRENE A. (1964). *Handbook of mathematical functions*, Natn Bur. Stand. Appl. Math. Series, 55 (U.S. Govt. Printing Office, Washington).

ADAM, M. G. (1952). *Mon. Not. R. astr. Soc.* **112,** 546.

—— (1955). *Mon. Not. R. astr. Soc.* **115,** 422.

—— and NICKOLS, S. (1958). *Mon. Not. R. astr. Soc.* **118,** 97.

ANDERSON, J. A. (1920). *Astrophys. J.* **51,** 263.

BAIRD, K. M. (1954). *J. opt. Soc. Am.* **44,** 11.

—— (1963). *Appl. Opt.* **2,** 471.

—— and HOWLETT, L. E. (1963). *Appl. Opt.* **2,** 455.

—— and SMITH, D. (1957). *Can. J. Phys.* **35,** 455.

BARRELL, H. (1946). *Proc. R. Soc.* A **186.** 164.

—— and SEARS, J. E. (1939). *Phil. Trans. R. Soc.* A **238,** 1.

—— and TEASDALE-BUCKELL, P. (1951). *Proc. phys. Soc.* **64,** 413.

BATES, R. H. T. (1969). *Mon. Not. R. astr. Soc.* **142,** 413.

BELL, E. E. (1967). *J. Phys., Paris* **28,** Colloque C.2, 18.

BENNETT, F. D. and KAHL, G. D. (1953). *J. opt. Soc. Am.* **43,** 71.

BENOÎT, J. R., FABRY, CH., and PEROT, A. (1913). *Trav. Mém. Bur. int. Poids Mes.* **15,** 3.

BERAN, M. J. and PARRENT, G. B. (1964). *Theory of partial coherence* (Prentice-Hall, New York).

BERGSTEIN, L. and SCHUCHTER, H. (1964). *J. opt. Soc. Am.* **54,** 887.

BLACKMAN, R. B. and TUKEY, J. W. (1959). *The measurement of power spectra* (Dover, New York).

BLAISE, J. (1958). *J. Phys. Radium, Paris* **19,** 335.

BLUM, E. J. (1960). *C. r. hebd. Séanc. Acad. Sci., Paris* **250,** 3279.

BORN, M. and WOLF, E. (1957). *Principles of optics* (Pergamon, London and Oxford).

BOSTROM, R. C. and VALI, V. (1968). *Nature, Lond.* **220,** 1018.

BOUCHERAINE, P. and CONNES, P. (1963). *J. Phys., Paris* **24,** 134.

BOYD, G. D. and GORDON, J. P. (1961). *Bell Syst. tech. J.* **40,** 489.

—— and KOGELNIK, H. (1962). *Bell Syst. tech. J.* **41,** 1.

BRACEWELL, R. N. (1958). *Proc. Inst. Radio Engrs* **46,** 97.

—— (1962). Radio astronomy techniques, *Handb. Phys.* (ed. Flugge) Bd. 54, 42 (Springer, Berlin).

BRADLEY, D. J., BATES, B., JUULMAN, C. O. L., and KOHNO, T. (1967). *J. Phys., Paris* **28,** Colloque C.2, 280.

BROSSEL, J. (1947). *Proc. phys. Soc.* **59,** 224.

BROTEN, N. W., LOCKE, J. C., LEGGE, T. H., McLEISH, C. W., RICHARDS, R. S., CHISHOLM, R. M., GUSH, H. P., YEN, J. L., and GALT, J. A. (1967). *Nature, Lond.* **215,** 38.

BROWN, R. HANBURY (1960). *N.P.L. Symposium No. 11, Interferometry* 335 (H.M.S.O., London).
—— (1964). *Sky Telesc.* **28,** 64.
—— (1968). *A. Rev. Astr. Astrophys.* **6,** 13.
—— DAVIS J. and ALLEN, L. R. (1964). *Nature, Lond.* **201,** 1111.
—— (1967). *Mon. Not. R. astr. Soc.* **137,** 375.
——, ——, —— and ROME, J. M. (1967). *Mon. Not. R. astr. Soc.* **137,** 393.
—— and TWISS, R. Q. (1954). *Phil. Mag.* **45,** 663.
—— —— (1956a). *Nature, Lond.* **177,** 27.
—— —— (1956b). *Nature, Lond.* **178,** 1046.
—— —— (1957a). *Proc. R. Soc.* A **242,** 300.
—— —— (1957b). *Proc. R. Soc.* A **243,** 291.
BRUCE, C. F. (1955a). *Aust. J. Phys.* **8,** 224.
—— (1955b). *J. opt. Soc.. Am.* **45,** 1084
—— (1957). *Optica Acta* **4,** 127.
—— (1966). *Appl. Opt.* **5,** 1447.
BUIJS, H. L. and GUSH H. P. (1967). *J. Phys., Paris* **28,** Colloque C.2, 105.
BURGESS, D. D. and COOPER, J. (1965). *J. scient. Instrum.* **42,** 829.
BURKE, B. F., MORAN, J. M., BARRETT, A. H., RYDBECK, O., HANSSON, B., ROGERS, A. E. E., BALL, J. A., and CUDABACK, D. D. (1968). *Astr. J.* **73,** S168.
CABRERA, N. and TERRIEN, J. (1941). *Revue Opt. théor. instrum.* **20,** 35.
CHABBAL, R. (1958). Thesis, Paris, Ed. *Revue Opt. théor. instrum.* Ser. A 3048, No. 3920.
—— (1958a). *J. Phys. Radium, Paris* **19,** 295.
—— and SOULET, M. (1958). *J. Phys. Radium, Paris* **19,** 274.
CHAMBERLAIN J. E., ANDERSON, A., and GEBBIE, H. A. (1965). *Spectrochim. Acta* **21,** 883.
—— CHANTRY, G. W., FINDLAY, F. D., GEBBIE, H. A., GIBBS, J. E., STONE, N. W. B., and WRIGHT, A. J. (1966). *Infrared Phys.* **6,** 195.
—— GIBBS, J. E. and GEBBIE, H. A. (1963). *Nature, Lond.* **198,** 874.
COHEN, M. H., JAUNCEY, D. L., KELLERMAN, K. I., and CLARK, B. G. (1968). *Science, N.Y.* **162,** 88.
CONNES, J. (1958). *J. Phys. Radium, Paris* **19,** 197.
—— and CONNES, P. (1966). *J. opt. Soc. Am.* **56,** 896.
——, —— and MAILLARD, J. P. (1967). *J. Phys., Paris* **28,** Colloque C.2., 120.
—— and GUSH, H. P. (1959). *J. Phys. Radium, Paris* **20,** 915.
CONNES, P. (1956). *Revue Opt. théor. instrum.* **35,** 37.
—— (1958). *J. Phys. Radium, Paris* **19,** 262.
—— (1971). *Physics Bull* **22,** 26–8.
CONWAY, R. G. and KRONBERG, P. P. (1969). *Mon. Not. R. astr. Soc.* **142,** 11.
COOK, A. H. (1957). *Br. J. appl. Phys.* **7,** 285.
—— (1960). *N.P.L. Symposium No. 11, Interferometry,* 387 (H.M.S.O., London).
—— (1961). *Phil. Trans. R. Soc.* A **254,** 125.

COOK, A. H. (1962). *Comité Int. Poids Mes.*, *Comité Consultatif pour la défi-nition du Mètre* 3ᵉ Session, 1962, Annexe 20, 129 (Gauthier–Villars, Paris).
—— (1967). *Phil. Trans. R. Soc.* A **261**, 211.
—— (1968). *Mon. Not. R. astr. Soc.* **139**, 141.
—— and HITCHINS, R. G. (1959). *J. scient. Instrum.* **36**, 337.
—— and RICHARDSON, HELEN M. (1959). *Proc. phys. Soc.* **73**, 661.
COURTÈS, G. (1958). *J. Phys. Radium, Paris* **19**, 342.
CULSHAW, W., RICHARDSON, J. M., and KERNS, D. M. (1960). *N.P.L. Symposium No. 11, Interferometry* (H.M.S.O., London).
CUSENIER, M. and PINARD, J. (1967). *J. Phys., Paris* **27**, Colloque C.2, 97.
DANJON, A. (1955). On the interferometric measurement of small angular distances. *Vistas Astr.* (ed. A. Beer) **1**, 377 (Pergamon, London and New York).
DAVIES, R. D., PONSONBY, J. E. B., POINTER, L., and DE JAGER, G. (1969). *Nature, Lond.* **222**, 933.
DE, M. (1956). *J. Ass. appl. Phys.* **111**, 51.
DIRAC, P. A. M. (1958). *The principles of quantum mechanics*, 4th edn (Clarendon Press, Oxford).
DUFFIEUX, P. M. (1939). *Revue Opt. théor. instrum.* **18**, 1, 207, 273, and 282.
ELGAROY, O., MORRIS, D., and ROWSON, B. (1962). *Mon. Not. R. astr. Soc.* **124**, 395.
ENGELHARDT, E. (1960). *N.P.L. Symposium No. 11, Interferometry*, **21** (H.M.S.O., London).
EVANS, J. W. (1949). *J. opt. Soc. Am.* **39**, 229.
FABRY, CH. and BUISSON, H. (1908). *J. Phys., Paris* (Ser. 4) **7**, 417.
—— (1919). *J. Phys., Paris* **9**, 189.
FABRY, CH. and PEROT, A. (1897). *Annls Chim. Phys.* Ser. 8. **12**, 459.
—— (1898a). *Annls Chim. Phys.* Ser. 8. **13**, 275.
—— (1898b). *Annls Chim. Phys.* Ser. 8. **13**, 404.
—— (1899). *Annls Chim. Phys.* Ser. 8. **16**, 115.
—— (1901). *Annls Chim. Phys.* Ser. 8. **22**, 564.
—— (1902). *Annls Chim. Phys.* Ser. 8. **25**, 98.
FELLGETT, P. (1958). *J. Phys. Radium, Paris* **19**, 237.
—— (1967). *J. Phys., Paris* **28**, Colloque C.2.
FIZEAU, H. L. (1862). *C. r. hebd. Seanc. Acad. Sci., Paris* **54**, 1237.
FLAMMER, C. (1957) *Spherical wave functions* (Stanford University Press, Palo Alto)
FORK, R. L., HERRIOTT, D. R., and KOGELNIK, H. (1964). *Appl. Opt.* **3**, 1471.
FORMAN, M. L. (1967). *J. Phys., Paris* **28**, Colloque C.2, 58
FORRESTER, A., GUDMUNSEN, R., and JOHNSON, P. (1955). *Phys. Rev.* **94**, 1691.
FOX, H. G. and LI, T. (1961). *Bell Syst. tech. J.* **40**, 453.
FRANCON, M. (1956). Interférences, diffraction et polarisation, *Handb. Phys.* (ed. Flugge) **24**, 171 (Springer, Berlin).
—— (1966). *Optical interferometry* (Academic Press, London).
FROOME, K. D. (1954). *Proc. R. Soc.* A **223**, 195.
—— (1958). *Proc. R. Soc.* A **247**, 109.

FROOME, K. D. and ESSEN, L. (1969). *The velocity of light and radio waves* (Academic Press, London and New York).

GATES, J. W. (1955). *Proc. phys. Soc.* B **68**, 1065.

GEAKE, J. E., RING, J., and WOLF, N. J. (1959). *Mon. Not. R. astr. Soc.* **119**, 616.

GEBBIE, H. A. (1957). *Phys. Rev.* **107**, 1194.

—— (1961). *Advances in quantum electronics* Pt. II (Ed. J. R. Singer) 155 (Columbia University Press, New York).

—— (1964). *Infrared Phys.* **4**, 85.

—— and BURROUGHS, W. J. (1968). *Nature, Lond.* **217**, 1241.

—— and STONE, N. W. B. (1963). *Proc. phys. Soc.* **82**, 309.

—— and TWISS, R. Q. (1966). *Rep. Prog. Phys.* **29**, 728.

GUBBAY, J. S. and ROBERTSON, D. S. (1967). *Nature, Lond.* **215**, 1157.

HANES, G. R. (1959). *Can. J. Phys.* **37**, 1283.

—— (1963). *Appl. Opt.* **2**, 465.

HART, K. H. and BAIRD, K. M. (1961). *Can. J. Phys.* **39**, 781.

—— and SAWABE, M. (1968). *Metrologia* **4**, 154.

HART, M. (1968). *J. Phys.* D **1**, 1405.

—— and BONSE, U. (1968). *Acta crystallogr.* A.A. **24**, 240.

HEAVENS, O. S. (1960). *Rep. Prog. Phys.* **23**, 1.

HERRIOTT, D. R. (1967). Some applications of lasers to interferometry in *Prog. Optics* **6** (ed. E. Wolf) (North-Holland, Amsterdam).

HILGER, A. and TWYMAN, F. (1918). Brit. Pat. 130224.

HILLIARD, R. L. and SHEPHERD, G. G. (1966). *J. opt. Soc. Am.* **56**, 362.

HINDMARSH, W. R. (1955). *Mon. Not. R. astr. Soc.* **113**, 270..

HOPKINS, H. H. (1957). *J. opt. Soc. Am.* **47**, 508.

HUNTEN, D. M. (1968). *Science, N.Y.* **162**, 313.

HUNZIGER, J. J. (1955). *Revue Opt. théor. instrum.* **34**, 512.

IGNATOWSKY, W. (1935). *Influence of the shape and position of the light source on measurements with Kösters interference comparator* (in Russian) (Moscow).

INGELSTAMM, E. (1960). *N.P.L. Symposium No. 11, Interferometry* 139 (H.M.S.O., London).

JACKSON, D. A. (1958). *J. Phys. Radium, Paris* **19**, 379.

JACQUINOT, P. (1958). *J. Phys. Radium, Paris* **19**, 223.

—— (1960). *Rep. Prog. Phys.* **23**, 267.

JACQUINOT, P. and DUFOUR, C. (1948). *J. Rech. Cent. natn. Rech. scient.* **6**, 1.

JARRETT, A. H. and V. KLÜBER, H. (1955). *Mon. Not. R. astr. Soc.* **115**, 343.

KENDERDINE, S., RYLE, M., and POOLEY, G. G. (1966). *Mon. Not. R. astr. Soc.* **134**, 189.

KING, G. C. P., BILHAM, R. G., GERRARD, V. B., DAVIES, D., and SYDENHAM, P. H. (1969). *Nature, Lond.* **223**, 818.

KINMAN, T. D. (1956). *Mon. Not. R. astr. Soc.* **116**, 77.

KO, H. C. (1967). *I.E.E.E. Trans., Antennas and Propagation* AP15, No. **1**, 188.

KÖSTERS, W. (1921). *Z. Feinmech.* **1**, 2, 19, 39.

—— (1926). *Z. Feinmech. Präzis.* **34**, 55.

—— (1938). *Werkstattstechnik* **32**, 527.

KÖSTERS, W. and LAMPE, K. (1934). *Phys. Z.* **35**, 233.

KUHL, J., STEUDEL, H., and WALTHER, A. (1967). *J. Phys., Paris* **28**, Colloque C.2, 308.

LANDWEHR, R. (1959*a*). *Optica Acta* **6**, 52.

—— (1959*b*). *J. opt. Soc. Am.* **49**, 733.

LINNIK, W. (1933). *C. r. Acad. Sci. U.R.S.S.* **1**, 18.

LOTSCH, H. K. V. (1967). *Optik, Stuttg.* **26**, 112.

—— (1968). *Optik, Stuttg.* **26**, 183.

LYOT, B. (1933). *C. r. hebd. Séanc. Acad. Sci., Paris* **197**, 1593.

—— (1944). *Annls Astrophys.* **7**, 31.

McCREADY, L. L., PAWSEY, J. L., and PAYNE-SCOTT, RUBY (1947). *Proc. R. Soc.* A **190**, 357.

MAGYAR, G. and MANDEL, L. (1963). *Nature, Lond.* **198**, 255.

—— (1964). *Quantum electronics* (ed. N. Bloembergen and P. Grivet), 1947 (Dunod et Cie, Paris).

MANDEL, L. and WOLF, E. (1965). *Rev. mod. Phys.* **37**, 231.

MARTON, L., SIMPSON, J. A., and SUDDETH, J. A. (1954). *Rev. scient. Instrum.* **25**, 1099.

MERTZ, L. (1959). *J. opt. Soc. Am.* **49**, iv.

—— (1965). *Transformations in optics* (Wiley, New York).

—— (1967*a*). *J. Phys., Paris* **28**, Colloque C.2, 11.

—— (1967*b*). *J. Phys., Paris* **28**, Colloque C.2, 87.

MICHEL, J. J. (1967). *J. Phys., Paris* **28**, Colloque C.2, 109.

MICHELSON, A. A. (1890). *Phil. Mag.* **30**, 1.

—— (1891). *Phil. Mag.* **31**, 338.

—— (1892). *Phil. Mag.* **34**, 280.

—— (1903). *Light waves and their uses* (University of Chicago Press, Chicago).

—— (1920). *Astrophys. J.* **51**, 257.

—— (1927). *Studies in optics* (Chicago Univ. Sci. Ser., Chicago).

—— and BENOIT, J. R. (1895). *Trav. Mém. Bur. int. Poids Mes.* **11**, 3.

—— and MORLEY, E. W. (1889). *Am. J. Sci.* **38**, 181.

—— and PEASE, F. G. (1921). *Astrophys. J.* **53**, 249.

MILLS, B. Y. and LITTLE, A. G. (1953). *Aust. J. Phys.* **6**, 272.

MORRIS, D., RADHAKRISHNAN, V., and SEIELSTAD, G. A. (1964). *Astrophys. J.* **139**, 551 and 560.

MURTY, M. V. R. K. (1960). *J. opt. Soc. Am.* **50**, 83.

NOMARSKI, G. (1955). *J. Phys., Paris* **16**, 9.

ÖHMAN, Y. (1938). *Nature, Lond.* **141**, 157, 291.

PAYNE-SCOTT, RUBY and LITTLE, A. G. (1950). *Observatory* **70**, 185.

—— (1951). *Aust. J. scient. Res.* A **4**, 489.

PEASE, F. G. (1931). *Ergebn. exakt. Naturw.* **10**, 84.

PECK, E. R. (1948). *J. opt. Soc. Am.* **38**, 66, 1015.

—— (1957). *J. opt. Soc. Am.* **47**, 250.

PÉRARD, A. (1928). *Revue Opt. théor. instrum.* **7**, 1.

—— (1953). *Réun. Inst. Opt.* **6**, 1.

PEROT, A. and FABRY, CH. (1899). *Annls Chim. Phys.* (Ser. 8) **16**, 289.

—— (1901). *Annls Chim. Phys.* (Ser. 8) **24**, 119.

POOLEY, G. G. (1969). *Mon. Not. R. astr. Soc.* **144**, 101.

—— and KENDERDINE, S. (1968). *Mon. Not. R. astr. Soc.* **135**, 529.

PRITCHARD, J. L., SAKAI, H., STEEL, W. H. and VANASSE, G. A. (1967). *J. Phys., Paris*, **28**. Suppl. 3–4, 92.

RAYLEIGH, LORD (1892). *Phil. Mag.* **34**, 407.

ROESLER, F. L. and MACK, J. E. (1967). *J. Phys., Paris* **28**, Colloque C.2, 313.

ROLT, F. H. and BARRELL, H. (1929). *Proc. R. Soc.* A **122**, 122.

ROWLEY, W. R. C. and HAMON, J. (1963). *Revue Opt. théor. instrum.* **42**, 519.

—— and STANLEY, V. W. (1965). *Instrum. Pract.* **19**, 1106.

RYLE, M. (1952). *Proc. R. Soc.* A **211**, 351.

—— (1957). *Nature, Lond.* **180**, 110.

—— and HEWISH, A. (1960). *Mon. Not. R. astr. Soc.* **120**, 220.

—— and NEVILLE, A. (1962). *Mon. Not. R. astr. Soc.* **125**, 39.

SCHUSTER, A. (1924). *Phil. Mag.* (Ser. 6) **48**, 609.

SEARS, J. E., and BARRELL, H. (1932). *Phil. Trans. R. Soc.* A **231**, 75.

—— (1934). *Phil. Trans. R. Soc.* A **233**, 143.

SHAFER, A. B., McGILL, L. R., and DROPPLEMAN, L. (1964). *J. opt. Soc. Am.* **54**, 879.

SIMPSON, J. A. (1954). *Rev. scient. Instrum.* **25**, 1105.

SMITH, D. S. (1960). *Can. J. Phys.* **38**, 983.

STEEL, W. H. (1963). *Optica Acta* **10**, 205.

—— (1967). *Interferometry* (Cambridge University Press, Cambridge).

TERRIEN, J. (1958). *J. Phys. Radium, Paris* **19**, 390.

—— (1959a). *J. Phys. Radium, Paris* **20**, 447.

—— (1959b). *Revue Opt. théor. instrum.* **38**, 29.

—— (1960). *N.P.L. Symposium No. 11, Interferometry* 435 (H.M.S.O., London).

—— (1967). *J. Phys., Paris* **28**, Colloque C.2, 3.

—— and HAMON, J. (1956). *C. r. hebd. Séanc. Acad. Sci., Paris* **243**, 740.

—— —— and MASUI, T. (1957). *C. r. hebd. Séanc. Acad. Sci. Paris* **245**, 776.

—— and MASUI, T. (1956). *C. r. hebd. Séanc. Acad. Sci., Paris* **243**, 776.

THOMSON, J. H. and PONSONBY, J. E. B. (1968). *Proc. R. Soc.* A **303**, 477.

TOLANSKI, S. (1944a). *Phil. Mag.* (Ser. 7) **35**, 120.

—— (1944b). *Phil. Mag.* (Ser. 7) **35**, 229.

—— (1945a). *J. scient. Instrum.* **22**, 161.

—— (1945b). *Phil. Mag.* (Ser. 7) **36**, 225.

—— (1948). *Multiple beam interferometry* (Clarendon Press, Oxford).

TREANOR, P. J. (1957). *Mon. Not. R. astr. Soc.* **117**, 22.

TWYMAN, F. and GREEN, A. (1916). Brit. Pat. 103832.

VANASSE, G. A. and SAKAI, H. (1967). Fourier Spectroscopy in *Prog. Optics* **6** (ed. Wolf) (North-Holland, Amsterdam).

VAN BUEREN H. G. (1969). *Physica, 's Grav.* **41**, 198.

VAN HEEL, A. C. S. (1950). *J. opt. Soc. Am.* **40**, 809.

—— (1961). Modern alignment devices in *Prog. Optics* **1** (ed. Wolf) (North-Holland, Amsterdam).

WATANABE, N. and IMAIZUMI, M. (1928). *Proc. imp. Acad. Japan* **4**, 350.

WHITTAKER, E. T. (1951). *History of the theories of aether and electricity: I—The classical theories* (Nelson, London).

—— and WATSON, G. N. (1940). *A course of modern analysis* (4th edn) (Cambridge University Press, Cambridge).

WOLF, E. (1955). *Vistas Astr.* I (ed. Beer), 377 (Pergamon, London and New York).

YOUNG, T. (1802). *Phil. Trans. R. Soc.* **92**, 387.

ZERNICKE, F. (1938). *Physica, 's Grav.* **5**, 785.

AUTHOR INDEX

SUBJECT INDEX

absorption spectra, 138
air-pressure scanning, 114, 119, 134
air, refractive index, 76, 77, 114, 156, 162, 163
Airy function, 7, 101, 107, 110, 165, 167
alignment interferometer, 210–14
amplitude, division of, 9
aperture
  errors due to size, 46–9, 50–2, 107
  synthesis, 204–7
apparatus function, 107–10, 125, 126
astronomical applications of interferometry, 207
astrophysical applications of interferometry, 114, 118, 224, 235
asymmetrical line shape, 92
auto-collimation for adjustment of interferometer, 59, 117, 133, 134
auto-correlation function, 23
axial symmetry, interferometer with, 181

beam divider, 56, 75, 103
beats
  optical, 217–20
  conditions for, 220
Brewster angle, 56
brightness of source, 179–81

cadmium, red line of, 151, 160
Cambridge aperture synthesis interferometer, 207
coherence, 4, 15–23
  area, 17
  function, ix, 20, 211–14
    mutual, ix, 20, 43–52, 190–1, 237
  length, 16
  time, 16
  volume, 18
coherency matrix, 25
commutation relations, 237
compensating plate, 37, 56, 57, 63
correlation, 225
  calculation by computer, 201
cross-correlation function, 23
cross-spectral density, 23
cube corner reflector, 58, 67

degeneracy, 17, 19
detection, 12–15, 225

diffraction loss in optical cavity, 149
direction, interferometric measurement, 197

exact fractions, method of, 64, 154
extended spectra, 95

fast Fourier transform, 95
filter
  birefringent, 86
  Fabry–Perot, 137–9
  multiple-beam, 87, 140
finesse, ix, 103, 128, 136, 186
Fizeau
  fringes, 1
  interference, multiple beam, 121, 165ff., 181
flatness, examination of, 67
focus conditions, 40
Fourier
  integral, 4
  transform, 5, 95, 193–5, 200, 210
    two-dimensional, 202, 205
    spectroscopy 5, 33, 88ff., 176, 182
free spectral range, 109
Fresnel integral, 51
fringes
  counting, 62, 65, 67, 154, 155, 164
  geometry of, 41, 132, 138
  localization of, 34–6, 40, 170
  of equal chromatic order, 172
  of superposition, 128

gauges, measurement of, 70
Gaussian
  beam, 147
  line shape, 88, 89

Haidinger rings, 32, 63, 103, 138
hydrogen 21-cm line, 98
hydroxyl radio sources, 201

intensity, ix, 3, 20
  interferometer, 224–36
interference
  microscope, 74, 75
  three-beam, 80–2
interferogram
  determination of phase, 62–4
  errors of interpretation, 75, 169–71